Hymns for Today's Church

MUSIC EDITION

Hymns for Today's Church

MUSIC EDITION

Consultant Editor: Michael Baughen,
Bishop of Chester

Hodder & Stoughton
LONDON SYDNEY AUCKLAND TORONTO

This title is also available in the USA from Hope Publishing Company, Carol Stream, Illinois 60188.

Also from Jubilate Hymns, published by Hodder and Stoughton:

Hymns for Today's Church – Words only
Hymns for Today's Church – Melody Edition
Carols for Today – Music Editions
Carols for Today – Words Edition
Church Family Worship
Carols for Christmas – Carol selection from Hymns for Today's Church

ISBN 0 340 41255 0

CONTENTS

PREFACE SECTION

Consultant Editor's Preface
Words Preface
Music Preface
Editorial Group
Legal Information
Music Acknowledgements

<table>
<tr><td>HYMN SECTION</td><td>Hymns</td></tr>
</table>

GOD

GOD'S WORLD

GOD'S CHURCH

INSIDE BACK COVER

Prayers and The Apostles' Creed

CONSULTANT EDITOR'S PREFACE

Hymns for Today's Church

Hymns for Today's Church began on 23rd May 1973 at a meeting in London. The small group that met on that day recorded their aim as the production of 'the first major new hymn book of the new era'. Even such a lofty ambition did not adequately prepare the members of the group for the enormous task ahead of them.

Matching today's translations

It was not long ago that most Christians in the English-speaking world used the Authorised Version of the Bible. The present stream of new translations would have seemed unthinkable at the time, yet now they are not only commonplace but widely accepted as enhancing our understanding of the Bible. Similarly, users of the Book of Common Prayer twenty years ago would hardly have anticipated the new liturgies taking such a hold in the 1980s. In many churches the most old-fashioned part of worship is the hymnody with its unrevised language. Yet hymnody is an essential part of 'addressing one another' and of worshipping God. That is often hampered by not being in the language of the present day. It is the enormous task of revising hymns to match today's Bible and liturgy translations that has been undertaken by the compilers of this new hymn book.

Refreshing our worship

Although much care has been taken over the music, the painstaking revision of the words has caused nine years of hard and meticulous work by the Words Group. There will be times when some will feel that the revisers could have chosen other ways of expressing a line or a verse – but one feels that about translations of the Bible, too. Yet no change has been made without the utmost care and re-examination. Our testing of the material in conferences and services encourages us to believe that the new hymn book will bring great refreshment to worship services, and will be a joy and inspiration to many Christians, worthily matching today's Bible translations and today's liturgies.

Thank you

As Consultant Editor I have not been greatly involved in the work of the book, but I have been able to see the great dedication of the words team and the music team. I particularly want to acknowledge the splendid work of the two chairmen – Michael Saward and David Wilson, of the first secretary Jim Seddon, and of Michael Perry and Christopher Idle. They have given a staggering amount of time, energy, thought and care to the book, together with the other members of the two groups. We also particularly want to thank the families and the churches of those who have been actively involved in the project from the start – they have given immense support and understanding.

Others have helped and advised in various ways, including Owen J. Thomas, Bunty Grundy, Mavis Seddon and Paul Wigmore. CPAS Publications generously supported the project in its formative years until Hodder and Stoughton took over the publishing responsibility – we thank them both for their trust and confidence in us. It is our hope that their confidence will be repaid, not only in the book being widely used, but in it bringing a renewal of hymnody in the worship of today's church to the glory of God.

MICHAEL BAUGHEN,
BISHOP OF CHESTER.

CONSULTANT EDITOR'S PREFACE TO THE
SECOND EDITION

The hopes expressed at the publication of this book in 1982 have been amply fulfilled; the appreciation of the refreshment it has brought to worship has been widespread. In this second edition we keep faith with the many churches and individuals who have already bought *Hymns for Today's Church* by retaining the same numbering scheme and essentially the same text. But we have been sensitive to reasoned criticism. This has meant including six more traditional texts to supplement previous revisions, three further important hymns in revised format, and very occasional and minimal adjustments to lines which have proved mistaken or unsatisfactory. No other changes apart from author's corrections have been made to the previous texts. We have also added ten canticle versions to complement those previously included and so match the full range of canticles in the Alternative Service Book 1980.

We particularly want to express warmest gratitude for their special contribution to this second edition to Michael Perry, David Wilson, David Iliff and Christopher Idle, supported fully by Bunty Grundy and Alan Pickering.

MICHAEL BAUGHEN
BISHOP OF CHESTER
1987

WORDS PREFACE

Until recent years, the editorial committee of a twentieth-century hymn book largely fulfilled its role by compiling an anthology of existing texts. Only a tiny handful of new hymns was likely to be available for possible inclusion. The words committee responsible for *Hymns for Today's Church* has faced a much more complicated task.

First, from the vast number of published hymns we have had to agree on a core of essential material. Many of the hymns in the older books are rarely used and in a time of inflation it has become impracticable to make room for them. These traditional hymns have then to be carefully scrutinised and brought into more contemporary language.

A second task has been to assemble a wide collection of hymns published since the 1950s and to select as many as seem capable of sustaining a place in the new book.

The third major responsibility has been to discover and encourage both existing and new writers in order to bring into being unpublished work of high quality in contemporary English.

Contents

For most of the past decade all three elements have been facing us side by side. By checking and rechecking the traditional texts we have produced a list of about three hundred and fifty hymns of which perhaps a handful are so indelibly impressed upon Christian consciousness that they have been treated as sacrosanct.

The new material has posed quite different problems. Many submissions lacked poetic style and theological content. Well meaning churchgoers have submitted pastiche Victoriana, new minted for the 1980s! The resulting book is, therefore, neither the usual anthology of traditional hymns nor is it an uncritical assemblage of the latest songs from the multitude of supplements which have mushroomed in recent years. Much of the material acceptable to them has been carefully evaluated and reluctantly dismissed by what has become known as the Jubilate Hymns team.

Shape

Past hymn books have usually been shaped either by a thematic doctrinal structure or by the demands of a liturgical calendar. A few have simply followed an alphabetical sequence of first lines. After consideration of the merits of each method we have decided on a thematic scheme, supported by an index relating to the church's year. In this way we hope to offer an approach equally acceptable to churches of various denominations. There is also a biblical index. It is our conviction that we are making available a more complete indexing system than has been the case in most previous hymn books.

Those churches which follow a lectionary offering a wide range of saints' days may be disappointed to discover that few hymns have been included relating to specific saints. The reason is purely economic. A modern hymn book is too expensive to produce if it allocates perhaps twenty per cent of its space to hymns used only once a year. Local churches are well able to find other ways of dealing with this need.

Modernisation

Hymns are the liturgy of the laity. Though it is usually the clergy who write hymns it is the laity who sing them, and some hymns have undoubtedly gone into the national bloodstream even more deeply than liturgies and Bible translations. To attempt, as our book unashamedly does, to revise older hymns requires some justification.

It is not always realised that many hymns have been revised in earlier hymn books and that some famous texts are significantly different from the original versions. 'Hark, the herald angels sing' is not what Charles Wesley wrote, and 'Lo, he comes' could not be sung in contemporary churches without shock or laughter if Cennick's original words were used. Most previous hymn books have therefore quietly emended words, not always successfully, and some have concealed the process by minimal markings.

The last few years have seen a major transformation in Christian worship. Liturgies and Bibles have been as radically translated as in the sixteenth century, and only the hymns have remained in the language of previous eras. To leave them unrevised in that situation is to create a verbal and cultural gulf which cannot be to the long-term advantage of Christians at worship.

Invisible mending

The Jubilate Hymns words team has aimed at three kinds of revision. The first, and least controversial, has been the change from 'thee' to 'you'. This has become such a liturgical commonplace that no justification seems necessary. Second, consistency has demanded that archaic endings such as '-est' and '-eth' be replaced and, in verse, these alterations have frequently required the re-shaping of whole lines. This has been done with as much sensitivity as we can muster, taking sound-patterns into consideration wherever possible. No one can hope to be completely successful in such an exercise, but we hope and trust that our work has been of high quality. Invisible mending is a hard skill to acquire, and we have been encouraged by the many favourable responses which have greeted sample revisions. These have been sung at a large number of conferences and in many congregations, by way of market research.

Our third aim has been the most difficult. Many hymns, especially from the nineteenth century, have reflected a style of emotive language which is not easily accepted by contemporary congregations. Such hymns are less and less used today, and we have tried to save the best of them for future generations by a judicious re-writing of the more sentimental sections. This has demanded further skills to avoid the intrusion of one century's idiomatic style into that of another.

Attribution

The question of attribution, when major revisions have taken place, is a delicate one. Where hymns have originated in another language we have omitted the device 'tr.' and in its place we have indicated 'from the Latin' etc., or 'after' the original author. When our own team has substantially revised an earlier text we have described it as 'in this version Jubilate Hymns' or, occasionally, by the reviser's own name. Very minor revisions (such as have commonly been made in earlier hymn books) have not been specifically mentioned. Readers should, however, assume that hymns from past generations have been changed from 'thee' and 'thou' form to 'you' and its concomitants, without indication, except in the section entitled 'Traditional Texts'.

First lines

We have been faced with a series of further questions to which some response must be given. If it be permitted to alter hymns, is it necessary or wise to alter first lines, especially when such lines are well known? To that we answer that we have only made such changes where archaisms have required them or, in a handful of cases, where the obscurity of the earlier version has positively called for a new and stronger beginning.

Capitals

It has not seemed vital to us to be totally consistent concerning the practice of using capital letters. We have, in common with modern practice, drastically reduced the occasions on which capitals have been used. The main titles of the Trinity are always given capitals as is the substantive 'Lord'. Other titles have capitals when used in the vocative or where confusion might otherwise result. Titles in relative clauses are not normally capitalised. If a hymn depends upon a title for its meaning, or a title is unique within a group (e.g. 'Prince of princes'), we have not hesitated to use capitals. Thus our primary aim has been to clarify each word's meaning within its context rather than to produce a wooden consistency.

Language

In recent years the churches have become more sensitive to the danger of linguistic sexism. We have responded to this with care and sympathy but not to the point of fatuity. Wherever it has been possible to reduce an unnecessarily masculine reference we have done so, including on occasion alterations to our own previously published hymns. The issue is one where moderation seems the wisest course and we have taken particular care to avoid wherever possible the introduction of sexist language in our own revisions of earlier hymns.

Many older hymn books include a 'Children's Section'. We have not done this for two reasons. First, because excellent modern books explicitly for children already exist and, second, because many of the earlier children's hymns sound patronising to modern ears. In our view, simple and direct hymns are usually understood by children, and we have included a number of such hymns.

Informal material

Popular Christian songs and choruses have proliferated in recent years and are widely used in local churches. It is quite beyond the scope of this book to include large numbers of these, but a supplement of thirty of the most popular has been added for use in more informal worship. Many of them may prove to be of a more transient nature than the material in the main part of the book and their inclusion in a separate supplement is intended to indicate the editorial team's awareness of this fact. It should be noted that certain popular texts are not included where authors refused to allow archaisms (written in the 1970s) to be altered, or who required disproportionate royalty payments.

Doctrine

Many previous hymn books have suffered from an inflexible doctrinal stance of one kind or another. Members of the Jubilate Hymns team come from both Anglican and Free Church backgrounds and it has been our intention that our work should be acceptable to as wide a range of Christians as possible. We have drawn on material from Anglican, Roman Catholic, Free Church and Orthodox sources, and the only conscious area of exclusion has been hymns in the Marian tradition. In the area of eucharistic doctrine we have made some modification in order to bring controversial language into the reconciling tradition of the Church of England's 'Rite A' order, and by this action we hope we have released some traditionally divisive hymns for wider usefulness. We shall be disappointed if our own personal traditions are taken to assume that the book will only be of interest to those of like conviction.

Authorship

Some explanation is due for the large number of hymns
written by members of the words team which have found
their way into the book. Over a thousand modern hymns
have been assessed by a process ensuring anonymity, and
no hymn has been included simply on the grounds of our
familiarity with an author's reputation. In this we believe
the book to be unique. Material submitted by team members has also gone through this selection process and there
has been no conscious bias in favour of their work.

Reaction

In all this we have been conscious that there is no pleasing
everybody. Those who want 'concrete' and 'protest' in
every hymn will regard us as compromising reactionaries.
Those who love pietistic language interspersed with the
endless repetition of 'Alleluias' will find us much too objective, while those who oppose change as a matter of course
will echo the words of a critic who, eighty years ago,
dismissed *Hymns Ancient and Modern* with the complaint
that it was 'vastly different . . . very inferior . . . and the
more I examine the book, the more I dislike it and the more
distressed I feel'. Bible translators, liturgists and hymn
book editors are all familiar with that cry. Jerome, Cranmer
and Isaac Watts heard it in their day.

Thanks

No successful project lasting nearly a decade from concep-
tion to birth can fail to produce a strong sense of mutual
confidence between the members of the team responsible. I
and my colleagues have met on over seventy occasions, and
the blend of argument, laughter, and high seriousness of
purpose will always be a treasured memory. It has been a
joy to work with the whole team. None will, I know,
begrudge it, if I make particular reference to the work of
Christopher Idle and Michael Perry. It has been an education to work with them. Finally it has been a privilege to
look to Michael Baughen as our consultant.
    Not one of us has been unmoved by the daunting task
which has faced us. If in any measure we have succeeded, it
has been because of the deep sense that we have been

following in a long tradition of Christian men and women who have provided for their fellow believers words of faith, hope and love. However inadequately, it is to the praise and glory of God that we have worked and it is in that same spirit that we commend the book to the churches.

MICHAEL SAWARD
Words Editor

Note: Words in the Second Edition

This second edition of *Hymns For Today's Church* is entirely compatible with the new Melody Edition, and with the new Words Edition. In relation to the first Music and Words Edition, and to the first (hardback) Words Edition, it is altered only in minor respects. For instance, it includes such revisions of words as were recommended to us by authors, and those thought necessary in the light of our slowly evolving language. Further important adjustments have been made in response to the call for inclusive language from English-speaking churches throughout the world.

While the numbering scheme remains the same, twenty-two new texts have been appended. These comprise more hymns in traditional form, standard hymns in revised form, additional canticle versions and two songs previously omitted. A small inset can be purchased by direct application to the publishers if churches wish to upgrade their existing first edition word books.

MICHAEL PERRY
Secretary: Jubilate Hymns

Note: The editors' principles of revision are set out more fully in *Hymns in Today's Language?*, Christopher Idle, Grove Books, 1982.

MUSIC PREFACE

A broad selection

In selecting tunes for *Hymns for Today's Church* we have surveyed some forty hymn books and over three thousand tunes. In our final choice we have given priority to a tune's current use in the several churches represented by those on the committee. Inevitably, however, since we are publishing a fair proportion of new words, we have commissioned some new music, especially in less common metres. The tunes chosen are therefore those much in use, rather than those that appeal to a particular musical taste. In fact the committee was drawn together to represent as wide a range of 'taste' as possible, precisely because that quality is so elusive and hard to make objective. We hope, therefore, that the tunes will be found singable and approachable and often familiar, so that the worshipper, who is grasping changes in the words, will not have too much new music to grasp at the same time.

Music for worship

We have endeavoured to compile music from many different eras and denominational traditions. We have tended to favour original harmonisations authentic to each composition, unless the re-introduction of early rhythms or harmonies, though authentic in a musical sense, would now be innovations because more recent versions have eclipsed them. We are aware that a good case can be made for research and that exciting things can be recovered, but we have felt it right for this book to provide a minimum of radical music as a vehicle for revised and new words which some may find radical enough.

Specialist material

We are particularly glad to include fifty or so descants, re-harmonisations or faux-bourdons. They provide interest along familiar lines for choirs and organists. However, in the last ten years, music in worship has evoked a wealth of talent, often backed by a resource of instrumental expertise. We hope that the new material especially will be used in as imaginative a way as possible, and that copyright holders will be generous to encourage this.

New Edition

This second edition has been devised in the same style as the first and is entirely compatible with it. We have been able through the print layout to add more alternative tunes, mostly established, some new, and more descants. The cross-indexing of alternative tunes is more extensive in the light of experience and reflection. This has occasionally involved moving a tune from one place to another, but that is rare, and no tune has been removed from the book. We commend this edition therefore as an even richer resource than the last and urge you to explore it increasingly in the sphere of worship open to you. To this end a Melody Edition is also available, which will commend itself for congregational use. Thanks are due to David Iliff, who has contributed much time to the preparation of these new editions. May God, who continues to give his people new songs to sing, use this book for his glory and our joy.

Closer to God

Ultimately, in music for worship as in everything else, it is true that 'apart from Christ we can do nothing'. Tunes, however well chosen, are dead things without the breath of the Spirit. In the time we have worked as a committee, we have been aware of God's loving help in so many ways. Here we wish to record our thanks to him and to the people from whom he has brought us help. We pray that he will enable you, as you use this book, to sing songs new and old on fire with his presence. Earthly worship can bring us close to heaven: may this work, with all its strengths and weaknesses, be used by God to do this for many.

DAVID WILSON
Music Editor

HYMNS FOR TODAY'S CHURCH
EDITORIAL GROUP

Chairman

Michael Baughen

Secretary

Michael Perry

Words Committee

Michael Saward (Chairman), Richard Bewes, Patrick Good-land, Kenneth Habershon, Christopher Idle, Alex Mitchell, Michael Perry, Clifford Roseweir, James Seddon.

Music Committee

David Wilson (Chairman), John Barnard, Simon Beckley, David Iliff, David Peacock, Christian Strover, Noël Tredinnick, Norman Warren.

Copyright Secretary

Bunty Grundy

Index Editor

Alan Pickering

LEGAL INFORMATION

Copyright

The Editors' use of copyright is to safeguard the interests of authors, composers, copyright holders and, in the case of Jubilate Hymns copyrights, of our publishers.

Reprinting

Those seeking to reprint hymns in this book which are the property of Jubilate Hymns Ltd., or of author or composer members of Jubilate Hymns (indicated by †), may write to The Copyright Secretary, Jubilate Hymns Ltd., c/o 47 Bedford Square, London WC1P 3DP. Alternatively these items may be used under the scheme operated by the Christian Music Association, Glyndley Manor, Stone Cross, Eastbourne, East Sussex BN24 5BS. Addresses of other authors can also be supplied. In all cases please enclose a reply-paid envelope. Hymns copyrighted Stainer & Bell Ltd. may not be reprinted or photocopied under any blanket licensing scheme but should be cleared individually with Stainer & Bell.

Recording and Broadcasting

Jubilate Hymns Ltd., as well as most author or composer members, are also members of the Performing Right Society and the Mechanical Copyright Protection Society.

Prayers

The Confession is from the ASB 1980 © Central Board of Finance of the Church of England.

The text of the Apostles' Creed is that of the International Consultation on English Texts (ICET). The Lord's Prayer is adapted from the ICET version.

MUSIC ACKNOWLEDGEMENTS

An asterisk following the number of the tune indicates the provision of a descant, faux-bourdon or special setting.

† In the case of Jubilate Hymns members, all copyrights are held by the composer, although permission to reprint may be obtained from Jubilate Hymns Limited (see Preface: Legal Information).

We apologise to any composers we have inadvertently failed to acknowledge and welcome information for future editions.

Composer/Arranger

Appleford, Patrick
417, 518: by permission of Josef Weinberger Limited

Archer, Malcolm David
603: by permission of the composer

Arnold, J. H.
142: from *The English Hymnal*, by permission of Oxford University Press

Ballinger, Bruce
S.29: © 1976 Sound III Inc., 2712 W. 104th Terrace, Leawood, KS 66206, USA

Barham Gould, A.
550: by permission of D. R. Gould

Barnard, John
2, 28, 30*, 33, 41, 45, 46*, 47*, 55, 81, 94*, 127, 128*, 141, 151*, 152*, 155*, 173*, 179*, 194, 207, 231*, 246, 280*, 284*, 290, 307*, 325, 327*, 328*, 349*, 366, 388, 424, 445, 459, 482, 497, 499, 505, 527, 546, 547, 591, 598*, 601*, 608*, 612*, S.19*, S.25, S.32: by permission of Jubilate Hymns Limited†

Baughen, M. A.
42, 60, 79, 97, 173, 201, 218, 328, 548, S.27: by permission of Jubilate Hymns Limited†

Beaumont, Geoffrey
33: by permission of Novello and Company Limited. Arrangement made and reproduced by permission of Paxton Music Limited
251: by permission of Novello and Company Limited
272, 316: by permission of Josef Weinberger Limited

Beckley, Simon
26, 141, 252, 314, 382: by permission of Jubilate Hymns Limited†

Bischoff, Paul
69: by permission of Gustav Bosse Verlag

Bonner, Carey
393: by permission of the National Christian Education Council

Harwood, Basil
   342, 401, 521, 536: reprinted by permission of the Executors of the late
   Dr. Basil Harwood

Hempel, Rolf
   69: by permission of Gustav Bosse Verlag

Holmes, Henry J. E.
   485: by permission of the Executors of the late Miss C. J. Holmes

Howells, Herbert
   228, 451: by permission of Novello and Company Limited

Humphreys, Philip
   255: by permission of the composer

Hurford, Peter
   143: by permission of Oxford University Press

Hymns Ancient and Modern Limited
   391: by permission of the proprietors

Iliff, David
   3, 42*, 56*, 152, 193*, 198, 233, 278, 321, 328, 496, 561, S.12: by
   permission of Jubilate Hymns Limited†

Ingham, T. H.
   494*, 583*: from *Songs of Praise*, by permission of Oxford University
   Press

Ireland, John
   136: by permission of the trustees of the John Ireland Trust

Iverson, Daniel
   S.23, S.24: from *Spirit of the Living God*, by Daniel Iverson, © Moody
   Press, 2101 West Harvard Street, Chicago, Illinois 60645, USA

Ives, Grayston
   474*: This tune is taken from Grayston Ives' *Tongues of Fire* and is
   reprinted by permission of the composer and Basil Ramsay
   Publishers of Music Limited

Jackson, Francis
   286: by permission of the composer

Jackson, Peter
   S.9: © Word Music (UK) Ltd., 9 Holdom Avenue, Bletchley, Milton
   Keynes, Bucks MK1 1QU

Jacques, Reginald
   80: from *Carols for Choirs 1*, by permission of Oxford University Press

Keys, Ivor
   44*, S.18*: by permission of the composer

Knight, Gerald
   580: by permission of Hymns Ancient and Modern Limited

Lang, C. S.
7*, 23*, 33*, 40*, 541*, 594*: by permission of Novello and Company Limited

Lee, J. V.
214: by permission of The United Reformed Church

Ley, Henry
397, 429: by permission of Chappell Music and International Music Publications

Lunt, Janet
S.6: by permission of Mustard Seed Music, 9 Holdom Avenue, Bletchley, Milton Keynes, Bucks MK1 1QU

McCarthy, David
500: by permission of Stainer & Bell Limited

Mansell, David
S.17: Springtide, by permission of Word Music (UK) Ltd, 9 Holdom Avenue, Bletchley, Milton Keynes, Bucks MK1 1QU

Maries, Andrew
405, S.6: by permission of the composer

Marsh, John
149: by permission of the composer

Micklem, Caryl
256: by permission of the composer

Mills, Pauline Michael
S.30: © 1963, 1975 by Fred Bock Music Company, all rights reserved, used by permission

Milner, Anthony
481: reproduced by permission of the publishers, McCrimmon Publishing Company Limited, Great Wakering, Essex

Morris, R. O.
62: by permission of Oxford University Press

Nicholson, S. H.
99*, 563: by permission of the Royal School of Church Music
142, 146, 171*, 176, 262, 331*, 353*, 371*, 508: by permission of Hymns Ancient and Modern Limited
226*, 351*, 515*: by permission of Oxford University Press

Owens, Jimmy
586, S.12, S.14: from *Come Together* © 1972 Lexicon Music Inc., used by permission of Word Music (UK) Ltd., 9 Holdom Avenue, Bletchley, Milton Keynes, Bucks MK1 1QU

Peacock, David
60, 76, 261, 339, 358, 471, 475, 503, 586, S.31: by permission of Jubilate Hymns Limited†

Perry, Michael
58, 91: by permission of Jubilate Hymns Limited†

Stanton, W. K.
209, 381: from the *BBC Hymn Book*, by permission of Oxford
University Press

Stassen, Linda
S.22: © 1974 Linda Stassen, New Song Ministries, PO Box 11662,
Costa Mesa, California 92627, USA

Strover, Christian
58, 340, 408, 443, S.10, S.11: by permission of Jubilate Hymns
Limited†

Taylor, Cyril
250, 489, 494: from the *BBC Hymn Book*, by permission of Oxford
University Press

Temple, Sebastian
S.19: by permission of Franciscan Communications, 1229 South
Santee Street, Los Angeles, California 90015, USA

Terry, R. R.
314, 422: by permission of Oxford University Press
362: by permission of Search Press Limited

Thalben-Ball, George T.
308, 538, 572: by permission of J. M. Thalben-Ball

Thiman, Eric
553: by permission of The United Reformed Church

Toolan, Suzanne
S.10: © 1971 GIA Publications Incorporated, used by permission

Traditional
S.25: copyright collected Boosey & Hawkes Inc., used by permission

Tredinnick, Noël
4, 17, 26, 32*, 42, 51, 60, 66, 73, 79, 82, 106, 122, 136*, 138, 147, 173,
177, 185, 208, 211, 218, 225, 252, 265, 285*, 314, 330, 382, 411, 502*,
506*, 548, S.14, S.16: by permission of Jubilate Hymns Limited†

Vaughan Williams, Ralph
13, 32, 50, 74, 88, 96, 131, 133, 157, 229, 231, 277, 282, 383, 392, 402,
429, 457, 477, 528, 534, 537, 549, 567, 579, 590: from *The English
Hymnal*, by permission of Oxford University Press
239: by permission of Stainer & Bell Limited
241: from *Enlarged Songs of Praise*, by permission of Oxford University
Press
420, 427, 528: by permission of Oxford University Press

Warren, Norman L.
44, 47, 53, 55, 68, 70, 97, 125, 127, 138, 152, 162, 186, 216, 218, 220,
243, 252, 288, 308, 319, 339, 365, 369*, 378, 410, 445, 455, 497, 611,
S.1, S.3, S.4, S.7, S.9, S.13, S.20, S.22*, S.26, S.28, S.29, S.32: by
permission of Jubilate Hymns Limited†

Westbrook, Francis
487: by permission of Oxford University Press

White, Peter
57: by permission of Jubilate Hymns Limited†

Willcocks, David
10*, 67*: from *Carols for Choirs 2*, by permission of Oxford University Press
59*, 65*, 84: from *Carols for Choirs 1*, by permission of Oxford University Press
140*, 356*: from *Hymns for Choirs*, by permission of Oxford University Press

Williams, Derek
335: by permission of the composer

Williams, T. J.
175, 248, 465: by permission of Eluned Crump and Dilys Evans, representatives of the late Gwenlyn Evans

Wilson, David G.
55, 75, 122, 188, 201, 234, 349, 438, 456, S.2, S.8, S.18, S.21: by permission of Jubilate Hymns Limited†

Wilson, John
245*, 494*: by permission of Oxford University Press

Wonnacott, Olwen
517, 526: by permission of the composer

It has been impossible to trace the copyright holders of tunes by the following composers. Omissions will be rectified where possible.

Allen, C. J.
Burleigh, H. T.
Hammond, Mary Jane
Kitson, C. H.
Matthews, Beryl
Rigby, Charles
Smith, K. D.

HYMN SECTION

GOD: HOLY TRINITY

1

FELMERSHAM   10 10 10 9   © Paul Edwards (born 1955)†

1 Father eternal, Lord of the ages,
  you who have made us, you who have called us:
  look on your children gathered before you;
  worship they bring you, Father of all.

2 Jesus our Saviour, born of a virgin,
  truth from high heaven you came to teach us;
  you are the way that leads to the Father:
  be now our life, both here and above.

3 Spirit all-holy, Spirit of mercy,
  bind us in one with Christ and the Father;
  give us all joy and peace in believing,
  firm on the rock of faith in our God.

4 Father eternal, Jesus redeemer,
  Spirit all-holy, Trinity perfect;
  Unity endless, Love everlasting:
  praise evermore we offer to you.

G. B. Timms (born 1910)
© Oxford University Press

Alternative tune: HARROW WEALD (2)

2

HARROW WEALD 5 5 5 5 5 5 5 4   © John Barnard (born 1948)†

1 Father in heaven,
   grant to your children
   mercy and blessing,
   songs never ceasing;
   love to unite us,
   grace to redeem us,
      Father in heaven,
      Father, our God.

2 Jesus redeemer,
   may we remember
   your gracious passion,
   your resurrection:
   worship we bring you,
   praise we shall sing you,
      Jesus redeemer,
      Jesus, our Lord.

3 Spirit descending,
   whose is the blessing,
   strength for the weary,
   help for the needy:
   sealed in our sonship,
   yours be our worship,
      Spirit descending,
      Spirit adored.

D. T. Niles (1908–1970)
in © Christian Conference of Asia Hymnal
Used by permission

Alternative tune: FELMERSHAM (1)

3

CHRISTE SANCTORUM   11 11 11 5

Melody from *Paris Antiphoner* 1681
© arranged David Iliff (born 1939)†

1 Father most holy, merciful and loving,
   Jesus, redeemer, ever to be worshipped,
   life-giving Spirit, comforter most gracious,
       God everlasting:

2 Three in a gracious unity unbroken,
   one perfect Godhead, bound in love unfailing,
   light of the angels, helper of the needy,
       hope of all living:

3 Let all creation honour its creator,
   let every creature praise you without ceasing!
   We too would bring our songs of true devotion:
       hear in your mercy!

4 Lord God Almighty, to your name be glory,
   One in Three persons, over all exalted;
   to you belong all honour, praise, and blessing,
       now and for ever.

from the Latin (c. tenth century)
A. E. Alston (1862–1927)

4

BARBARA ALLEN   8 7 8 7

English traditional melody
© arranged Noël Tredinnick (born 1949)†

1 My Lord of light who made the worlds,
   in wisdom you have spoken;
   but those who heard your wise commands
   your holy law have broken.

2 My Lord of love who knew no sin,
   a sinner's death enduring:
   for us you wore a crown of thorns,
   a crown of life securing.

3 My Lord of life who came in fire
   when Christ was high ascended:
   your burning love is now released,
   our days of fear are ended.

4 My Lord of lords, one Trinity,
   to your pure name be given
   all glory now and evermore,
   all praise in earth and heaven.

© Christopher Idle (born 1938)†

5

ST. PATRICK 8 8 8 8 D

Irish traditional hymn melodies
arranged C. V. Stanford (1852–1924)

1 *f* I bind my-self to God to-day, the strong and
ho - ly Tri - ni - ty, to know his name and
make him known, the Three-in - One and One - in-Three.

Unison

2 *mf* I bind my-self_ to God_ for_ e - ver, to Je - sus
3 I bind my-self to God_ to - day, _ to his _ great

in _ his in - car - na-tion, bap - tized_ for_ me _ in
power to hold and lead, _ his eye____ to _ watch me

Jor - dan ri - ver and_cru - ci - fied_ for my sal - va - tion;__
on my way,_ his_ ear to _ lis - ten to my need;___

2 __ he burst the pri - son __ of his tomb, as -
3 __ the wis - dom of my __ God to teach, his

- cen - ded to __ the heaven - ly throne, re - turn - ing __ at __ the
hand to guide, his shield to ward, the word __ of __ God __ to

day of doom: by __ faith I __ make his life my own.
give me speech, his __ hea - venly host __ to be my guard.

GARTAN 4444448

Unison

5 *f* I bind my - self _ to God _ to - day, _ the strong _ and ho - ly

Tri - ni - ty, to know _ his _ name and make him known, the _

Three-in - One _ and One - in - Three; ____ from him all na - ture

has cre - a -tion, e - ter -nal Fa-ther, Spi - rit, Word: praise God, _ my_

strength and my sal - va - tion; praise in the Spi -rit through Christ the

Lord! _____ A - men.

after Patrick (c. 385–461)
Cecil F. Alexander (1818–1895)
© in this version Jubilate Hymns†

6

TRINITY 86867788 © Kenneth Coates (born 1917)

and though our tongues are earth-bound clay,

light them with flam - ing fire to - day.

1 O Trinity, O Trinity,
          the uncreated One;
O Unity, O Unity
          of Father, Spirit, Son:
you are without beginning,
your life is never ending;
          and though our tongues are earthbound clay,
          light them with flaming fire today.

2 O Majesty, O Majesty,
          the Father of our race;
O Mystery, O Mystery,
          we cannot see your face:
your justice is unswerving,
your love is overpowering;
          and though . . .

3 O Virgin-born, O Virgin-born,
          of humankind the least;
O Victim torn, O Victim torn,
          both spotless lamb and priest:
you died and rose victorious,
you reign above all-glorious;
          and though . . .

4 O Wind of God, O Wind of God,
          invigorate the dead;
O Fire of God, O Fire of God,
          your burning radiance spread:
your fruit our lives renewing,
your gifts, the church transforming;
          and though . . .

5 O Trinity, O Trinity,
          the uncreated One;
O Unity, O Unity
          of Father, Spirit, Son:
you are without beginning,
your life is never-ending;
          and though . . .

from the Lenten Triodion of the Orthodox Church
© Michael Saward (born 1932)†

7(i)

NICAEA   11 12 12 10

J. B. Dykes (1823–1876)
descant C. S. Lang (1891–1971)
descant © Novello & Co Ltd

Descant

4 Ho-ly, ho-ly, ho - ly, Lord God al - might - y!

all your works shall praise your name, in earth and sky and sea:

Ho - ly, ho - ly, ho - ly! — mer - ci-ful and might - y,

God   in three   per - sons,   glo - rious_ Tri - ni - ty.

1 *f* Holy, holy, holy, Lord God almighty!
early in the morning our song of praise shall be:
Holy, holy, holy! – merciful and mighty,
God in three persons, glorious Trinity.

2 *mf* Holy, holy, holy! All the saints adore you
casting down their golden crowns
around the glassy sea,
cherubim and seraphim falling down before you:
you were and are, and evermore shall be!

3 *mf* Holy, holy, holy! Though the darkness hide you,
though the sinful human eye
your glory may not see,
you alone are holy, there is none beside you,
perfect in power, in love and purity.

4 *f* Holy, holy, holy, Lord God almighty!
all your works shall praise your name,
in earth and sky and sea:
Holy, holy, holy! – merciful and mighty,
God in three persons, glorious Trinity.

R. Heber (1783–1826)

(see also traditional version, 594)

7(ii)

TERSANCTUS 11 12 12 10

Gordon Hartless (born 1913)
© Josef Weinberger Ltd

1 Holy, holy, holy, Lord God almighty!
early in the morning our song of praise shall be:
Holy, holy, holy! – merciful and mighty,
God in three persons, glorious Trinity.

2 Holy, holy, holy! All the saints adore you
casting down their golden crowns
    around the glassy sea,
cherubim and seraphim falling down before you:
you were and are, and evermore shall be!

3 Holy, holy, holy! Though the darkness hide you,
   though the sinful human eye
         your glory may not see,
   you alone are holy, there is none beside you,
   perfect in power, in love and purity.

4 Holy, holy, holy, Lord God almighty!
   all your works shall praise your name,
         in earth and sky and sea:
   Holy, holy, holy! – merciful and mighty,
   God in three persons, glorious Trinity.

R. Heber (1783–1826)

8

STUTTGART   8 7 8 7

C. F. Witt (1660–1716)
© arranged K. D. Smith (born 1928)

1 Praise the Father, God of justice:
   sinners tremble at his voice,
   crowns and creatures fall before him,
   saints triumphantly rejoice.

2 Praise the Son, who comes with burning,
   purging sin and healing pain,
   by whose cross and resurrection
   we have died to rise again.

3 Praise the Spirit: power and wisdom,
   peace that like a river flows,
   word of Christ and consolation,
   life by whom his body grows.

4 Praise the Father, Son and Spirit,
   One-in-Three and Three-in-One,
   God our judge and God our saviour,
   God our heaven on earth begun!

© Michael Perry (born 1942)†

9

LEONI 6 6 8 4 D

Transcribed by M. Lyon (1751–1797)
and adapted by T. Olivers (1725–1799)
from a synagogue melody for the Yigdal (doxology)

1 The God of Abraham praise
 who reigns enthroned above;
 the ancient of eternal days
 and God of love!
 The Lord, the great I AM,
 by earth and heaven confessed –
 we bow before his holy name
 for ever blessed.

2 To him we lift our voice
  at whose supreme command
  from death we rise to gain the joys
  at his right hand:
  we all on earth forsake –
  its wisdom, fame, and power;
  the God of Israel we shall make
  our shield and tower.

3 Though nature's strength decay,
  and earth and hell withstand,
  at his command we fight our way
  to Canaan's land:
  the water's deep we pass
  with Jesus in our view,
  and through the howling wilderness
  our path pursue.

4 He by his name has sworn –
  on this we shall depend,
  and as on eagles' wings upborne
  to heaven ascend:
  there we shall see his face,
  his power we shall adore,
  and sing the wonders of his grace
  for evermore.

5 There rules the Lord our king,
  the Lord our righteousness,
  victorious over death and sin,
  the prince of peace:
  on Zion's sacred height
  his kingdom he maintains,
  and glorious with his saints in light
  for ever reigns.

6 Triumphant hosts on high
  give thanks eternally
  and 'Holy, holy, holy' cry,
  'great Trinity!'
  Hail Abraham's God and ours!
  one mighty hymn we raise,
  all power and majesty be yours
  and endless praise!

from a Hebrew doxology
T. Olivers (1725–1799)
© in this version Jubilate Hymns†

10

CORDE NATUS 8 7 8 7 8 7 7

Melody from *Piae Cantiones* 1582
arranged David Willcocks (born 1919)
arrangement © Oxford University Press

An arrangement of the tune on 2 staves will be found at 56.

1   We believe in God Almighty,
      maker of the earth and sky;
      all we see and all that's hidden
      is his work unceasingly:
      God our Father's loving kindness
      with us till the day we die –
        evermore and evermore.

2   We believe in Christ the Saviour,
      Son of God and Son of Man;
      born of Mary, preaching, healing,
      crucified, yet risen again:
      he ascended to the Father
      there in glory long to reign –
        evermore and evermore.

3   We believe in God the Spirit,
      present in our lives today;
      speaking through the prophets' writings,
      guiding travellers on their way:
      to our hearts he brings forgiveness
      and the hope of endless joy –
        evermore and evermore.

© David Mowbray (born 1938)†

11

CROFT'S 136th   6 6 6 6 8 8

W. Croft (1678–1727)

1 We give immortal praise
   to God the Father's love
   for all our comforts here
   and better hopes above:
         he sent his own
         eternal Son,
         to die for sins
         that we had done.

2 To God the Son belongs
   immortal glory too,
   who bought us with his blood
   from everlasting woe:
         and now he lives,
         and now he reigns,
         and sees the fruit
         of all his pains.

3 To God the Spirit's name
   immortal worship give,
   whose new-creating power
   makes the dead sinner live:
         his work completes
         the great design,
         and fills the soul
         with joy divine.

4 To God the Trinity
   be endless honours done,
   the undivided Three,
   and the mysterious One:
         where reason fails
         with all her powers,
         there faith prevails,
         and love adores.

I. Watts (1674–1748)

12

CAPETOWN 7775   F. Filitz (1804–1876)

1   Three-in-One and One-in-Three,
    ruler of the earth and sea:
    hear our praise, O Trinity,
    holy chant and psalm.

2   Light of lights, with morning shine,
    bring to us your light divine;
    make our lives your holy shrine –
    set our hearts aflame.

3   Light of lights, when falls the even,
    let it close on sins forgiven;
    guard us in the peace of heaven –
    spread your holy calm.

4   Three-in-One and One-in-Three,
    faint our songs on earth may be;
    yet in heaven's glory we
    shall adore your name.

G. Rorison (1821–1869)
© in this version Jubilate Hymns†

For other hymns on this theme, see:
Sunday Themes index
    Section 35, The Trinity (p. xiv)
Song Section:
    Father, we adore you (S.5)
    Holy, holy, holy, holy (S.14)

GOD: LORD AND FATHER
Creating and Sustaining

13

EASTER SONG   8 8 4 4 8 8 and Alleluias

Geistliche Kirchengesang
Cologne 1623
arranged R. Vaughan Williams (1872–1958)
arrangement © Oxford University Press

1 *f* All creatures of our God and king,
lift up your voice and with us sing
Alleluia, alleluia!
mf Bright burning sun with golden beam,
soft shining moon with silver gleam,
O praise him, O praise him,
Alleluia, alleluia, alleluia!

2　Swift rushing wind so wild and strong,
　　white clouds that sail in heaven along,
　　　　O praise him, alleluia!
　　New rising dawn in praise rejoice,
　　you lights of evening find a voice;
　　　　O praise him . . .

3　Cool flowing water, pure and clear,
　　make music for your Lord to hear,
　　　　Alleluia, alleluia!
　　Fierce fire so masterful and bright
　　giving to us both warmth and light,
　　　　O praise him . . .

4　Earth ever fertile, day by day
　　bring forth your blessings on our way,
　　　　O praise him, alleluia!
　　All fruit and crops that richly grow,
　　all trees and flowers God's glory show;
　　　　O praise him . . .

5　People and nations, take your part,
　　love and forgive with all your heart;
　　　　Alleluia, alleluia!
　　All who long pain and sorrow bear,
　　trust God and cast on him your care;
　　　　O praise him . . .

6 *f*　Death, once the ancient enemy,
　　hear now our Easter melody,
　　　　O praise him, alleluia!
　　You are the pathway home to God,
　　our door to life through Christ our Lord;
　　　　O praise him . . .

7 *ff*　Let all things their creator bless
　　and worship him in lowliness,
　　　　Alleluia, alleluia!
　　Praise, praise the Father, praise the Son,
　　and praise the Spirit, Three-in-One,
　　　　O praise him . . .

after Francis of Assisi (1182–1226)
W. H. Draper (1855–1933)
© in this version Jubilate Hymns†

14 and 15

OLD 100th   8 8 8 8 (LM)   Melody from the *Genevan Psalter* 1551

Alternative version with melody in tenor   arranged J. Dowland (1563–1626)

14

1 *f* All people that on earth do dwell,
sing to the Lord with cheerful voice:
serve him with joy, his praises tell,
come now before him and rejoice!

2 *mf* Know that the Lord is God indeed,
he formed us all without our aid;
we are the flock he loves to feed,
the sheep who by his hand are made.

3 *f* O enter then his gates with praise,
and in his courts his love proclaim;
give thanks and bless him all your days:
let every tongue confess his name.

4 *mf* The Lord our mighty God is good,
his mercy is for ever sure;
his truth at all times firmly stood,
and shall from age to age endure.

5 *f* Praise God the Father, God the Son,
and God the Spirit evermore;
all praise to God the Three-in-One,
let heaven rejoice and earth adore!

from *Jubilate Deo* (Psalm 100)
W. Kethe (died 1594)
© in this version Jubilate Hymns†

15

1 Before Jehovah's awesome throne,
you nations, bow with sacred joy;
know that the Lord is God alone –
he can create, and he destroy.

2 His sovereign power, without our aid,
formed us and fashioned us of old;
and when like wandering sheep we strayed,
he brought us back into his fold.

3 We'll crowd your gates with thankful songs,
high as the heavens our voices raise;
and earth with her ten thousand tongues
shall fill your courts with sounding praise.

4 Wide as the world is your command,
vast as eternity your love;
firm as a rock your truth shall stand,
when rolling years shall cease to move.

from *Jubilate Deo* (Psalm 100)
I. Watts (1674–1748)
and J. Wesley (1703–1791)

16

FULDA 8 8 8 8 (LM)   W. Gardiner *Sacred Melodies* 1815

1 *f* Come with all joy to sing to God
        our saving rock, the living Lord:
        in glad thanksgiving seek his face
        with songs of victory and grace.

2   In holiness and light arrayed
       above all gods that we have made,
       he is the one almighty king
       and his the glory that we sing.

3 *mf* The earth is his from east to west,
         from ocean-floor to mountain-crest;
         he made the seas and formed the lands,
         he shaped the islands by his hands.

4   Come near to worship! come with faith,
       bow down to him who gives us breath:
       God is our shepherd, he alone;
       we are his people, all his own.

5 *mp* But if you hear God's voice today
         do not reject what he will say:
         when Israel wandered from God's path
         they suffered forty years of wrath.

6   That generation went astray;
       they did not want to know his way:
       they put their saviour to the test,
       and saw his power, but lost their rest.

7 *f* So to the God of earth and heaven,
the Father, Spirit, Son, be given
praise now, as praise has ever been
and ever shall be praise – Amen!

from *Venite* (Psalm 95)
© Christopher Idle (born 1938)†

17

COME REJOICE   8 7 8 7   © Noël Tredinnick (born 1949)†

1 Come, rejoice before your maker
all you peoples of the earth;
serve the Lord your God with gladness,
come before him with a song!

2 Know for certain that Jehovah
is the true and only God:
we are his, for he has made us;
we are sheep within his fold.

3 Come with grateful hearts before him,
enter now his courts with praise;
show your thankfulness towards him,
give due honour to his name.

4 For the Lord our God is gracious –
everlasting in his love;
and to every generation
his great faithfulness endures.

from *Jubilate Deo* (Psalm 100)
© Michael Baughen (born 1930)†

18

O QUANTA QUALIA   11 10 11 10   *Paris Antiphoner* 1681

1   Come, worship God who is worthy of honour,
    enter his presence with thanks and a song!
    he is the rock of his people's salvation,
    to whom our jubilant praises belong.

2   Ruled by his might
            are the heights of the mountains,
    held in his hands are the depths of the earth;
    his is the sea, his the land, for he made them,
    king above all gods, who gave us our birth.

3   We are his people, the sheep of his pasture,
    he is our maker and to him we pray;
    gladly we kneel in obedience before him –
    great is the God whom we worship this day!

4 Now let us listen, for God speaks among us,
   open our hearts and receive what he says:
   peace be to all who remember his goodness,
   trust in his promises, walk in his ways!

from *Venite* (Psalm 95)
© Michael Perry (born 1942)†

Alternative tune: EPIPHANY HYMN (338)

19

ADORAMUS 8 8 8 8   © Peggy Spencer Palmer (born 1900)

1 Now praise the protector of heaven,
   the purpose and power of the Lord;
   all praise for his work shall be given –
   our guide and defender and God.

2 In God's wise and wonderful plan
   was made every marvellous thing;
   in him all our blessings began –
   the Father of glory, the king.

3 He first made the sky's lofty dome,
   our holy creator and guard;
   then furnished the earth for our home –
   almighty, eternal, the Lord.

after Cædmon (c.670)
© Christopher Idle (born 1938)†

Alternative tune: CELESTE (450)

20

MONMOUTH 888888

G. Davis (c.1768–1824)

1 I'll praise my maker while I've breath,
  and when my voice is lost in death,
  praise shall possess my noblest powers;
  my days of praise are never past
  while life and thought and being last
  or immortality endures.

2 Happy are those whose hopes rely
  on God the Lord, who made the sky,
  the earth, the sea, the night and day;
  his truth for ever stands secure,
  he keeps his promise to the poor,
  and none who seeks is turned away.

3 The Lord gives eyesight to the blind,
  he calms and heals the troubled mind,
  he sends the wounded conscience peace;
  he helps the stranger in distress,
  the widow and the fatherless,
  and grants the prisoner glad release.

4 I'll praise him while he lends me breath,
  and when my voice is lost in death
  praise shall employ my noblest powers;
  my days of praise are never past
  while life and thought and being last
  or immortality endures.

I. Watts (1674–1748)
© in this version Jubilate Hymns†

21

ST. DENIO 11 11 11 11   Welsh hymn melody 1839

1 Immortal, invisible, God only wise,
  in light inaccessible hid from our eyes;
  most holy, most glorious, the ancient of days,
  almighty, victorious, your great name we praise.

2 Unresting, unhasting, and silent as light,
  nor wanting nor wasting, you rule us in might;
  your justice like mountains high soaring above,
  your clouds
        which are fountains of goodness and love.

3 To all life you give, Lord, to both great and small,
  in all life you live, Lord, the true life of all:
  we blossom and flourish, uncertain and frail;
  we wither and perish, but you never fail.

4   We worship before you, great Father of light,
    while angels adore you, all veiling their sight;
    our praises we render, O Father, to you
    whom only the splendour of light
        hides from view.

W. C. Smith (1824–1908)
© in this version Jubilate Hymns†

4 We wor - ship be -fore you, great Fa-ther_of light, while an - gels a -

-dore you, all _ veil-ing their sight; our prais-es_we_ ren-der, O Fa - - ther, to

you   whom on - ly the   splen-dour of _ light hides from view.

22

RUSSIAN ANTHEM 11 10 12 10 A. F. Lvov (1799–1870)

1   King of the universe, Lord of the ages,
     maker of all things, sustainer of life;
     source of authority, wise and just creator,
     hope of the nations: we praise and adore.

2   Powerful in majesty, throned in the heavens –
     sun, moon and stars by your word are upheld;
     time and eternity bow within your presence,
     Lord of the nations: we praise and adore.

3   Wisdom unsearchable, fathomless knowledge
     past understanding by our clever brain;
     ground of reality, basis of all order,
     guide to the nations: we praise and adore.

4   Justice and righteousness, holy, unswerving –
     all that is tainted shall burn in your flame;
     sword-bearing deity, punisher of evil,
     judge of the nations: we praise and adore.

5   Ruler and potentate, sage and lawgiver,
     humbled before you, unworthy we bow:
     in our extremity, show us your forgiveness,
     merciful Father: we praise and adore.

© Michael Saward (born 1932)†

23

MONKLAND 7777

Melody J. Freylinghausen (1670–1739)
adapted and harmonised J. B. Wilkes (1785–1869)
descant C. S. Lang (1891–1971)
descant © Novello & Co Ltd

7 Glo-ry then to God on high, 'Glo - ry!' let cre - a - tion cry:

for his mer - cy— shall en-dure, — ev - er faith-ful, ev - er sure.

for his mer - cy— shall en-dure, ev - er faith - ful, ev - er sure.

1 Let us gladly with one mind
  praise the Lord, for he is kind:
    for his mercy shall endure,
    ever faithful, ever sure.

2 He has made the realms of space,
  all things have their ordered place:
    for his mercy . . .

3 He created sky and sea,
  field and mountain, flower and tree:
    for his mercy . . .

4 Every creature, great and small –
  God alone has made them all:
    for his mercy . . .

5 Then he fashioned humankind,
  crown of all that he designed:
    for his mercy . . .

6 He has shaped our destiny –
  heaven for all eternity:
    for his mercy . . .

7 Glory then to God on high,
  'Glory!' let creation cry:
    for his mercy . . .

after J. Milton (1608–1674)
© in this version Michael Saward (born 1932)†

24

HANOVER 10 10 11 11

A Supplement to the New Version 1708
probably by W. Croft (1678–1727)
descant A. Gray (1855–1935)

6 O mea-sure-less Might, un-change-a-ble Love, whom an-gels de-light to wor-ship a - bove! your ran-somed cre-a-tion with glo-ry a - blaze, in true a-dor-a-tion shall sing to your praise!

1 *f* O worship the King all glorious above,
and gratefully sing his power and his love,
our shield and defender, the Ancient of Days,
pavilioned in splendour and girded with praise.

2 O tell of his might and sing of his grace,
whose robe is the light, whose canopy space;
his chariots of wrath
the deep thunder-clouds form,
and dark is his path on the wings of the storm.

3 *mf* The earth, with its store of wonders untold,
Almighty, your power has founded of old,
established it fast by a changeless decree,
and round it has cast like a garment the sea.

4 Your bountiful care what tongue can recite?
it breathes in the air, it shines in the light;
it streams from the hills, it descends to the plain,
and sweetly distils in the dew and the rain.

5 *mp* We children of dust are feeble and frail –
in you we will trust, for you never fail;
your mercies how tender, how firm to the end!
our maker, defender, redeemer and friend.

6 *f* O measureless Might, unchangeable Love,
whom angels delight to worship above!
your ransomed creation with glory ablaze,
in true adoration shall sing to your praise!

after W. Kethe (died 1594)
R. Grant (1779–1838)

25

ST. HELENS   12 13 13 10   © Kenneth Coates (born 1917)

1 Praise him, praise him, praise him,
    powers and dominations;
 praise his name in glorious light,
    you creatures of the day:
 moon and stars, ring praises
    through the constellations –
 Lord God, whose word
        shall never pass away!

2 Praise him, praise him, praise him,
    ocean depths and waters;
 elements of earth and heaven,
    your several praises blend:
 birds and beasts and cattle,
    Adam's sons and daughters,
 worship the king
        whose reign shall never end!

3 Praise him, praise him, praise him,
    saints of God who fear him;
 to the highest name of all,
    concerted anthems raise,
 all you seed of Israel,
    holy people near him
 whom he exalts to power
        and crowns with praise!

from Psalm 148
© Michael Perry (born 1942)†

Alternative tune: NICAEA (7)

26(i)

FRIARMERE VICARAGE 12 11 12 11

© Simon Beckley (born 1938)†
© arranged Noël Tredinnick (born 1949)†

Unison

1 The works of the Lord are created in wisdom,
   we view the earth's wonders and call him to mind;
   we hear what he says in the world we discover,
   and God shows his glory in all that we find.

2 Not even the angels have ever been granted
   to tell the full story of nature and grace;
   but open to God is all human perception,
   the mysteries of time and the secrets of space.

3 The sun every morning lights up his creation,
   the moon marks the rhythm
            of months in their turn;
   the glittering stars are arrayed in his honour,
   adorning the years as they ceaselessly burn.

26(ii)

STREETS OF LAREDO   12 11 12 11   American traditional melody
© arranged Noël Tredinnick (born 1949)†

Unison

4   The wind is his breath
          and the clouds are his signal,
   the rain and the snow are the robes of his choice;
   the storm and the lightning,
          his watchmen and heralds,
   the crash of the thunder, the sound of his voice.

5   The song is unfinished; how shall we complete it,
   and where find the skill to perfect all his praise?
   At work in all places, he cares for all peoples –
   how great is the Lord to the end of all days!

from Ecclesiasticus 42–43
© Christopher Idle (born 1938)†

27(i)

NORICUM 777777   F. James (1858–1922)

1 Who can measure heaven and earth?
God was present at their birth;
who can number seeds or sands?
every grain is in his hands:
through creation's countless days
every dawn sings out his praise.

2 Who can tell what wisdom brings,
first of all created things?
One alone is truly wise,
hidden from our earthbound eyes:
knowledge lies in him alone –
God, the Lord upon his throne!

3 Wisdom in his plans he laid,
planted her in all he made;
granted her to humankind,
sowed her truth in every mind:
but with richest wisdom blessed
those who love him first and best.

27(ii)

LUCERNA LAUDONIAE 7 7 7 7 7 7

D. Evans (1874–1948)
© Oxford University Press

4 Wisdom gives the surest wealth,
   brings her children life and health;
   teaches us to fear the Lord,
   marks a universe restored:
   heaven and earth she will outlast –
   happy those who hold her fast!

from Ecclesiasticus 1
© Christopher Idle (born 1938)†

For other hymns on this theme, see:
Sunday Themes index
    Section 1, The Creation (p. vii)
    Section 29 (2) The Good Shepherd (p. xii)
Song Section
    You are worthy (S.30)

GOD: LORD AND FATHER
Gracious and Merciful

28

AMAZING GRACE   8 6 8 6 (CM)

Traditional
© arranged John Barnard (born 1948)†

1 Amazing grace – how sweet the sound –
  that saved a wretch like me!
  I once was lost, but now am found;
  was blind, but now I see.

2 God's grace first taught my heart to fear,
  his grace my fears relieved;
  how precious did that grace appear
  the hour I first believed!

3 Through every danger, trial and snare
  I have already come;
  his grace has brought me safe thus far,
  and grace will lead me home.

4 The Lord has promised good to me,
   his word my hope secures;
   my shield and stronghold he shall be
   as long as life endures.

5 And when this earthly life is past,
   and mortal cares shall cease,
   I shall possess with Christ at last
   eternal joy and peace.

J. Newton (1725–1807)
© in this version Jubilate Hymns†

29

PASTOR PASTORUM   6 5 6 5   P. F. Silcher (1789–1860)

1 Faithful Shepherd, feed me
  in the pastures green;
  faithful Shepherd, lead me
  where your steps are seen:

2 Hold me fast, and guide me
  in the narrow way;
  so, with you beside me,
  I need never stray:

3 Daily bring me nearer
  to the heavenly shore;
  make my faith grow clearer,
  help me love you more:

4 Consecrate each pleasure,
  every joy and pain;
  you are all my treasure,
  all I hope to gain:

5 Day by day prepare me
  as you purpose best,
  mercy shall pursue me
  to your promised rest.

T. B. Pollock (1836–1896)
© in this version Jubilate Hymns†

30

REGENT SQUARE 8 7 8 7 8 7   H. T. Smart (1813–1879)

1 Fill your hearts with joy and gladness,
   sing and praise your God and mine!
   Great the Lord in love and wisdom,
   might and majesty divine!
   He who framed the starry heavens
   knows and names them as they shine.

2 Praise the Lord, his people, praise him!
   wounded souls his comfort know;
   those who fear him find his mercies,
   peace for pain and joy for woe;
   humble hearts are high exalted,
   human pride and power laid low.

3 Praise the Lord for times and seasons,
   cloud and sunshine, wind and rain;
   spring to melt the snows of winter
   till the waters flow again;
   grass upon the mountain pastures,
   golden valleys thick with grain.

4   Fill your hearts with joy and gladness,
     peace and plenty crown your days;
     love his laws, declare his judgements,
     walk in all his words and ways;
     he the Lord and we his children –
     praise the Lord, all people, praise!

from Psalm 147
© Timothy Dudley-Smith (born 1926)

Descant and arrangement © John Barnard (born 1948)†

31(i)

RIMINGTON   8 8 8 8 (LM)

F. Duckworth (1862–1941)
© Mrs. B. A. Duckworth

1   Give to our God immortal praise,
    mercy and truth are all his ways;
    wonders of grace to God belong:
    repeat his mercies in your song.

2   Give to the Lord of lords renown,
    the King of kings with glory crown:
    his mercies ever shall endure
    when lords and kings are known no more.

3   He built the earth, he spread the sky,
    and fixed the starry lights on high;
    wonders of grace to God belong:
    repeat his mercies in your song.

31(ii)

TRURO   8 8 8 8 (LM)   T. Williams' *Psalmodia Evangelica* 1789

4   He fills the sun with morning light,
    he bids the moon direct the night;
    his mercies ever shall endure
    when suns and moons shall shine no more.

5   He sent his Son with power to save
    from guilt and darkness and the grave;
    wonders of grace to God belong:
    repeat his mercies in your song.

6   All through this world he guides our feet
    and leads us to his heavenly seat;
    his mercies ever shall endure
    when this our world shall be no more.

I. Watts (1674–1748)
© in this version Jubilate Hymns†

32(i)

OLD YEAVERING 8887

© Noël Tredinnick (born 1949)†

Unison

v. 3 Melody in tenor

3 Like the Sum-mer breez-es play-ing, like the tall trees soft - ly sway-ing,

tall trees soft-ly sway-ing,

like the lips of sil - ent pray - ing is the per-fect peace of God.

like the lips of sil-ent

32(ii)

QUEM PASTORES LAUDAVERE   8 8 8 7

German carol melody
fourteenth century
arranged R. Vaughan Williams (1872–1958)
arrangement © Oxford University Press

1   Like a mighty river flowing,
     like a flower in beauty growing,
     far beyond all human knowing
        is the perfect peace of God.

2   Like the hills serene and even,
     like the coursing clouds of heaven,
     like the heart that's been forgiven
        is the perfect peace of God.

3   Like the summer breezes playing,
     like the tall trees softly swaying,
     like the lips of silent praying
        is the perfect peace of God.

4   Like the morning sun ascended,
     like the scents of evening blended,
     like a friendship never ended
        is the perfect peace of God.

5   Like the azure ocean swelling,
     like the jewel all-excelling,
     far beyond our human telling
        is the perfect peace of God.

© Michael Perry (born 1942)†

33(i)

NUN DANKET   6 7 6 7 6 6 6 6

Later form of melody by
J. Crüger (1598–1662)

1 Now thank we all our God
  with hearts and hands and voices;
  such wonders he has done!
  in him the world rejoices.
  He, from our mothers' arms,
  has blessed us on our way
  with countless gifts of love,
  and still is ours today.

2 So may this generous God
  through all our life be near us;
  to fill our hearts with joy,
  and with his peace to cheer us:
  to keep us in his grace,
  and guide us when perplexed;
  to free us from all ills
  in this world and the next.

3 All praise and thanks to God
  who reigns in highest heaven,
  to Father and to Son
  and Spirit now be given:
  this one eternal God,
  whom heaven and earth adore,
  is he who was, is now,
  and shall be evermore.

after M. Rinkart (1586–1649)
Catherine Winkworth (1827–1878)

A descant and arrangement for verse 3 is printed overleaf.

Descant and arrangement C. S. Lang (1891–1971)

3 All praise and thanks to God __

__ who reigns __ in high - est hea - ven,

to Fa-ther and to Son __ and Spir - it now __ be giv - en:

this one e - ter - nal God, __
_ whom heaven __ and earth a - dore,
is he who was, is now, __ and shall __ be ev - er - more.

33(ii)

GRACIAS 67 67 6 6 6 6

G. P. Beaumont (1903–1970)
arranged John Barnard (born 1948)
by permission of © Paxton Music Ltd

The unison and harmony versions are harmonically compatible.

1 Now thank we all our God
with hearts and hands and voices;
such wonders he has done!
in him the world rejoices.
He, from our mothers' arms,
has blessed us on our way
with countless gifts of love,
and still is ours today.

2 So may this generous God
through all our life be near us;
to fill our hearts with joy,
and with his peace to cheer us:
to keep us in his grace,
and guide us when perplexed;
to free us from all ills
in this world and the next.

3 All praise and thanks to God
who reigns in highest heaven,
to Father and to Son
and Spirit now be given:
this one eternal God,
whom heaven and earth adore,
is he who was, is now,
and shall be evermore.

after M. Rinkart (1586–1649)
Catherine Winkworth (1827–1878)

34

VENICE 6 6 8 6 (SM)   W. Amps (1824–1910)

1 O bless the Lord, my soul!
   let all within me join
   and help my tongue to praise his name
   whose mercies are divine.

2 O bless the Lord, my soul!
   let not his mercies lie
   forgotten in unthankfulness,
   from lack of praise to die.

3 For God forgives our sins
   and God relieves our pain;
   the Lord who heals our sicknesses
   renews our strength again.

4 He crowns our life with love
   when ransomed from the grave;
   he who redeemed my soul from hell
   has sovereign power to save.

5 The Lord provides our food
   and gives the sufferers rest;
   the Lord has judgement for the proud
   and justice for the oppressed.

6 His mighty works and ways
   by Moses he made known,
   but gave the world his truth and grace
   by his belovèd Son.

                                    I. Watts (1674–1748)

35

MARTYRDOM 8 6 8 6 (CM)   H. Wilson (1766–1824)

1 O God of Jacob, by whose hand
   your children still are fed;
   who through this earthly pilgrimage
   your people safely led:

2 Our vows, our prayers, we now present
   before your gracious throne;
   as you have been their faithful God,
   so always be our own!

3 Through each perplexing path of life
   our wandering footsteps guide;
   give us today our daily bread,
   and for our needs provide.

4 O spread your covering wings around
   till all our wanderings cease,
   and at our heavenly Father's home
   we shall arrive in peace.

P. Doddridge (1702–1751)
© in this version Jubilate Hymns†

36

THAXTED   13 13 13 13 13 13

G. T. Holst (1874–1934)

1 O God beyond all praising,
    we worship you today
and sing the love amazing
    that songs cannot repay;
for we can only wonder
    at every gift you send,
at blessings without number
    and mercies without end:
we lift our hearts before you
    and wait upon your word,
we honour and adore you,
    our great and mighty Lord.

2 Then hear, O gracious Saviour,
    accept the love we bring,
that we who know your favour
    may serve you as our king;
and whether our tomorrows
    be filled with good or ill,
we'll triumph through our sorrows
    and rise to bless you still:
to marvel at your beauty
    and glory in your ways,
and make a joyful duty
    our sacrifice of praise.

37

ST. ANNE   8 6 8 6 (CM)   *A Supplement to the New Version* 1708
                                                probably by W. Croft (1678–1727)

1 *f* O God, our help in ages past,
       our hope for years to come,
       our shelter from the stormy blast,
       and our eternal home:

2 *mf* Beneath the shadow of your throne
        your people lived secure;
        sufficient is your arm alone,
        and our defence is sure.

3   Before the hills in order stood,
        or earth from darkness came,
        from everlasting you are God,
        to endless years the same.

4   A thousand ages in your sight
        are like an evening gone;
        short as the watch that ends the night,
        before the rising sun.

5 *mp* Time, like an ever-rolling stream,
        will bear us all away;
        we pass forgotten, as a dream
        dies with the dawning day.

6 *f* O God, our help in ages past,
       our hope for years to come:
       be our defence while life shall last,
       and our eternal home!

I. Watts (1674–1748)

Descant and arrangement by G. T. Shaw (1879–1943)
© Novello & Co Ltd

6 O God, our help in a - ges past, our hope for years to come: be our de-fence while life shall last, and our e - ter-nal home!

38

PRAISE, MY SOUL   878787

J. Goss (1800–1880)
descant © Robin Sheldon (born 1932)

1 *f* Praise, my soul, the king of hea - ven! to his feet your tri - bute bring: ran-somed, healed, re- stored, for - gi - ven, who like me his praise should sing? Al - le - lu - ia,

al - le - lu - ia! praise the e - ver - last - ing king!

Harmony

2 mf Praise him for his grace and fa - vour to our fa - thers

in dis - tress; Praise him still the same as e - ver,

slow to blame and swift to bless: Al - le - lu - ia,

- lu - ia, al - le - lu - ia! wide-ly as his mer-cy flows.

Descant
4 *f* An-gels, help us to a-dore him — you be-hold him

Unison
4 *f* An-gels, help us to a-dore him — you be-hold him

face to face; sun and moon, bow down be-fore him,

face to face; sun and moon, bow down be-fore him,

H. F. Lyte (1793–1847)

39

CONTEMPLATION 8 6 8 6 (CM)

F. A. G. Ouseley (1825–1889)

1   When all your mercies, O my God,
    my thankful soul surveys,
    uplifted by the view, I'm lost
    in wonder, love and praise.

2   Unnumbered blessings to my soul
    your tender care bestowed
    before my infant heart perceived
    from whom these blessings flowed.

3   Ten thousand thousand precious gifts
    my daily thanks employ;
    nor is the least a thankful heart
    that takes those gifts with joy.

4   In health and sickness, joy and pain,
    your goodness I'll pursue;
    and after death, in distant worlds,
    the glorious theme renew.

5   Throughout eternity, O Lord,
    a joyful song I'll raise;
    but all eternity's too short
    to utter all your praise!

J. Addison (1672–1719)
© in this version Jubilate Hymns†

40

LOBE DEN HERREN 14 14 4 7 8   *Stralsund Gesangbuch* 1665
descant C. S. Lang (1891–1971)
descant © Novello & Co Ltd

4 Praise to the Lord— O let all that is in me a - dore — him! All that has

life and breath, come now with prais-es be-fore — him! Let the 'A-men!' sound

— from his peo-ple a - gain— glad-ly with praise we a - dore ____ him!

1   Praise to the Lord,
        the almighty, the king of creation!
    O my soul, praise him,
        for he is your health and salvation!
    Come, all who hear;
        brothers and sisters, draw near,
    praise him in glad adoration!

2   Praise to the Lord,
        above all things so mightily reigning;
    keeping us safe at his side,
        and so gently sustaining.
    Have you not seen
        all you have needed has been
    met by his gracious ordaining?

3   Praise to the Lord,
        who shall prosper our work and defend us;
    surely his goodness and mercy
        shall daily attend us.
    Ponder anew
        what the almighty can do,
    who with his love will befriend us.

4   Praise to the Lord –
        O let all that is in me adore him!
    All that has life and breath,
        come now with praises before him!
    Let the 'Amen!'
        sound from his people again –
    gladly with praise we adore him!

> after J. Neander (1650–1680)
> Catherine Winkworth (1827–1878) and others

41

WEALDSTONE 8 7 8 7 D

1   Tell his praise in song and story,
    bless the Lord with heart and voice;
    in my God is all my glory –
    come before him and rejoice:
    join to praise his name together,
    he who hears his people's cry;
    tell his praise, come wind or weather,
    shining faces lifted high.

2   To the Lord whose love has found them
    cry the poor in their distress;
    swift his angels camped around them
    prove him sure to save and bless.
    God it is who hears our crying
    though the spark of faith be dim:
    taste and see! beyond denying
    blessed are those who trust in him.

3   Taste and see! In faith draw near him,
    trust the Lord with all your powers;
    seek and serve him, love and fear him,
    life and all its joys are ours –
    true delight in holy living,
    peace and plenty, length of days:
    come, my children, with thanksgiving
    bless the Lord in songs of praise.

4   In our need he walks beside us,
    ears alert to every cry;
    watchful eyes to guard and guide us,
    love that whispers 'It is I'.
    Good shall triumph, wrong be righted,
    God has pledged his promised word;
    so with ransomed saints united
    join to praise our living Lord!

            from Psalm 34
            © Timothy Dudley-Smith (born 1926)

Alternative tune: ABBOT'S LEIGH (494)

42(i)

WOODLANDS 10 10 10 10

W. Greatorex (1877–1949)
© Oxford University Press
descant © David Iliff (born 1939)†

4 Tell out, my soul, the glo-ries of his word!___ firm is his_
pro-mise and his mer-cy sure: tell out my soul,___ the great - ness
of the Lord to child-ren's child-ren and for _____ ev-er - more!

42(ii)

GO FORTH   10 10 10 10

© Michael Baughen (born 1930)†
© arranged Noël Tredinnick (born 1949)†

1 Tell out, my soul, the greatness of the Lord!
   unnumbered blessings, give my spirit voice;
   tender to me the promise of his word –
   in God my saviour shall my heart rejoice.

2 Tell out, my soul, the greatness of his name!
   make known his might,
           the deeds his arm has done;
   his mercy sure, from age to age the same –
   his holy name: the Lord, the mighty one.

3 Tell out, my soul, the greatness of his might!
   powers and dominions lay their glory by;
   proud hearts and stubborn wills are put to flight,
   the hungry fed, the humble lifted high.

4 Tell out, my soul, the glories of his word!
   firm is his promise, and his mercy sure:
   tell out, my soul, the greatness of the Lord
   to children's children and for evermore!

from *Magnificat* (Luke 1)
© Timothy Dudley-Smith (born 1926)

43

SPIRITUS VITAE   9 8 9 8

Mary Jane Hammond (1878–1964)
© information sought

1   Thank you, O Lord of earth and heaven,
    thank you for all your love has planned;
    thank you for food and daily blessings,
    gifts from your ever-gracious hand.

2   Thank you for such a great salvation,
    mercy as boundless as the sea;
    thank you for love which died to save us,
    love which gave all to set us free.

3   Thank you for means of grace and guidance,
    gifts of your Spirit, strength divine;
    thank you for word and prayer and symbol,
    food for our souls in bread and wine.

4   Thank you for that blessed hope of glory,
    great day when Christ shall come again,
    day when, in perfect love and justice
    he in his majesty shall reign.

5   Grant us, because of all your mercies,
    lips which proclaim our thanks and praise;
    lives which, in loving glad surrender,
    serve and adore you all their days.

6   Glory to God our heavenly Father,
    glory to Jesus, God the Son,
    glory to God the Holy Spirit,
    glory to God the Three-in-One.

from *A General Thanksgiving*
by E. Reynolds (1599–1676)
J. E. Seddon (1915–1983)
© Mrs M. Seddon†

44(i)

DOMINUS REGIT ME 8 7 8 7   J. B. Dykes (1823–1876)

1 *mf* The king of love my shepherd is,
       whose goodness fails me never;
       I nothing lack if I am his
       and he is mine for ever.

2   Where streams of living water flow
      a ransomed soul, he leads me;
      and where the fertile pastures grow,
      with food from heaven feeds me.

3   Perverse and foolish I have strayed,
      but in his love he sought me;
      and on his shoulder gently laid,
      and home, rejoicing, brought me.

4 *mp* In death's dark vale I fear no ill
       with you, dear Lord, beside me;
       your rod and staff my comfort still,
       your cross before to guide me.

5 *mf* You spread a banquet in my sight
       of love beyond all knowing;
       and O the gladness and delight
       from your pure chalice flowing!

6 *f* And so through all the length of days
      your goodness fails me never:
      Good Shepherd, may I sing your praise
      within your house for ever!

H. W. Baker (1821–1877)
© in this version Jubilate Hymns†

44(ii)

THE FOLLOWERS   8 7 8 7

The Followers, © Nick Whitley
© arranged Norman Warren (born 1934)†
descants © Ivor Keys (born 1919)

Descant 1 is for part of the congregation to sing.
Descant 2 is for choir or instrument.

Alternative tune: ST. COLUMBA (404)

45(i)

BEDFORDSHIRE MAY-DAY CAROL   8 6 8 6 (CM)   English traditional melody
© arranged Paul Edwards (born 1955)†

1   The Lord my shepherd rules my life
    and gives me all I need;
    he leads me by refreshing streams,
    in pastures green I feed.

2   The Lord revives my failing strength,
    he makes my joy complete;
    and in right paths, for his name's sake,
    he guides my faltering feet.

3   Though in a valley dark as death,
    no evil makes me fear;
    your shepherd's staff protects my way,
    for you are with me there.

4   While all my enemies look on
    you spread a royal feast;
    you fill my cup, anoint my head,
    and treat me as your guest.

45(ii)

BROTHER JAMES' AIR 8 6 8 6 (CM) extended

J. L. MacBeth Bain
© arranged John Barnard (born 1948)†

When this tune is used the last two lines of each verse are repeated.

5 Your goodness and your gracious love
   pursue me all my days;
   your house, O Lord, shall be my home –
   your name, my endless praise.

6 To Father, Son, and Spirit, praise!
   to God whom we adore
   be worship, glory, power and love,
   both now and evermore.

from Psalm 23
© in this version Christopher Idle (born 1938)†

(see also traditional version, 591)

Alternative tune: CRIMOND (591)

46

WILTSHIRE   8 6 8 6 (CM)   G. T. Smart (1776–1867)

1 *mf* Through all the changing scenes of life,
          in trouble and in joy,
          the praises of my God shall still
          my heart and tongue employ.

2 *f*   O glorify the Lord with me,
          with me exalt his name!
          when in distress, to him I called –
          he to my rescue came.

3 *mf* The hosts of God encamp around
          the dwellings of the just;
          his saving help he gives to all
          who in his mercy trust.

4   O taste his goodness, prove his love!
          experience will decide
          how blessed they are, and only they,
          who in his truth confide.

5   Fear him, you saints, and you will then
          have nothing else to fear;
          his service shall be your delight,
          your needs shall be his care.

6 *f* To Father, Son and Spirit, praise!
to God whom we adore
be worship, glory, power and love,
both now and evermore!

from Psalm 34
N. Tate (1652–1715) and
N. Brady (1659–1726)
© in this version Jubilate Hymns†

Descant and arrangement © John Barnard (born 1948)†

47(i)

PATRIXBOURNE 878787

© John Barnard (born 1948)†

The descant should be sung to *Ah*

Alternative tune: ALL SAINTS (561)

47(ii)

TIMELESS LOVE   8 7 8 7 8 7   © Norman Warren (born 1934)†

1 Timeless love! We sing the story,
   praise his wonders, tell his worth;
   love more fair than heaven's glory,
   love more firm than ancient earth!
   Tell his faithfulness abroad –
   who is like him? Praise the Lord!

2 By his faithfulness surrounded,
   north and south his hand proclaim;
   earth and heaven formed and founded,
   skies and seas, declare his name!
   Wind and storm obey his word –
   who is like him? Praise the Lord!

3 Truth and righteousness enthrone him,
   just and equal are his ways;
   more than happy, those who own him,
   more than joy, their songs of praise!
   Sun and shield and great reward –
   who is like him? Praise the Lord!

from Psalm 89
© Timothy Dudley-Smith (born 1926)

48

ALBERTA   10 4 10 4 10 10

W. H. Harris (1883–1973)

1   Unto the hills around me
                I lift up my longing eyes;
    whence shall my hope and my salvation come
                and whence arise?
    From God the Lord shall come my certain aid,
    from God the Lord,
                who heaven and earth has made.

2   Your God will never let your footsteps stray,
                his grasp is sure;
    he will not sleep, but holds your life in his;
                you are secure:
    God never slumbers; he is always there,
    and keeps his people in his tender care.

3   God is the Lord, your stronghold and defence,
                your shield and shade;
    he will protect by his almighty power
                the life he made:
    no sun shall harm by day, nor moon by night;
    he is your guardian, you are his delight.

4   From every evil he shall keep your soul,
                from every sin;
    God shall preserve your life as you go out,
                as you come in:
    guarding above you, he whom we adore
    will keep you henceforth and for evermore.

                    from Psalm 121
                    J. D. S. Campbell (1845–1914)
                    © in this version Jubilate Hymns†

For other hymns on this theme, see:
Sunday Themes index
    Section 29 (2), The Good Shepherd (p. xii)
King of glory, king of peace (603)
Song Section
    Praise him, praise him (S.21)

GOD: LORD AND SAVIOUR
Promised and Incarnate

49

ES IST EIN' ROS'   7 6 7 6 6 7 6

Old German tune harmonised by
M. Praetorius (1571–1621)

Re - peat the hymn a - gain: ____ 'To God on high be glo - ry, and peace on ____ earth. ____ A - men.'

1 A great and mighty wonder:
redemption drawing near!
the virgin bears the infant,
the prince of peace is here!
Repeat the hymn again:
'To God on high be glory,
and peace on earth. Amen.'

2 The Word becomes incarnate
and yet remains on high;
the shepherds hear the anthem
as glory fills the sky –
repeat the hymn again:
'To God on high . . .

3 The angels sing the story:
rejoice, O distant lands!
you valleys, forests, mountains,
and oceans, clap your hands!
Repeat the hymn again:
'To God on high . . .

4 He comes to save all nations:
let all now hear his word!
approach and bring him worship,
the saviour and the Lord!
Repeat the hymn again:
'To God on high . . .

after Germanus (c.634–732)
J. M. Neale (1818–1866)
© in this version Jubilate Hymns†

50

THIS ENDRIS NYGHT 8 6 8 6 (CM)

English carol melody
fifteenth century
arranged R. Vaughan Williams (1872–1958)
arrangement © Oxford University Press

1   Behold, the great Creator makes
himself a house of clay;
a robe of human form he takes
for ever from this day.

2   Hear this! – the wise eternal Word
as Mary's infant cries;
a servant is our mighty Lord,
and God in cradle lies.

3   Glad shepherds run to view this sight,
a choir of angels sings;
wise men from far with pure delight
adore the King of kings.

4   These wonders all the world amaze
and shake the starry frame;
the host of heaven stand to gaze,
and bless the Saviour's name.

5   Join then, all hearts that are not stone,
and all our voices prove
to celebrate the holy one,
the God of peace and love.

T. Pestel (c.1585–1660)
© in this version Jubilee Hymns†

51

BUNESSAN   10 8 10 8

Gaelic melody
© arranged Noël Tredinnick (born 1949)†

1   Child in the manger, infant of Mary,
    outcast and stranger, Lord of all!
    child who inherits all our transgressions,
    all our demerits on him fall.

2   Once the most holy child of salvation
    gentle and lowly lived below:
    now as our glorious mighty redeemer,
    see him victorious over each foe.

3   Prophets foretold him, infant of wonder;
    angels behold him on his throne:
    worthy our saviour of all their praises;
    happy for ever are his own.

                    after Mary MacDonald (1789–1872)
                    L. Macbean (1853–1931)

52

CROSS OF JESUS   8 7 8 7   J. Stainer (1840–1901)

1 Come, O long-expected Jesus,
   born to set your people free!
   from our fears and sins release us,
   Christ in whom our rest shall be.

2 Israel's strength and consolation,
   born salvation to impart;
   dear desire of every nation,
   joy of every longing heart:

3 Born your people to deliver,
   born a child and yet a king;
   born to reign in us for ever,
   now your gracious kingdom bring:

4 By your own eternal Spirit
   rule in all our hearts alone;
   by your all-sufficient merit
   raise us to your glorious throne.

C. Wesley (1707–1788)
© in this version Jubilate Hymns†

53(i)

MORWENSTOW   899998

Christopher Dearnley (born 1930)
© Oxford University Press

1 Child of the stable's secret birth,
   the Lord by right of the lords of earth;
   let angels sing of a king new-born –
   the world is weaving a crown of thorn:
   a crown of thorn for that infant head
   cradled soft in the manger bed.

2 Eyes that shine in the lantern's ray;
   a face so small in its nest of hay –
   face of a child who is born to scan
   the world he made, through the eyes of man:
   and from that face in the final day
   earth and heaven shall flee away.

3 Voice that rang through the courts on high
   contracted now to a wordless cry,
   a voice to master the wind and wave,
   the human heart and the hungry grave:
   the voice of God through the cedar trees
   rolling forth as the sound of seas.

53(ii)

SECRET BIRTH   899998   © Norman Warren (born 1934)†

vv. 2,3,4

4   Infant hands in a mother's hand,
    for none but Mary may understand
    whose are the hands and the fingers curled
    but his who fashioned and made our world;
    and through these hands in the hour of death
    nails shall strike to the wood beneath.

5   Child of the stable's secret birth,
    the Father's gift to a wayward earth,
    to drain the cup in a few short years
    of all our sorrows, our sins and tears –
    ours the prize for the road he trod:
    risen with Christ; at peace with God.

© Timothy Dudley-Smith (born 1926)

54

LINGWOOD   8 7 8 7 8 7   C. Armstrong Gibbs (1889–1960)
© J. Curwen & Sons Ltd/William Elkin Music Services

1 Earth was waiting, spent and restless,
   with a mingled hope and fear,
   faithful men and women praying,
   'Surely, Lord, the day is near:
   the Desire of all the nations –
   it is time he should appear!'

2 Then the Spirit of the Highest
   to a virgin meek came down,
   and he burdened her with blessing,
   and he pained her with renown;
   for she bore the Lord's anointed
   for his cross and for his crown.

3 Earth has groaned and laboured for him
   since the ages first began,
   for in him was hid the secret
   which through all the ages ran –
   Son of Mary, Son of David,
   Son of God, and Son of Man.

                                    W. C. Smith (1824–1908)

55(i)

FAITHFUL VIGIL   6 5 6 5

© David Wilson (born 1940)†
© arranged John Barnard (born 1948)†

(ii)

FAWLEY LODGE   6 5 6 5

© Norman Warren (born 1934)†

1 Faithful vigil ended,
watching, waiting cease:
Master, grant your servant
his discharge in peace.

2 All the Spirit promised,
all the Father willed,
now these eyes behold it
perfectly fulfilled.

3 This your great deliverance
sets your people free;
Christ their light uplifted
all the nations see.

4 Christ, your people's glory!
watching, doubting cease;
grant to us your servants
our discharge in peace.

from *Nunc Dimittis* (Luke 2)
© Timothy Dudley-Smith (born 1926)

56

CORDE NATUS 8 7 8 7 8 7 7

Melody from *Piae Cantiones* 1582
© arranged with descant David Iliff (born 1939)†

Descant

5 Christ be praised with God the Fa - ther, and the Ho - ly

Unison

Spi - rit, praised! hymns of wor-ship, high thanks - giv - ing

e - cho, e - cho through a world a - mazed:

Hon - our, ma - jes - ty, do - min - ion! songs of vic - to -

-ry be raised ev - er - more and ev - er - more!

1 God of God, the uncreated,
   love before the world began;
   he the source and he the ending,
   Son of God and Son of Man,
   Lord of all the things that have been,
   master of the eternal plan,
        evermore and evermore.

2 He is here, whom generations
   sought throughout the ages long;
   promised by the ancient prophets,
   justice for a world of wrong,
   God's salvation for the faithful:
   him we praise in endless song
        evermore and evermore.

3 Happy is that day for ever
   when, by God the Spirit's grace,
   lowly Mary, virgin mother,
   bore the saviour of our race.
   Man and child, the world's redeemer
   now displays his sacred face
        evermore and evermore.

4 Praise him, heaven of the heavens,
   praise him, angels in the height;
   priests and prophets, bow before him,
   saints who longed to see this sight.
   Let no human voice be silent,
   in his glory hearts unite
        evermore and evermore!

5 Christ be praised with God the Father,
   and the Holy Spirit, praised!
   hymns of worship, high thanksgiving
   echo through a world amazed:
   Honour, majesty, dominion!
   songs of victory be raised
        evermore and evermore!

after Prudentius (348–c.413)
J. M. Neale (1818–1866) and
H. W. Baker (1821–1877)
© in this version Jubilate Hymns†

57

BEACON HILL 10 10 10 10

© Peter White (born 1937)†

1 *mp* Had he not loved us
he had never come,
yet is he love
and love is all his way;
low to the mystery
of the virgin's womb
Christ bows his glory –
born on Christmas Day.

2 Had he not loved us
he had never come;
had he not come
he need have never died,
nor won the victory
of the vacant tomb,
the awful triumph
of the crucified.

3 Had he not loved us
he had never come;
still were we lost
in sorrow, sin and shame,
the doors fast shut
on our eternal home
mf which now stand open –
for he loved and came.

© Timothy Dudley-Smith (born 1926)

Alternative tune: SURSUM CORDA (399)

58(i)

BIRABUS 8 7 8 7

Peter Cutts (born 1937)
© Oxford University Press

(ii)

EVERSLEY 8 7 8 7

© Michael Perry (born 1942)†
© arranged Christian Strover (born 1932)†

1 Jesus, hope of every nation,
  light of heaven upon our way;
  promise of the world's salvation,
  spring of life's eternal day!

2 Saints by faith on God depending
  wait to see Messiah born;
  sin's oppressive night is ending
  in the glory of the dawn.

3 Look, he comes! – the long-awaited
  Christ, redeemer, living Word;
  hope and faith are vindicated
  as with joy we greet the Lord.

4 Glory in the highest heaven
  to the Father, Spirit, Son;
  and on earth let praise be given
  to our God, the Three-in-One!

Alternative tunes: SHIPSTON (282)
HALTON HOLGATE (370)

from *Nunc Dimittis* (Luke 2)
© Michael Perry (born 1942)†

59

MENDELSSOHN   7 7 7 7 D and refrain   F. Mendelssohn (1809–1847)

f Hark! the he-rald an-gels sing glo - ry — to the new-born King.

1   Hark! the herald angels sing
    glory to the new-born King;
    peace on earth and mercy mild,
    God and sinners reconciled!
    Joyful all you nations rise,
    join the triumph of the skies;
    with the angelic host proclaim,
    'Christ is born in Bethlehem':
        Hark! the herald angels sing
        glory to the new-born King.

2   Christ, by highest heaven adored,
    Christ, the everlasting Lord;
    late in time behold him come,
    offspring of a virgin's womb:
    veiled in flesh the Godhead see,
    hail the incarnate Deity!
    pleased as man with us to dwell,
    Jesus our Emmanuel:
        Hark! the herald . . .

3   Hail the heaven-born Prince of peace,
    hail the Sun of righteousness;
    light and life to all he brings,
    risen with healing in his wings:
    mild, he lays his glory by,
    born that we no more may die;
    born to raise us from the earth,
    born to give us second birth:
        Hark! the herald . . .

C. Wesley (1707–1788) and others

A descant and arrangement for verse 3 is printed overleaf.

Descant and arrangement by David Willcocks (born 1919)
© Oxford University Press

more may die; born to raise us from the earth,

born to give us se - cond birth: Hark! the he - rald

an - gels sing glo - ry to the new - born King.

60(i)

FAIRMILE 7 7 7 7   © David Peacock (born 1949)†

1 Holy child, how still you lie!
  safe the manger, soft the hay;
  faint upon the eastern sky
  breaks the dawn of Christmas Day.

2 Holy child, whose birthday brings
  shepherds from their field and fold,
  angel choirs and eastern kings,
  myrrh and frankincense and gold:

3 Holy child – what gift of grace
  from the Father freely willed!
  In your infant form we trace
  all God's promises fulfilled.

4 Holy child, whose human years
  span like ours delight and pain;
  one in human joys and tears,
  one in all but sin and stain:

5 Holy child, so far from home,
  all the lost to seek and save,
  to what dreadful death you come,
  to what dark and silent grave!

60(ii)

HOLY CHILD 7777D

© Michael Baughen (born 1930)†
© arranged Noël Tredinnick (born 1949)†

6 Holy child, before whose name
powers of darkness faint and fall;
conquered, death and sin and shame –
Jesus Christ is Lord of all!

7 Holy child, how still you lie!
safe the manger, soft the hay;
clear upon the eastern sky
breaks the dawn of Christmas Day.

© Timothy Dudley-Smith (born 1926)

Alternative tune: SAVANNAH (150)

61

PICARDY 878787

French traditional carol
as in *The English Hymnal* 1906

Unison

1 *mp* Let all mortal flesh keep silence,
      and with fear and trembling stand;
      set your minds on things eternal,
      for with blessing in his hand
      Christ our God to earth descending
      comes our homage to command.

2 *mf* King of kings, yet born of Mary,
      once upon the earth he stood;
      Lord of lords we now perceive him
      in his body and his blood –
      he will give to all the faithful
      his own self for heavenly food.

3   Rank on rank the host of heaven
      stream before him on the way;
      as the Light of light descending
      from the realms of endless day
   f vanquishes the powers of evil,
      clears the gloom of hell away.

4 At his feet the six-winged seraphs,
  cherubim with sleepless eye,
  veil their faces in his presence
  as with ceaseless voice they cry:
  Alleluia, alleluia,
  alleluia, Lord most high!

after the *Liturgy of James*
G. Moultrie (1829–1885)
© in this version Jubilate Hymns†

62

HERMITAGE   6 7 6 7

R. O. Morris (1886–1948)
© Oxford University Press

Unison

1 Love came down at Christmas,
  love all lovely, love divine;
  love was born at Christmas –
  star and angels gave the sign.

2 Worship we the Godhead,
  love incarnate, love divine;
  worship we our Jesus –
  what shall be our sacred sign?

3 Love shall be our token,
  love be yours and love be mine;
  love to God and neighbour,
  love for prayer and gift and sign.

Christina Rossetti (1830–1894)
© in this version Jubilate Hymns†

63

BERGERS · 9 8 9 8 9 8

French traditional carol
arranged M. E. F. Shaw (1875–1958)
arrangement © Oxford University Press

1. Lord, you were rich beyond all splendour,
   yet, for love's sake, became so poor;
   leaving your throne in glad surrender,
   sapphire-paved courts for stable floor:
   Lord, you were rich beyond all splendour,
   yet, for love's sake, became so poor.

2. You are our God beyond all praising,
   yet, for love's sake, became a man;
   stooping so low, but sinners raising
   heavenwards, by your eternal plan:
   you are our God, beyond all praising,
   yet, for love's sake, became a man.

3 Lord, you are love beyond all telling,
  Saviour and King, we worship you;
  Emmanuel, within us dwelling,
  make us and keep us pure and true:
  Lord, you are love beyond all telling,
  Saviour and King, we worship you.

F. Houghton (1894–1972)
© Overseas Missionary Fellowship
and in this version Jubilate Hymns†

64

EISENACH   8 8 8 8 (LM)   J. H. Schein (1586–1630)

1 To us a child of royal birth,
  heir of the promises, is given;
  the Invisible appears on earth,
  the Son of Man, the God of heaven.

2 A saviour born, in love supreme
  he comes our fallen souls to raise;
  he comes his people to redeem
  with all the fulness of his grace.

3 The Christ foretold by prophecy
  and filled with all the Spirit's power,
  our prophet, priest and king is he,
  the mighty Lord whom we adore.

4 The Lord of hosts, the God most high
  who leaves his throne to live on earth,
  with joy we welcome from the sky
  and take into our hearts by faith.

C. Wesley (1707–1788)
© in this version Jubilate Hymns†

65

ADESTE FIDELES   Irregular

Eighteenth-century melody probably by
J. F. Wade (1711–1786)
arranged mainly W. H. Monk (1823–1889)

O come, let us a - dore him, O come, let us a-

-dore him, O come, let us a - dore him, ─ Christ ─ the Lord!

1 O come, all you faithful,
   joyful and triumphant!
   O come now, O come now, to Bethlehem!
   Come and behold him, born the king of angels:
        O come, let us adore him,
        O come, let us adore him,
   O come, let us adore him, Christ the Lord!

2 God from God,
   Light from light,
   he who abhors not the virgin's womb;
   very God, begotten, not created:
        O come . . .

3 Sing, choirs of angels,
   sing in exultation!
   Sing, all you citizens of heaven above,
   'Glory to God in the highest!'
        O come . . .

4 Yes, Lord, we greet you,
   born for our salvation;
   Jesus, to you be glory given!
   Word of the Father now in flesh appearing:
        O come . . .

OR on Christmas morning:

4 Yes, Lord, we greet you,
   born this happy morning;
   Jesus, to you be glory given!
   Word of the Father now in flesh appearing:
        O come . . .

                    after J. F. Wade (1711–1786)
                    F. Oakeley (1802–1880) and others

(see also traditional long version, 597)

A descant and arrangement for verse 3 is printed overleaf.
For alternative descant and arrangement see 597.

Descant and arrangement David Willcocks (born 1919)
© Oxford University Press

For alternative descant and arrangement see 597.

66

VENI EMMANUEL 888888

Fifteenth-century plainsong melody
© arranged Noël Tredinnick (born 1949)†

1 O come, O come, Emmanuel
  and ransom captive Israel
  who mourns in lonely exile here
  until the Son of God draws near:
      Rejoice, rejoice!
  Emmanuel shall come to you, O Israel.

2 O come, true Branch of Jesse, free
  your children from this tyranny;
  from depths of hell your people save
  to rise victorious from the grave:
      Rejoice, rejoice . . .

3 O come, bright Daybreak, come and cheer
  our spirits by your advent here;
  dispel the long night's lingering gloom
  and pierce the shadows of the tomb:
      Rejoice, rejoice . . .

4 O come, strong Key of David, come
  and open wide our heavenly home;
  make safe the way that leads on high,
  and close the path to misery:
      Rejoice, rejoice . . .

5 O come, O come, great Lord of might
  who long ago on Sinai's height
  gave all your tribes the ancient law,
  in cloud and majesty and awe:
      Rejoice, rejoice . . .

from the Latin (thirteenth century)
J. M. Neale (1818–1866) and others
© in this version Jubilate Hymns†

67

IRBY   8 7 8 7 7 7

H. J. Gauntlett (1805–1876)

1 Once in royal David's city
   stood a lowly cattle shed,
   where a mother laid her baby
   in a manger for his bed:
   Mary was that mother mild,
   Jesus Christ, her little child.

2 He came down to earth from heaven
   who is God and Lord of all;
   and his shelter was a stable
   and his cradle was a stall:
   with the poor and meek and lowly
   lived on earth our saviour holy.

3   And through all his wondrous childhood
    he would honour and obey,
    love and watch the gentle mother
    in whose tender arms he lay:
    Christian children all should be
    kind, obedient, good as he.

4   For he is our childhood's pattern:
    day by day like us he grew;
    he was little, weak and helpless;
    tears and smiles like us he knew:
    and he feels for all our sadness,
    and he shares in all our gladness.

5   And our eyes at last shall see him,
    through his own redeeming love;
    for that child, so dear and gentle,
    is our Lord in heaven above:
    and he leads his children on
    to the place where he has gone.

6   Not in that poor lowly stable
    with the oxen standing by,
    we shall see him, but in heaven,
    set at God's right hand on high:
    there his children gather round
    bright like stars, with glory crowned.

Cecil F. Alexander (1818–1895)

Descant and arrangement David Willcocks (born 1919)
© Oxford University Press

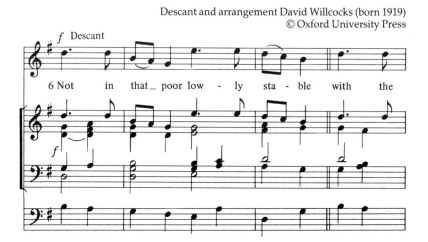

f Descant

6 Not   in   that_ poor low - ly   sta - ble   with   the

68

SAIGON 6 6 8 6 (SM)   © Norman Warren (born 1934)†

1 The darkness turns to dawn,
     the dayspring shines from heaven;
     for unto us a child is born,
     to us a Son is given.

2 The Son of God most high,
     before all else began,
     a virgin's son behold him lie,
     the new-born Son of Man.

3 God's Word of truth and grace
     made flesh with us to dwell;
     the brightness of the Father's face,
     the child Emmanuel.

4 How rich his heavenly home!
     How poor his human birth!
     As mortal man he stoops to come,
     the light and life of earth.

5 A servant's form, a slave,
     the Lord consents to share;
     our sin and shame, our cross and grave,
     he bows himself to bear.

6 Obedient and alone
     upon that cross to die,
     and then to share the Father's throne
     in majesty on high.

7 And still God sheds abroad
     that love so strong to send
     a saviour, who is Christ the Lord,
     whose reign shall never end.

© Timothy Dudley-Smith (born 1926)

69

ICH REDE 7676D

Paul Bischoff
arranged Rolf Hempel
© Gustav Bosse Verlag

1. When things began to happen,
   before the birth of time,
   the Word was with the Father
   and shared his holy name:
   without him there was nothing –
   all life derives from him;
   his light shines in the darkness –
   an unextinguished beam.

2. He came to his creation,
   the work of his own hand;
   he entered his own country
   but they would not respond:
   yet some gave their allegiance
   of life and heart and mind;
   thus they became his subjects
   and he became their friend.

3. Conceived by heaven's mercy,
   this was no human birth;
   for they are God's own children
   redeemed from sin and death:
   and they beheld his glory,
   so full of grace and truth;
   in Christ, God's Son, our saviour,
   whom we adore by faith.

from John 1
© Michael Saward (born 1932)†

Alternative tune: CRÜGER (190)

70

LORD OF LOVE   8 8 8 7   © Norman Warren (born 1934)†

1 Within a crib my saviour lay,
   a wooden manger filled with hay,
   come down for love on Christmas Day:
       all glory be to Jesus!

2 Upon a cross my saviour died,
   to ransom sinners crucified,
   his loving arms still open wide:
       all glory be to Jesus!

3 A victor's crown my saviour won,
   his work of love and mercy done,
   the Father's high-ascended Son:
       all glory be to Jesus!

© Timothy Dudley-Smith (born 1926)

71

DUNDEE   8 6 8 6 (CM)   *Scottish Psalter* Edinburgh 1615

1   The people who in darkness walked
    have seen a glorious light:
    that light shines out on those who lived
    in shadows of the night.

2   To greet you, Sun of righteousness,
    the gathering nations come;
    rejoicing as when reapers bring
    their harvest treasures home.

3   For now to us a child is born,
    to us a son is given;
    and on his shoulder ever rests
    all power in earth and heaven.

4   His name shall be the prince of peace,
    eternally adored;
    most wonderful of counsellors,
    the great and mighty Lord.

5   His peace and righteous government
    shall over all extend;
    on judgement and on justice based,
    his reign shall never end.

from Isaiah 9
J. Morison (1750–1798)
© in this version Jubilate Hymns†

For other hymns on this theme, see:

Sunday Themes index
   Section 10, The Incarnation (p. viii)

Additional Hymns
   O bless the God of Israel (599)
   On Jordan's bank (601)
   You servants of the Lord (598)

GOD: LORD AND SAVIOUR
Born: Christmas Seasonal

72

CRADLE SONG   11 11 11 11   W. J. Kirkpatrick (1838–1921)

1   Away in a manger, no crib for a bed,
    the little Lord Jesus laid down his sweet head;
    the stars in the bright sky
            looked down where he lay;
    the little Lord Jesus asleep on the hay.

2   The cattle are lowing, the baby awakes,
    but little Lord Jesus no crying he makes:
    I love you, Lord Jesus – look down from on high
    and stay by my side until morning is nigh.

3   Be near me, Lord Jesus; I ask you to stay
    close by me for ever and love me, I pray;
    bless all the dear children in your tender care,
    and fit us for heaven to live with you there.

verses 1, 2 unknown (nineteenth century)
verse 3 J. T. McFarland (c.1906)

73

O TANNENBAUM 88888887

Traditional melody
© arranged Noël Tredinnick (born 1949)†

1 *mf* A mes-sen-ger named Ga - bri - el came to the land of
2 *f* An - gel - ic hosts of God most high with ra - diant glo - ry
3 *p* In awe-some fear and bit - ter cold the shep-herds hud - dle
4 With-in the sa - cred sta - ble -shrine they see the ho - ly
5 *mf* Since then have passed two thou-sand years of hu-man mis - e -

Is - ra - el; and he pro-claimed that Ma - ry's son was
fill the sky; en - rap-tured voi - ces joy - ful sing to
in their fold; then since the mes - sage is for them they
child di - vine; the man - ger stands a - midst the straw and
- ry and tears; yet Christ a - lone can bring re - lease: he

God's mes - si - ah, ho - ly One.
wel - come Christ, the new-born king.
make their way to Beth - le - hem. O Je - sus Christ, strong
hum - ble folk their God a - dore.
loves us still— the prince of peace.

Son of God, once born for us_____ at Beth - le - hem: we

lis - ten to the an - gels' song and wor-ship you__ for__ ev - er.

74

QUEM PASTORES LAUDAVERE   8 8 8 7

German carol melody
fourteenth century
arranged R. Vaughan Williams (1872–1958)
arrangement © Oxford University Press

1 Shepherds came, their praises bringing,
who had heard the angels singing:
'Far from you be fear unruly,
Christ is king of glory born.'

2 Wise men whom a star had guided
incense, gold, and myrrh provided,
made their sacrifices truly
to the king of glory born.

3 Jesus born the king of heaven,
Christ to us through Mary given,
to your praise and honour duly
be resounding glory done.

from *Quem Pastores Laudavere* (fifteenth century)
G. B. Caird (1917–1984)
revised by the author 1981
© Mrs V. M. Caird

75(i)

CHERRY TREE CAROL   7 6 8 6   English traditional carol melody

1   A song was heard at Christmas
    to wake the midnight sky:
    a saviour's birth, and peace on earth,
    and praise to God on high.
    The angels sang at Christmas
    with all the hosts above,
    and still we sing the newborn King,
    his glory and his love.

2   A star was seen at Christmas,
    a herald and a sign,
    that all might know the way to go
    to find the child divine.
    The wise men watched at Christmas
    in some far eastern land,
    and still the wise in starry skies
    discern their Maker's hand.

3   A tree was grown at Christmas,
    a sapling green and young:
    no tinsel bright with candlelight
    upon its branches hung.
    But he who came at Christmas
    our sins and sorrow bore,
    and still we name his tree of shame
    our life for evermore.

75(ii)

HOLY APOSTLES 7 6 8 6 D

4 A child was born at Christmas
   when Christmas first began:
   the Lord of all a baby small,
   the Son of God made man.
   For love is ours at Christmas,
   and life and light restored,
   and so we praise through endless days
   the Saviour, Christ the Lord.

76(i)

ALL MY HEART   8 3 3 6 D   © David Peacock (born 1949)†

1 *f* All my heart this night rejoices,
            as I hear,
            far and near,
        sweetest angel voices.
        'Christ is born!' their choirs are singing,
            till the air
            everywhere
        now with joy is ringing.

2 *mf* Listen! from a humble manger
            comes the call,
            'One and all,
        run from sin and danger!
        Christians come, let nothing grieve you:
            you are freed!
            All you need
        I will surely give you.'

76(ii)

BONN 8 3 3 6 D

J. G. Ebeling (1637–1676)

3   Gather, then, from every nation;
         here let all,
         great and small,
     kneel in adoration;
     love him who with love is yearning:
         Hail the star
         that from far
     bright with hope is burning!

4   You, my Lord, with love I'll cherish,
         live to you,
         and with you
     dying, shall not perish,
     f but shall dwell with you for ever
         far on high,
         in the joy
     that can alter never.

after P. Gerhardt (1607–1676)
Catherine Winkworth (1827–1878)
© in this version Jubilate Hymns†

77

IRIS 8 7 8 7 and refrain

French carol melody
arranged M. E. F. Shaw (1875–1958)
arrangement © Oxford University Press

Come _____ and

Come _____ and

1st wor - ship Christ the new-born king; _____
2nd wor - ship, wor-ship Christ the new - born , king.

1 Angels from the realms of glory,
  wing your flight through all the earth;
  heralds of creation's story
  now proclaim Messiah's birth!
      Come and worship
      Christ, the new-born king;
      come and worship,
      worship Christ the new-born king.

2 Shepherds in the fields abiding,
  watching by your flocks at night,
  God with us is now residing:
  see, there shines the infant light!
      Come and worship
      Christ, the new-born king;
      come and worship,
      worship Christ the new-born king.

3 Wise men, leave your contemplations!
  brighter visions shine afar;
  seek in him the hope of nations,
  you have seen his rising star:
      Come and worship
      Christ, the new-born king;
      come and worship,
      worship Christ the new-born king.

4 Though an infant now we view him,
  he will share his Father's throne,
  gather all the nations to him;
  every knee shall then bow down:
      Come and worship
      Christ, the new-born king;
      come and worship,
      worship Christ the new-born king.

J. Montgomery (1771–1854)
© in this version Jubilate Hymns†

78

YORKSHIRE   10 10 10 10 10 10   J. Wainwright (1723–1768)
                                          arranged W. H. Monk (1823–1889)

1   Christians, awake, salute the happy morn
    on which the saviour of the world was born;
    rise to adore the mystery of love
    which hosts of angels chanted from above!
    With them the joyful tidings first begun
    of God incarnate and the virgin's Son.

2   First, to the watchful shepherds it was told,
    who heard the herald angel's voice: 'Behold,
    I bring good news of your Messiah's birth
    to you and all the nations here on earth!
    This day has God fulfilled his promised word;
    this day is born a saviour, Christ the Lord!'

3   To Bethlehem these eager shepherds ran
    to see the wonder of our God made man;
    they found, with Joseph and the holy maid,
    her son, the saviour, in a manger laid.
    Amazed, with joy this story they proclaim,
    the first apostles of his infant fame.

4   Let us, like those good shepherds, now employ
    our grateful voices to declare the joy:
    Christ, who was born on this most happy day,
    round all the earth his glory shall display.
    Saved by his love, unceasing we shall sing
    eternal praise to heaven's almighty king.

J. Byrom (1692–1763)
© in this version Jubilate Hymns†

79

MABLEDON   8 7 8 7 3 3 7

© Michael Baughen (born 1930)†
© arranged Noël Tredinnick (born 1949)†

1 Christmas for God's holy people
is a time of joy and peace:
so, all Christian men and women,
hymns and carols let us raise
to our God
come to earth,
Son of Man, by human birth.

2 Child of Mary, virgin mother,
peasant baby, yet our king,
cradled there among the oxen:
joyful carols now we sing
to our God . . .

3 Angel armies sang in chorus
at our Christ's nativity –
he who came to share our nature:
so we sing with gaiety
to our God . . .

4 Shepherds hurried to the manger,
saw the babe in Bethlehem,
glorified the God of heaven:
now we join to sing with them
to our God . . .

5 Infant lowly, born in squalor,
prophet, king and great high priest,
Word of God, to us descending:
still we sing, both great and least,
to our God . . .

© Michael Saward (born 1932)†

Alternative tune: MICHAEL (228)

80

GALLERY CAROL   11 11 11 11

English traditional carol
arranged R. Jacques (1894–1969)
arrangement © Oxford University Press

1   Come all you good people and burst into song!
    be joyful and happy, your praises prolong;
    remember the birthday of Jesus our king,
    who brings us salvation: his glory we sing.

2   His mother, a virgin so gentle and pure,
    was told of God's promise, unchanging and sure,
    foretelling the birthday of Jesus our king,
    who brings us salvation: his glory we sing.

3   To Bethlehem hurried the shepherds amazed,
    with stories of angels and heavens that blazed,
    proclaiming the birthday of Jesus our king,
    who brings us salvation: his glory we sing.

4   So come let us honour the babe in the hay
    and give him our homage and worship today,
    recalling the birthday of Jesus our king,
    who brings us salvation: his glory we sing.

from an old Dorset carol
© Michael Saward (born 1932)†

81

ALL THROUGH THE NIGHT   8 4 8 4 8 8 8 4   Welsh traditional melody
© arranged John Barnard (born 1948)†

1   Come and sing the Christmas story
        this holy night!
    Christ is born: the hope of glory
        dawns on our sight.
    Alleluia! earth is ringing
    with a thousand angels singing –
    hear the message they are bringing
        this holy night.

2   Jesus, Saviour, child of Mary
        this holy night,
    in a world confused and weary
        you are our light.
    God is in a manger lying,
    manhood taking, self denying,
    life embracing, death defying
        this holy night.

3   Lord of all! Let us acclaim him
        this holy night;
    king of our salvation name him,
        throned in the height.
    Son of Man – let us adore him,
    all the earth is waiting for him;
    Son of God – we bow before him
        this holy night.

82

O WALY WALY   8 8 8 8 (LM)   English traditional melody
© arranged Noël Tredinnick (born 1949)†

1 *f*   Glad music fills the Christmas sky –
        a hymn of praise, a song of love;
        the angels worship high above
        and Mary sings her lullaby.

2 *mf* Of tender love for God she sings,
        the chosen mother of the Son;
        she knows that wonders have begun,
        and trusts for all the future brings.

3   The angel chorus of the skies
        who come to tell us of God's grace
        have yet to know his human face,
        to watch him die, to see him rise.

4   Let praise be true and love sincere,
        rejoice to greet the saviour's birth;
        let peace and honour fill the earth
        and mercy reign – for God is here!

5 *f*   Then lift your hearts and voices high,
        sing once again the Christmas song:
        for love and praise to Christ belong –
        in shouts of joy, and lullaby.

© Michael Perry (born 1942)†

Alternative tune: DEUS TUORUM MILITUM (580)

83

PUER NOBIS   7 6 7 7

Piae Cantiones 1582
arranged G. T. Shaw (1879–1943)
arrangement © Oxford University Press

1 Jesus Christ the Lord is born,
   all the bells are ringing!
   angels greet the holy One
       and shepherds hear them singing,
       and shepherds hear them singing:

2 'Go to Bethlehem today,
   find your king and saviour:
   glory be to God on high,
       to earth his peace and favour,
       to earth his peace and favour!'

3 Held within a cattle stall,
   loved by love maternal,
   see the master of us all,
       our Lord of lords eternal,
       our Lord of lords eternal!

4 Soon shall come the wise men three,
   rousing Herod's anger;
   mothers' hearts shall broken be
       and Mary's son in danger,
       and Mary's son in danger.

5 Death from life and life from death,
   our salvation's story:
   let all living things give breath
       to Christmas songs of glory,
       to Christmas songs of glory!

after German authors (fifteenth century)
© Michael Perry (born 1942)†

84

GOD REST YOU MERRY Irregular

English traditional carol
arranged David Willcocks (born 1919)
arrangement © Oxford University Press

1 God rest you merry, gentlemen,
   let nothing you dismay!
   for Jesus Christ our saviour
   was born on Christmas Day,
   to save us all from Satan's power
   when we had gone astray:
        O tidings of comfort and joy,
        comfort and joy;
        O tidings of comfort and joy!

2   At Bethlehem in Judah
      the holy babe was born;
      they laid him in a manger
      on this most happy morn,
      at which his mother Mary
      did neither fear nor scorn:
           O tidings of comfort and joy . . .

3   From God our heavenly Father
      a holy angel came;
      the shepherds saw the glory
      and heard the voice proclaim
      that Christ was born in Bethlehem –
      and Jesus is his name:
           O tidings of comfort and joy . . .

4   Fear not, then said the angel,
      let nothing cause you fright;
      to you is born a saviour
      in David's town tonight,
      to free all those who trust in him
      from Satan's power and might:
           O tidings of comfort and joy . . .

5   The shepherds at these tidings
      rejoiced in heart and mind,
      and on the darkened hillside
      they left their flocks behind,
      and went to Bethlehem straightway
      this holy child to find:
           O tidings of comfort and joy . . .

6   And when to Bethlehem they came
      where Christ the infant lay;
      they found him in a manger
      where oxen fed on hay,
      and there beside her newborn child
      his mother knelt to pray:
           O tidings of comfort and joy . . .

7   Now to the Lord sing praises,
      all people in this place!
      with Christian love and fellowship
      each other now embrace,
      and let this Christmas festival
      all bitterness displace:
           O tidings of comfort and joy . . .

traditional (eighteenth century)
© in this version Jubilate Hymns†

85

IN DULCI JUBILO
66777855

Later form of fourteenth-century German carol melody
arranged J. Stainer (1840–1901)
based on harmony by R. L. Pearsall (1795–1856)

1 Good Christians all, rejoice
   with heart and soul and voice!
   listen now to what we say,
   Jesus Christ is born today;
   ox and ass before him bow
   and he is in the manger now!
        Christ is born today;
        Christ is born today!

2 Good Christians all, rejoice
   with heart and soul and voice!
   hear the news of endless bliss,
   Jesus Christ was born for this:
   he has opened heaven's door
   and we are blessed for evermore!
        Christ was born for this;
        Christ was born for this.

3 Good Christians all, rejoice
   with heart and soul and voice!
   now you need not fear the grave;
   Jesus Christ was born to save:
   come at his most gracious call
   to find salvation, one and all!
        Christ was born to save;
        Christ was born to save!

from *In Dulci Jubilo* (fourteenth century)
J. M. Neale (1818–1866)

86

INFANT HOLY 87878877

Polish carol
arranged A. E. Rusbridge (1917–1969)
arrangement © Mrs. R. Rusbridge

1 *p* Infant holy, infant lowly,
for his bed a cattle stall;
oxen lowing, little knowing
Christ the babe is Lord of all.
mf Swift are winging angels singing,
nowells ringing, tidings bringing:
Christ the babe is Lord of all;
Christ the babe is Lord of all!

2 *mp* Flocks were sleeping, shepherds keeping
vigil till the morning new,
saw the glory, heard the story –
tidings of a gospel true.
mf Thus rejoicing, free from sorrow,
praises voicing greet tomorrow:
Christ the babe was born for you;
Christ the babe was born for you!

from the Polish
Edith M. G. Reed (1885–1933)

87

NOEL   8 6 8 6 D (DCM)

English traditional melody
arranged A. S. Sullivan (1842–1900)

1 It came upon the midnight clear,
   that glorious song of old,
   from angels bending near the earth
   to touch their harps of gold:
   'Through all the earth, goodwill and peace
   from heaven's all-gracious king!'
   The world in solemn stillness lay
   to hear the angels sing.

2 With sorrow brought by sin and strife
   the world has suffered long
   and, since the angels sang, have passed
   two thousand years of wrong:
   the nations, still at war, hear not
   the love-song which they bring:
   O hush the noise and cease the strife,
   to hear the angels sing!

3 And those whose journey now is hard,
   whose hope is burning low,
   who tread the rocky path of life
   with painful steps and slow:
   O listen to the news of love
   which makes the heavens ring!
   O rest beside the weary road
   and hear the angels sing!

4 And still the days are hastening on –
   by prophets seen of old –
   towards the fulness of the time
   when comes the age foretold:
   then earth and heaven renewed shall see
   the prince of peace, their king;
   and all the world repeat the song
   which now the angels sing.

E. H. Sears (1810–1876)
© in this version Jubilate Hymns†

88(i)

FOREST GREEN   8 6 8 6 D (DCM)

English traditional melody
arranged R. Vaughan Williams (1872–1958)
arrangement © Oxford University Press

1 *mf* O little town of Bethlehem,
   how still we see you lie!
   Above your deep and dreamless
      sleep
   the silent stars go by:
   yet in your dark streets shining
   is everlasting light;
   the hopes and fears of all the years
   are met in you tonight.

2   For Christ is born of Mary
   and, gathered all above
   while mortals sleep,
      the angels keep
   their watch of wondering love:
f O morning stars, together
   proclaim the holy birth,
   and praises sing to God the king,
   and peace to all the earth.

88(ii)

CHRISTMAS CAROL   8 6 8 6 D (DCM)

H. Walford Davies (1869–1941)
© Oxford University Press

3 *p* How silently, how silently
the wondrous gift is given!
So God imparts to human hearts
the blessings of his heaven:
no ear may hear his coming,
but in this world of sin,
where meek souls will receive him –
   still
the dear Christ enters in.

4 *mf* O holy child of Bethlehem,
descend to us, we pray;
cast out our sin and enter in,
be born in us today!
f We hear the Christmas angels
the great glad tidings tell –
O come to us, abide with us,
our Lord Emmanuel.

P. Brooks (1835–1893)

89

RECTORY MEADOW Irregular

E. R. Routley (1917–1982)
© Oxford University Press

1 O Prince of peace whose pro-mised birth the an - gels
2 O Child who found to lay your head no place __ but
3 O Christ whom shep - herds came to find, their joy ___ be
4 O Sa - viour Christ, as - cen - ded Lord, our ri - sen

1 sang with 'Peace __ on earth,' peace be to us and
2 in a man - ger bed, come where our doors stand
3 ours in heart __ and mind; let grief and care be
4 prince of life ___ re - stored, our love who once for

vv. 2,3,4

1 all be - side, __ peace to us all — __
2 o - pen wide, __ peace to us all — __ peace to the
3 laid a - side, __ peace to us all — __ peace to the
4 sin - ners died, __ peace to us all — __ peace to the

vv. 3,4   v. 4

1
2 world —
3 world — peace in our homes — __
4 world — peace in our homes — __ peace in our hearts — __

Org. v. 2 only

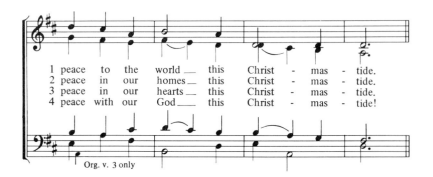

1 peace to the world — this Christ - mas - tide.
2 peace in our homes — this Christ - mas - tide.
3 peace in our hearts — this Christ - mas - tide.
4 peace with our God — this Christ - mas - tide!

Org. v. 3 only

1 O Prince of peace whose promised birth
   the angels sang with 'Peace on earth,'
   peace be to us and all beside,
       peace to us all –
   peace to the world this Christmastide.

2 O Child who found to lay your head
   no place but in a manger bed,
   come where our doors stand open wide,
       peace to us all –
       peace to the world –
   peace in our homes this Christmastide.

3 O Christ whom shepherds came to find,
   their joy be ours in heart and mind;
   let grief and care be laid aside,
       peace to us all –
       peace to the world –
       peace in our homes –
   peace in our hearts this Christmastide.

4 O Saviour Christ, ascended Lord,
   our risen prince of life restored,
   our love who once for sinners died,
       peace to us all –
       peace to the world –
       peace in our homes –
       peace in our hearts –
   peace with our God this Christmastide!

90

J. Goss (1800–1880)

Hail, O ev-er-bless-èd morn; hail, re-demp-tion's hap-py dawn;

sing through all Je - ru - sa - lem: 'Christ is born in Beth-le-hem!'

1   See, amid the winter snow,
    born for us on earth below;
    see, the gentle Lamb appears,
    promised from eternal years:
        Hail, O ever-blessèd morn;
        hail, redemption's happy dawn;
        sing through all Jerusalem:
        'Christ is born in Bethlehem!'

2   Low within a manger lies
    he who built the starry skies;
    he who, throned in height sublime,
    reigns above the cherubim:
        Hail, O ever-blessèd morn . . .

3   Say, you humble shepherds, say
    what's your joyful news today?
    tell us why you left your sheep
    on the lonely mountain steep:
        Hail, O ever-blessèd morn . . .

4   'As we watched at dead of night,
    all around us shone a light;
    angels singing Peace on earth
    told us of a Saviour's birth.'
        Hail, O ever-blessèd morn . . .

5   Sacred infant, king most dear,
    what a tender love was here,
    thus to come from highest bliss
    down to such a world as this!
        Hail, O ever-blessèd morn . . .

6   Holy saviour, born on earth,
    teach us by your lowly birth;
    grant that we may ever be
    taught by such humility.
        Hail, O ever-blessèd morn . . .

E. Caswall (1814–1878)
© in this version Jubilate Hymns†

91

CALYPSO CAROL   Irregular

© Michael Perry (born 1942)†
© arranged Stephen Coates (born 1952)

the prince of glo - ry when he came. _____

Verse 4 may be concluded as vv.1–3, ending with a pause on the first chord of the last bar on the facing page.

1 See him lying on a bed of straw:
   a draughty stable with an open door;
   Mary cradling the babe she bore –
   the prince of glory is his name.
       O now carry me to Bethlehem
       to see the Lord appear to men –
       just as poor as was the stable then,
       the prince of glory when he came.

2 Star of silver, sweep across the skies,
   show where Jesus in the manger lies;
   shepherds, swiftly from your stupor rise
   to see the saviour of the world!
       O now carry . . .

3 Angels, sing again the song you sang,
   bring God's glory to the heart of man;
   sing that Bethl'em's little baby can
   be salvation to the soul.
       O now carry . . .

4 Mine are riches, from your poverty;
   from your innocence, eternity;
   mine, forgiveness by your death for me,
   child of sorrow for my joy.
       O now carry . . .

© Michael Perry (born 1942)†

92

THE INFANT KING   4 9 4 8 9 9 4

Possibly from an old Basque noël
arranged C. E. Pettman (1866–1943)
arrangement © 1984 H. Freeman and Co.
EMI Music Publishing Ltd and International Music Publications

1 *mp*   Sing lullaby!
       lullaby baby, now reclining:
          sing lullaby!
       Hush, do not wake the infant king;
       angels are watching, stars are shining
       over the place where he is lying:
          sing lullaby.

2   Sing lullaby!
       lullaby baby, sweetly sleeping:
          sing lullaby!
       Hush, do not wake the infant king;
  p soon will come sorrow with the morning,
       soon will come bitter grief and weeping:
          sing lullaby!

3 *mp*   Sing lullaby!
       lullaby baby, gently dozing:
          sing lullaby!
       Hush, do not wake the infant king;
  p soon comes the cross, the nails, the piercing,
       then in the grave at last reposing:
          sing lullaby!

4 *mp*   Sing lullaby!
       lullaby! Is the baby waking?
          sing lullaby!
  mf Hush, do not stir the infant king,
       dreaming of Easter, joyful morning,
       conquering death, its bondage breaking:
          sing lullaby!

S. Baring-Gould (1834–1924)

THE FIRST NOWELL   Irregular

English traditional carol
arranged J. Stainer (1840–1901)

Now - ell, ___ now - ell, now - ell, ___ now-
-ell, ___ born is the king __ of Is - ra - el!

1   The first nowell the angel did say
    was to Bethlehem's shepherds
              in fields as they lay;
    in fields where they lay keeping their sheep
    on a cold winter's night that was so deep:
         Nowell, nowell, nowell, nowell,
         born is the king of Israel!

2   Then wise men from a country far
    looked up and saw a guiding star;
    they travelled on by night and day
    to reach the place where Jesus lay:
         Nowell, nowell . . .

3   At Bethlehem they entered in,
    on bended knee they worshipped him;
    they offered there in his presence
    their gold and myrrh and frankincense:
         Nowell, nowell . . .

4   Then let us all with one accord
    sing praises to our heavenly Lord;
    for Christ has our salvation wrought
    and with his blood our life has bought:
         Nowell, nowell . . .

                    unknown (c. seventeenth century)
                    © in this version Word & Music†

94

WINCHESTER OLD   8 6 8 6 (CM)

T. Este's *Psalmes* 1592
arranged W. H. Monk (1823–1889)

1   While shepherds watched their flocks by night
    all seated on the ground,
    the angel of the Lord came down
    and glory shone around.

2   'Fear not,' said he – for mighty dread
    had seized their troubled mind –
    'Good news of greatest joy I bring
    to you and all mankind.

3   'To you in Bethlehem this day
    is born of David's line
    a saviour, who is Christ the Lord.
    And this shall be the sign:

4   'The heavenly babe you there shall find
    to human view displayed,
    in simple clothing tightly wrapped
    and in a manger laid.'

5   Thus spoke the seraph, and forthwith
    appeared a shining throng
    of angels praising God, who thus
    addressed their joyful song:

6   'All glory be to God on high,
    and to the earth be peace!
    To those on whom his favour rests
    goodwill shall never cease.'

N. Tate (1652–1715)

Descant

6 'All ___ glo - ry be to God ___ on high, and
to ___ the earth be peace! To those on ___ whom his
fa - vour rests good - will ___ shall ne - ver cease.'

95

STILLE NACHT   Irregular

F. X. Gruber (1787–1863)
arrangement from *The Australian Hymn Book* 1977

1 Silent night! holy night!
  all is calm, all is bright
  round the virgin and her child:
  holy infant, so gentle and mild,
  sleep in heavenly peace;
  sleep in heavenly peace!

2 Silent night! holy night!
  shepherds quail at the sight,
  glory streams from heaven afar:
  heavenly hosts sing, 'Alleluia,
  Christ the saviour is born,
  Christ the saviour is born.'

3 Silent night! holy night!
  Son of God, love's pure light:
  radiant beams your holy face
  with the dawn of saving grace,
  Jesus, Lord, at your birth,
  Jesus, Lord, at your birth.

after J. Möhr (1792–1848)
J. F. Young (1820–1885)

For other hymns on this theme, see:
Sunday Themes index
  Section 10, The Incarnation (p. viii)
Additional Hymns
  In the bleak mid-winter (600)

Before the heaven and earth (612)
Lord, now let your servant (611)
Song Section
  The virgin Mary (S.25)

GOD: LORD AND SAVIOUR
Growing, Teaching, Serving

96

QUEM PASTORES LAUDAVERE   8 8 8 7

German carol melody
fourteenth century
arranged R. Vaughan Williams (1872–1958)
arrangement © Oxford University Press

1 Jesus, good above all other,
  gentle child of gentle mother;
  in a stable born our brother,
  whom the angel hosts adore:

2 Jesus, cradled in a manger,
  keep us free from sin and danger;
  and to all, both friend and stranger,
  give your blessing evermore.

3 Jesus, for your people dying,
  risen master, death defying;
  Lord of heaven, your grace supplying,
  come to us – be present here!

4 Lord, in all our doings guide us:
  pride and hate shall not divide us;
  we'll go on with you beside us,
  and with joy we'll persevere.

from the Latin (twelfth century)
J. M. Neale (1818–1866) verses 1 and 2
P. Dearmer (1867–1936) verses 3 and 4

97(i)

HIGHEST HEAVEN   8 7 8 7 7 7

© Michael Baughen (born 1930)†
© arranged Norman Warren (born 1934)†

1 *mf* Lord, who left the highest heaven
for a homeless human birth
and, a child within a stable,
came to share the life of earth –
with your grace and mercy bless
all who suffer homelessness.

2 *mp* Lord, who sought by cloak of darkness
refuge under foreign skies
from the swords of Herod's soldiers,
ravaged homes, and parents' cries –
may your grace and mercy rest
on the homeless and oppressed.

3 *mf* Lord, who lived secure and settled,
safe within the Father's plan,
and in wisdom, stature, favour
growing up from boy to man –
with your grace and mercy bless
all who strive for holiness.

97(ii)

OTTAWA 878777

L. Mason (1792–1872)

4   Lord, who leaving home and kindred,
     followed still as duty led,
     sky the roof and earth the pillow
     for the prince of glory's head –
     with your grace and mercy bless
     sacrifice for righteousness.

5 *mp* Lord, who in your cross and passion
     hung beneath a darkened sky,
     yet whose thoughts were for your mother,
     and a thief condemned to die –
     may your grace and mercy rest
     on the helpless and distressed.

6 *f* Lord, who rose to life triumphant
     with our whole salvation won,
     risen, glorified, ascended,
     all the Father's purpose done –
     may your grace, all conflict past,
     bring your children home at last.

© Timothy Dudley-Smith (born 1926)

98(i)

ST. EDMUND 7777D

C. Steggall (1826–1905)

1 Songs of thankfulness and praise,
Jesus, Lord, to you we raise;
once revealed, when heaven's star
brought the wise men from afar;
branch of royal David's stem
in your birth at Bethlehem,
      Word before the world began,
      God revealed to us in man.

2 God revealed at Jordan's stream,
prophet, priest and king supreme;
once revealed in power divine
changing water into wine;
Cana's holy wedding guest
keeping to the last the best;
      Word before . . .

98(ii)

ST. GEORGE'S, WINDSOR   7 7 7 7 D   G. J. Elvey (1816–1893)

3 God revealed in valiant fight,
   conquering the devil's might;
   sins forgiven, sickness healed,
   life restored and God revealed:
   once revealed in gracious will
   ever bringing good from ill,
       Word before . . .

4 Stars shall fall and heavens fade,
   sun and moon shall dark be made;
   Christ will then like lightning shine,
   all will see the glorious sign;
   all will then the trumpet hear,
   all will see the Son appear,
       Word before . . .

            C. Wordsworth (1807–1885)
            © in this version Jubilate Hymns†

99

DIX 777777

C. Kocher (1786–1872)
arranged W. H. Monk (1823–1889)
descant S. H. Nicholson (1875–1947)
descant © Royal School of Church Music

5 In the heaven-ly ci - ty bright none shall need cre - a - ted light —
you, its _ light, its joy, its _ crown,_you its sun which goes_ not_ down;
there for _ e - ver may we _ sing al - le - lu - ias to our king.

The harmony of bars 1–4 may be repeated for bars 5–8, if preferred.

1 *f* As with gladness men of old
did the guiding star behold,
as with joy they hailed its light,
leading onward, gleaming bright:
so, most gracious Lord, may we
evermore your splendour see.

2 *mf* As with joyful steps they sped
to that lowly manger bed,
there to bend the knee before
Christ whom heaven and earth adore:
so with ever-quickening pace
may we seek your throne of grace.

3 As they offered gifts most rare
at your cradle plain and bare,
so may we with holy joy
pure and free from sin's alloy,
all our costliest treasures bring,
Christ, to you, our heavenly king.

4 *mp* Holy Jesus, every day
keep us in the narrow way,
and when earthly things are past,
bring our ransomed souls at last:
where they need no star to guide,
where no clouds your glory hide.

5 *f* In the heavenly city bright
none shall need created light –
you, its light, its joy, its crown,
you its sun which goes not down;
there for ever may we sing
alleluias to our king.

W. C. Dix (1837–1898)
© in this version Jubilate Hymns†

100

NEUMARK 989888

G. Neumark (1621–1681)
arranged E. R. Routley (1917–1982)
arrangement © Mrs. M. Routley

1 Wise men, they came to look for wisdom,
    finding one wiser than they knew;
    rich men, they met with one yet richer –
    King of the kings, they knelt to you:
        Jesus, our wisdom from above,
        wealth and redemption, life and love.

2 Pilgrims they were, from unknown countries,
    searching for one who knows the world;
    lost are their names, and strange their journeys,
    famed is their zeal to find the child:
        Jesus, in you the lost are claimed,
        aliens are found, and known, and named.

3 Magi, they stooped to see your splendour,
    led by a star to light supreme;
    promised Messiah, Lord eternal,
    glory and peace are in your name.
        Joy of each day, our Song by night,
        shine on our path your holy light.

4 Guests of their God, they opened treasures,
    incense and gold and solemn myrrh;
    welcoming one too young to question
    how came these gifts, and what they were.
        Gift beyond price of gold or gem,
        make among us your Bethlehem.

101

SLANE 10 11 11 12

Irish traditional melody
arranged M. E. F. Shaw (1875–1958)
arrangement © Oxford University Press

1 Lord of all hopefulness, Lord of all joy,
   whose trust, ever childlike,
                 no cares could destroy:
   be there at our waking, and give us, we pray,
   your bliss in our hearts, Lord,
                 at the break of the day.

2 Lord of all eagerness, Lord of all faith,
   whose strong hands were skilled
                 at the plane and the lathe:
   be there at our labours, and give us, we pray,
   your strength in our hearts, Lord,
                 at the noon of the day.

3 Lord of all kindliness, Lord of all grace,
   your hands swift to welcome,
                 your arms to embrace:
   be there at our homing, and give us, we pray,
   your love in our hearts, Lord,
                 at the eve of the day.

4 Lord of all gentleness, Lord of all calm,
   whose voice is contentment,
                 whose presence is balm:
   be there at our sleeping, and give us, we pray,
   your peace in our hearts, Lord,
                 at the end of the day!

Jan Struther (1901–1953)

102

EVERTON   8 7 8 7 D

H. T. Smart (1813–1879)

1 Son of God, eternal saviour,
  source of life and truth and grace;
  Son of Man whose birth among us
  hallows all our human race:
  Christ our head, for all your people
  you have never ceased to plead;
  fill us with your love and pity,
  heal our wrongs, and help our need.

2 Lord, as you have lived for others,
  so may we for others live;
  freely have your gifts been granted,
  freely may your servants give:
  yours the gold and yours the silver,
  all the wealth of sea and land;
  we but stewards of your riches
  held in trust at your command.

3 Come, O Christ, and reign among us,
  king of love, and prince of peace;
  hush the storm of strife and passion,
  bid its cruel discords cease:
  by your patient years of toiling,
  by your silent hours of pain,
  quench our fevered thirst for pleasure,
  shame our selfish greed for gain.

4 Son of God, eternal saviour,
  source of life and truth and grace;
  Son of Man, whose birth among us
  hallows all our human race:
  you have prayed and you have purposed
  that your people shall be one;
  grant to us our hope's fulfilment –
  here on earth your will be done!

                    S. T. C. Lowry (1855–1932)

103

HEINLEIN 7 7 7 7

Melody from the *Nürnbergisches Gesangbuch* 1676
attributed to M. Herbst (1654–1681)

1 *mf* Forty days and forty nights
    you were fasting in the wild;
    forty days and forty nights
    tempted and yet undefiled.

2 *mp* Burning heat throughout the day,
    bitter cold when light had fled;
    prowling beasts around your way,
    stones your pillow, earth your bed.

3   Shall not we your trials share,
    learn your discipline of will;
    and with you by fast and prayer
    wrestle with the powers of hell?

4   So if Satan, pressing hard,
    soul and body would destroy:
    Christ who conquered, be our guard;
    give to us the victor's joy.

5 *mf* Saviour, may we hear your voice –
    keep us constant at your side;
  f   and with you we shall rejoice
    at the eternal Eastertide.

G. H. Smyttan (1822–1870)
© in this version Jubilate Hymns†

104

ST. ANDREW 8 7 8 7   E. H. Thorne (1834–1916)

1 Jesus calls us! – in the tumult
   of our life's wild restless sea;
   day by day his voice re-echoes
   saying, 'Christian, follow me!'

2 As of old, apostles heard it
   by the Galilean lake,
   turned from home and toil and kindred,
   leaving all for his dear sake.

3 Jesus calls us – from the worship
   of the vain world's golden store,
   from each rival that would claim us,
   saying, 'Christian, love me more!'

4 In our joys and in our sorrows,
   days of toil and hours of ease,
   still he calls, in cares and pleasures,
   'Christian, love me more than these!'

5 Jesus calls us! – by your mercies,
   Saviour, make us hear your call,
   give to you our heart's obedience,
   serve and love you best of all.

Cecil F. Alexander (1818–1895)

105

BISHOPTHORPE 8 6 8 6 (CM)   J. Clarke (c. 1674–1707)

1 Immortal love for ever full,
   for ever flowing free,
   for ever shared, for ever whole,
   a never-ebbing sea!

2 Upon our lips we bear the name
   all other names above;
   yet love alone knows whence it came,
   that all-embracing love.

3 We may not climb the heavenly steeps
   to bring the Lord Christ down;
   in vain we search the lowest deeps,
   for him no depths can drown.

4 But warm, sweet, tender, even yet
   a present help is he;
   and faith has still its Olivet,
   and love its Galilee.

5 The margin of his robe we feel
   through sorrow and through pain;
   we touch the Lord whose love can heal,
   and we are whole again.

6 Through him the earliest prayers are said
that children's lips can frame;
the last low whispers of our dead
are burdened with his name.

7 Alone, O Love no words can tell,
your saving name is given;
to turn aside from you is hell,
to walk with you is heaven!

J. G. Whittier (1807–1892)
© in this version Jubilate Hymns†

106

ENIGMA   4 8 8 4   © Noël Tredinnick (born 1949)†

1 With loving hands,
at work among the suffering
and broken hearts, he ministers,
who is their king.

2 With wounded hands,
outstretched upon a cruel tree,
he lies and then is lifted up
in agony.

3 With pleading hands,
towards the world he longs to bless,
he waits, with heaven's life to fill
our emptiness.

© Randle Manwaring (born 1912)

107

OFFERTORIUM 7 6 7 6 D

From J. M. Haydn (1737–1806)

1 My Lord, I did not choose you
  for that could never be;
  my heart would still refuse you
  had you not chosen me:
  you took the sin that stained me,
  you cleansed me, made me new,
  for you, Lord, had ordained me
  that I should live in you.

2 Unless your grace had called me
  and taught my opening mind
  the world would have enthralled me
  to heavenly glories blind:
  my heart knows none above you;
  for you I long, I thirst,
  and know that, if I love you,
  Lord, you have loved me first.

J. Conder (1789–1855)

Alternative tune: EWING (573)

108

BEULAH   8 6 8 6 (CM)   G. M. Garrett (1834–1897)

1 O changeless Christ, for ever new,
   who walked our earthly ways,
   still draw our hearts as once you drew
   the hearts of other days.

2 As once you spoke by plain and hill
   or taught by shore and sea,
   so be today our teacher still,
   O Christ of Galilee.

3 As wind and storm their master heard
   and his command fulfilled,
   may troubled hearts receive your word,
   the tempest-tossed be stilled.

4 And as of old to all who prayed
   your healing hand was shown,
   so be your touch upon us laid,
   unseen but not unknown.

5 In broken bread, in wine outpoured,
   your new and living way
   proclaim to us, O risen Lord,
   O Christ of this our day.

6 O changeless Christ, till life is past
   your blessing still be given;
   then bring us home, to taste at last
   the timeless joys of heaven.

© Timothy Dudley-Smith (born 1926)

Alternative tunes: ABRIDGE (374)
                     BALLERMA (374)

109

LITHEROP   878787

Peter Cutts (born 1937)
© Oxford University Press

1 Jesus, come! for we invite you,
   guest and master, friend and Lord;
   now, as once at Cana's wedding,
   speak, and let us hear your word:
   lead us through our need or doubting,
   hope be born and joy restored.

2 Jesus, come! transform our pleasures,
   guide us into paths unknown;
   bring your gifts, command your servants,
   let us trust in you alone:
   though your hand may work in secret,
   all shall see what you have done.

3 Jesus, come in new creation,
   heaven brought near in power divine;
   give your unexpected glory
   changing water into wine:
   rouse the faith of your disciples –
   come, our first and greatest Sign!

4 Jesus, come! surprise our dullness,
   make us willing to receive
   more than we can yet imagine,
   all the best you have to give:
   let us find your hidden riches,
   taste your love, believe, and live!

from John 2
© Christopher Idle (born 1938)†

Alternative tune: MANNHEIM (525)

110

FRANCONIA   6 6 8 6 (SM)   *Harmonischer Liederschatz* 1738

1 Blessed are the pure in heart,
   for they shall see our God;
   the secret of the Lord is theirs,
   their soul is Christ's abode.

2 The Lord, who left the heavens
   our life and peace to bring;
   to dwell in lowliness with us,
   our pattern and our king:

3 Still to the lowly soul
   himself he will impart;
   and for his dwelling and his throne
   chooses the pure in heart.

4 Lord, we your presence seek:
   our inner life renew;
   give us a pure and lowly heart,
   a temple fit for you.

J. Keble (1792–1866)
and W. J. Hall (1793–1861)

A descant and arrangement for verse 4 is printed overleaf.

Descant and arrangement G. T. Shaw (1879–1943)

4 Lord, we your pre-sence seek: our in - ner life_ re - new;

give us a pure and low-ly heart, a _ tem - ple fit for_ you.

111

BANGOR 8 6 8 6 (CM)   W. Tans'ur's *Harmony of Syon* 1734

1 'Forgive our sins as we forgive,'
  you taught us, Lord, to pray;
  but you alone can grant us grace
  to live the words we say.

2 How can your pardon reach and bless
  the unforgiving heart
  that broods on wrongs, and will not let
  old bitterness depart?

3 In blazing light your cross reveals
  the truth we dimly knew:
  what trivial debts are owed to us,
  how great our debt to you!

4 Lord, cleanse the depths within our souls
  and bid resentment cease;
  then, bound to all in bonds of love,
  our lives will spread your peace.

Rosamond Herklots (born 1905)
© Oxford University Press

Alternative tune: ST. BERNARD (484)

112

WINCHESTER NEW   8 8 8 8 (LM)   *Musikalisches Handbuch* Hamburg 1690

1   Lord Jesus, once you spoke to men,
    upon the mountain, in the plain:
    O help us listen now, as then,
    and wonder at your words again.

2   We all have secret fears to face,
    our minds and motives to amend;
    we seek your truth, we need your grace,
    our living Lord and present friend.

3   The gospel speaks – and we receive
    your light, your love, your own command:
    O help us live what we believe
    in daily work of heart and hand.

113

ST. JAMES   8 6 8 6 (CM)   R. Courteville (1675–1735)

1 *mf* You are the way, to you alone
    from sin and death we run:
    and those who would the Father seek
    must seek him through the Son.

2   You are the truth, your word alone
    true wisdom can impart:
    you only can inform the mind
    and purify the heart.

3 *f* You are the life, the empty tomb
    proclaims your conquering arm:
    and those who put their trust in you,
    nor death nor hell shall harm.

4 *mf* You are the way, the truth, the life:
    grant us that way to see,
    that truth to keep, that life to know
    through all eternity.

G. Doane (1799–1859)

114

BRESLAU   8 8 8 8 (LM)   Melody in *As Hymnodus Sacer* Leipzig 1625

1 'Take up your cross,' the Saviour said,
   'if you would my disciple be;
   deny yourself, forsake the world,
   and humbly follow after me.'

2 Take up your cross – let not its weight
   fill your weak soul with vain alarm;
   his strength shall bear your spirit up,
   and brace your heart, and nerve your arm.

3 Take up your cross, nor heed the shame
   nor let your foolish pride rebel;
   the Lord for you the cross endured
   to save your soul from death and hell.

4 Take up your cross, then, in his strength,
   and calmly every danger brave;
   he guides us to a better home,
   and leads to conquest of the grave.

5 Take up your cross and follow Christ,
   nor think till death to lay it down;
   for only they who bear the cross
   may hope to win the glorious crown.

C. W. Everest (1814–1877)

115

ST. ALBINUS   7 8 7 8 4   H. J. Gauntlett (1805–1876)

Al - le - lu - ia!

1   Christ upon the mountain peak
    stands alone in glory blazing;
    let us, if we dare to speak,
    with the saints and angels praise him –
        Alleluia!

2   Trembling at his feet we saw
    Moses and Elijah speaking:
    all the prophets and the law
    shout through them their joyful greeting –
        Alleluia!

3   Swift the cloud of glory came,
    God proclaiming in its thunder
    Jesus as his Son by name!
    nations, cry aloud in wonder –
        Alleluia!

4   This is God's belovèd Son!
    law and prophets fade before him,
    First and Last, and only One:
    let creation now adore him –
        Alleluia!

Brian Wren (born 1936)
© Oxford University Press

116

DAS NEUGEBORNE KINDELEIN
888888

From a medieval melody by
M. Vulpius (c. 1560–1616)

1 Our Saviour Christ once knelt in prayer
with none but three disciples there,
upon a lonely mountain high
beneath a blue expanse of sky –
below them, far as eye could see,
the little hills of Galilee.

2 There as he prays a radiance bright
transfigures all his form to light;
his robe in dazzling splendour shows
a purer white than sunlit snows,
while on his countenance divine
transcendent glories burn and shine.

3 So for a moment stands revealed
what human form and flesh concealed;
while Moses and Elijah share
in earth and heaven mingled there,
with him whom prophecy foresaw,
the true fulfiller of the law.

4 The shadowed summit, wrapped in cloud,
sounds to a voice that echoes loud:
'This is my true belovèd Son,
listen to him, my chosen one.'
The glory fades; with all its pains
the road to Calvary remains.

5 Give to us, Lord, the eyes to see
as saw those first disciples three:
a teacher true, a friend indeed,
the risen saviour sinners need,
the Son whose praise eternal rings,
the Lord of lords and King of kings!

© Timothy Dudley-Smith (born 1926)

Alternative tune: SURREY (117)

117

SURREY 888888

Later form of melody by
H. Carey (c. 1687–1743)

1   When Jesus led his chosen three
    to lift the shadow from their sight,
    and on the mountain let them see
    his face transfigured, crowned with light:
    what grace that day to them was given!
    to men on earth, a glimpse of heaven.

2   There Moses and Elijah stood
    and spoke about his exodus,
    their freedom purchased by his blood,
    a passover most marvellous!
    The law and prophets meet their Lord,
    see God revealed, and man restored.

3   Then from the cloud there came a voice,
    'This is my own belovèd Son;'
    the scriptures' theme, the Father's choice,
    their master stood supreme, alone:
    they saw his glory, and they heard
    the one eternal, living Word.

4   So may we see and know this grace –
    the truth which like a burning light
    illuminates the darkest place
    till Christ himself shall end the night:
    when to his people's longing eyes
    God's day shall dawn, his sun shall rise.

Alternative tune: DAS NEUGEBORNE KINDELEIN (116)

118

SPLENDOUR   8 8 8 8 (LM)

M. Praetorius (1571–1621)

1   My Lord, you wore no royal crown;
    you did not wield the powers of state,
    nor did you need a scholar's gown
    or priestly robe, to make you great.

2   You never used a killer's sword
    to end an unjust tyranny;
    your only weapon was your word,
    for truth alone could set us free.

3   You did not live a world away
    in hermit's cell or desert cave,
    but felt our pain and shared each day
    with those you came to seek and save.

4   You made no mean or cunning move,
    chose no unworthy compromise,
    but carved a track of burning love
    through tangles of deceit and lies.

5   You came unequalled, undeserved,
    to be what I was meant to be;
    you came to serve, not to be served,
    a light for all the world to see.

6   So when I stumble, set me right;
    command my life as you require;
    let all your gifts be my delight
    and you, my Lord, my one desire.

119

WINCHESTER NEW   8 8 8 8 (LM)   *Musikalisches Handbuch* Hamburg 1690

1   Ride on, ride on in majesty
    as all the crowds 'Hosanna!' cry:
    through waving branches slowly ride,
    O Saviour, to be crucified.

2   Ride on, ride on in majesty,
    in lowly pomp ride on to die:
    O Christ, your triumph now begin
    with captured death, and conquered sin!

3   Ride on, ride on in majesty –
    the angel armies of the sky
    look down with sad and wondering eyes
    to see the approaching sacrifice.

4   Ride on, ride on in majesty,
    the last and fiercest foe defy:
    the Father on his sapphire throne
    awaits his own anointed Son.

5   Ride on, ride on in majesty,
    in lowly pomp ride on to die:
    bow your meek head to mortal pain,
    then take, O God, your power and reign!

H. Milman (1791–1868)
© in this version Jubilate Hymns†

120

ST. THEODULPH 7 6 7 6 D

M. Teschner (1584–1635)
arranged W. H. Monk (1823–1889)

All glo-ry, praise and hon - our, to you, re-deem-er, king,

to whom the lips of child - ren made sweet ho - san-nas ring.

f   All glory, praise and honour,
to you, redeemer, king,
to whom the lips of children
made sweet hosannas ring.

1 *mf* You are the king of Israel,
great David's greater son;
you ride in lowly triumph,
the Lord's anointed one!
f   All glory, praise . . .

2   The company of angels
are praising you on high,
and we with all creation
together make reply:
All glory, praise . . .

3 *mf* The people of the Hebrews
with palms before you went;
our praise and prayer and anthems
before you we present.
f   All glory, praise . . .

4 *mf* To you before your passion
they sang their hymns of praise;
f   to you, now high exalted,
our melody we raise:
All glory, praise . . .

5   As you received their praises,
accept the prayers we bring,
for you delight in goodness
O good and gracious king!
All glory, praise . . .

after Theodulph (c.750–821)
J. M. Neale (1818–1866)
© in this version Jubilate Hymns†

121

CREDO   888888

J. Stainer (1840–1901)

A little slower

1 We were not there to see you come
   to this poor world of sin and death,
   nor did we see your humble home,
   your childhood spent in Nazareth:
        but we believe your footsteps trod
        its streets and paths, O Son of God.

2 We did not see you lifted high
   or feel the taunts they flung at you,
   nor were we there to hear your cry,
   'Forgive, they know not what they do!'
        Yet we believe the deed was done
        which shook the earth and veiled the sun.

3 We did not stand beside the tomb
   upon that resurrection day,
   nor met you in the upper room,
   nor walked with you along the way:
        but we believe the angel said,
        'Why seek the living with the dead?'

4 We were not with the chosen few
   who saw you vanish from their sight,
   nor could we fall and worship you,
   the risen, ascended, Lord of might:
        yet we believe that mortal eyes
        from that far mountain saw you rise.

5 And now you reign enthroned on high
   and bless your waiting people here;
   we still may look up to the sky
   yet cannot see your glory there:
        but we believe your faithful word –
        O come to us, exalted Lord!

Ann Richter (1792–1857) and others
© in this version Jubilate Hymns†

For other hymns on this theme, see:
Sunday Themes index
   Section 17, Revelation: Parables (p. x)

GOD: LORD AND SAVIOUR
Suffering and Dying

122

A PURPLE ROBE   8 6 8 6 Triple

© David Wilson (born 1940)†
© arranged Noël Tredinnick (born 1949)†

1 A pur - ple robe, a crown of thorn, a reed in his___ right
4 He hangs, by whom the world was made, be - neath the dark - ened

hand;___ be - fore the sol - diers' spite and scorn I see my sav - iour
sky;___ the ev - er - last - ing ran - som paid, I see my sav - iour

stand.___ 2 He bears be-tween the Ro - man guard the weight of all___ our
die.___ 5 He shares on high___ his Fa - ther's throne who once in mer - cy

woe; _____ a stum-bling fig-ure bowed and scarred I see my sav-iour
came; _____ for all his love to sin - ners shown I sing my sav-iour's

Fine

go.__ 3 Fast to the cross's spread-ing span, high in the sun-lit air, _____
name..

all the un-num-bered sins_ of man I see_ my sav-iour bear. _____

123

HERZLIEBSTER JESU   11 11 11 5   Later form of melody by J. Crüger (1598–1662)
arranged J. S. Bach (1685–1750)

1   Ah, holy Jesus, how have you offended
    that man to judge you has in hate pretended? –
    by foes derided, by your own rejected,
        O most afflicted!

2   Who was the guilty? who brought this upon you?
    It is my treason, Lord, that has undone you;
    and I, O Jesus, it was I denied you,
        I crucified you.

3   See how the Shepherd for the sheep is offered,
    the slave has sinned and yet the Son has suffered;
    for our atonement hangs the saviour bleeding,
        God interceding.

4   For me, kind Jesus, was your incarnation,
    your dying sorrow and your life's oblation;
    your bitter passion and your desolation,
        for my salvation.

5 O mighty Saviour, I cannot repay you,
   I do adore you and will here obey you:
   recall your mercy and your love unswerving,
        not my deserving.

after J. Heerman (1585–1647)
R. Bridges (1844–1930)
© in this version Jubilate Hymns†

124

WALSALL 8 6 8 6 (CM)   W. Anchors' *A Choice Collection* c. 1721

1 Alas! and did my saviour bleed,
   and did my sovereign die?
   Did he devote that sacred head
   for such a one as I?

2 Was it for sins that I had done
   he suffered on the tree?
   amazing pity, grace unknown
   and love beyond degree!

3 Well might the sun in darkness hide
   and shut his glories in
   when Christ, the mighty maker, died
   to bear the creature's sin.

4 Dear Saviour, how can I repay
   the debt of love I owe?
   Lord, take my very self I pray
   your work, your will to do.

I. Watts (1674–1748)

125

LONDON ROAD 888888   © Norman Warren (born 1934)†

1 Downtrodden Christ, to you we pray
   who at the third hour of the day
   were led away and nailed up high
   in naked shame beneath the sky:
        Show through the pain
            that scars your face
        the love of God, and our disgrace.

2 Uplifted Christ, to you we pray
   who at the sixth hour of the day
   took all our guilt upon that tree
   in darkness, blood, and agony:
        Look on our pride and unbelief,
        grant us repentance and relief.

3 Outstretching Christ, to you we pray
   who at the ninth hour of the day
   alone dismissed your final breath
   and opened heaven by your death:
        Come to our dying world and reign,
        that we with you may live again.

© Christopher Idle (born 1938)†

Alternative tune: MELITA (273)

126

CASWALL 6565   F. Filitz (1804–1876)

1 *mf* Glory be to Jesus,
     who, in bitter pains,
     poured for me the life-blood
     from his sacred veins.

2   Grace and life eternal
     in that blood I find:
     blessed be his compassion
     wonderfully kind!

3   Abel's blood for vengeance
     pleaded to the skies,
     but the blood of Jesus
     for our pardon cries.

4   When that blood is sprinkled
     on our guilty hearts,
     Satan in confusion
     terror-struck departs.

5   When this earth exulting
     lifts its praise on high,
     angel hosts rejoicing
     make their glad reply.

6 *f* Raise your thankful voices,
     swell the mighty flood;
     louder still and louder
     praise the Lamb of God!

from the Italian c.1815
E. Caswall (1814–1878)

127(i)

KENOSIS   10 10 7 7   © Norman Warren (born 1934)†

Unison

1 Empty he came
   as a man to our race,
   equal with God
   yet forsaking his place –
       humbly he served in our world,
       humbly he served in our world.

2 Lowlier still,
   he was willing to die
   nailed to a cross
   as the people passed by –
       bravely he died in our world,
       bravely he died in our world.

3 Raised by our God
   for us all to revere,
   given a name
   that shall stand without peer –
       honoured as Lord in our world,
       honoured as Lord in our world.

127(ii)

BEKESBOURNE   10 10 7 7   © John Barnard (born 1948)†

4   Give us that mind
    that refuses to claim
    even our rights,
    make our outlook the same –
        humbly to serve in our world,
        humbly to serve in our world.

from *The Song of Christ's Glory* (Philippians 2)
© Gavin Reid (born 1934)

128

REGENT SQUARE   8 7 8 7 8 7

H. T. Smart (1813–1879)

1 *mf* Hark! the voice of love and mercy
  sounds aloud from Calvary;
  see, it tears the temple curtain,
  shakes the earth and veils the sky:
    'It is finished, it is finished!' –
  hear the dying Saviour cry.

2 Finished – all the types and shadows
  of the ceremonial law;
  God fulfils what he has promised –
  death and hell shall reign no more:
    'It is finished, it is finished!' –
  Christ has opened heaven's door.

3 *f* Saints and angels shout his praises,
  his great finished work proclaim;
  all on earth and all in heaven
  join to bless Emmanuel's name:
    'Alleluia, alleluia,
  endless glory to the Lamb!'

J. Evans (1748–1809)
© in this version Jubilate Hymns†

3 Saints and an-gels shout his prais-es, his great fin-ished work pro-claim;

all on earth and all in hea - ven join to bless Em-man-uel's name:

'Al - le - lu — ia, al - le - lu - ia, end-less glo - ry___ to the Lamb!'

129

ST. JOHN 666688

J. B. Calkin (1827–1905)

1 *mp* He stood before the court
   on trial instead of us;
   he met its power to hurt,
   condemned to face the cross:
   our king, accused
   of treachery;
   our God, abused
   for blasphemy!

2   These are the crimes that tell
   the tale of human guilt;
   our sins, our death, our hell –
   on these the case is built:
   to this world's powers
   their Lord stays dumb;
   the guilt is ours,
   no answers come.

3   The sentence must be passed,
   the unknown prisoner killed;
   the price is paid at last,
   the law of God fulfilled:
   he takes our blame,
mf and from that day
   the accuser's claim
   is wiped away.

4   Shall we be judged and tried?
   in Christ our trial is done;
f we live, for he has died,
   our condemnation gone:
   in Christ are we
   both dead and raised,
   alive and free –
   his name be praised!

© Christopher Idle (born 1938)†

130

MAN OF SORROWS 7 7 7 8 P. P. Bliss (1838–1876)

1 *mf* Man of sorrows! what a name
    for the Son of God, who came
    ruined sinners to reclaim:
        Alleluia! what a saviour!

2   Mocked by insults harsh and crude,
    in my place condemned he stood;
    sealed my pardon with his blood:
        Alleluia! what a saviour!

3 *mp* Guilty, helpless, lost were we:
    blameless Lamb of God was he,
    sacrificed to set us free:
  mf   Alleluia! what a saviour!

4 *mp* He was lifted up to die:
    'It is finished!' was his cry;
  mf now in heaven exalted high:
        Alleluia! what a saviour!

5 *f* When he comes, our glorious king,
    all his ransomed home to bring;
    then again this song we'll sing:
        'Alleluia! what a saviour!'

            P. P. Bliss (1838–1876)

131(i)

HERONGATE   8 8 8 8 (LM)

English traditional melody
arranged R. Vaughan Williams (1872–1958)
arrangement © Oxford University Press

(ii)

GIDEON   8 8 8 8 (LM)

T. B. Southgate (1814–1868)

1 *mf* It is a thing most wonderful –
almost too wonderful to be –
that God's own Son should come from heaven
and die to save a child like me.

2 And yet I know that it is true:
he came to this poor world below,
and wept and toiled, and mourned and died,
only because he loved us so.

3 I cannot tell how he could love
a child so weak and full of sin;
his love must be most wonderful
if he could die my love to win.

4 *mp* I sometimes think about the cross,
and shut my eyes, and try to see
the cruel nails, and crown of thorns,
and Jesus crucified for me.

5 But, even could I see him die,
I could but see a little part
of that great love which, like a fire,
is always burning in his heart.

6 *mf* How wonderful it is to know
his love for me so free and sure;
 mp but yet more wonderful to see
my love for him so faint and poor.

7 *mf* And yet I want to love you, Lord:
O teach me how to grow in grace,
that I may love you more and more
until I see you face to face.

W. W. How (1823–1897)
© in this version Jubilate Hymns†

132

ABINGDON 888888

E. R. Routley (1917–1982)

1 Lord Christ, we praise your sacrifice,
   your life in love so freely given:
   for those who took your life away
   you prayed, that they might be forgiven;
   and there, in helplessness arrayed,
   God's power was perfectly displayed.

2 Once helpless in your mother's arms,
   dependent on her mercy then,
   you made yourself again, by choice,
   as helpless in the hands of men;
   and at their mercy crucified,
   you claimed your victory and died.

3 Though helpless and rejected then
   you're now as risen Lord acclaimed;
   for ever, by your victory,
   is God's eternal love proclaimed –
   the love which goes through death to find
   new life and hope for humankind.

4 So, living Lord, prepare us now
   your willing helplessness to share;
   to give ourselves in sacrifice
   to overcome the world's despair;
   in love to give our lives away
   and claim your victory today.

© Alan Gaunt (born 1935)

133(i)

DANIEL   8 8 8 8 (LM)

Irish traditional melody
arranged M. E. F. Shaw (1875–1958)
arrangement © Oxford University Press

(ii)

ST. LAURENCE   8 8 8 8 (LM)

L. G. Hayne (1836–1883)

133(iii)

HERONGATE   8 8 8 8 (LM)

English traditional melody
arranged R. Vaughan Williams (1872–1958)
arrangement © Oxford University Press

1   Lord Jesus, for my sake you come,
    the Son of Man, and God most high;
    you leave behind your Father's home
    to live and serve, to love and die.

2   Your eyes seek out our world's distress
    through insult, grief and agony;
    they meet our tears with tenderness
    yet blaze upon our blasphemy.

3   Are these the robes that make men proud,
    is this the crown that you must wear?
    your face is set, your head is bowed,
    and silently you persevere.

4   You never grasped at selfish gain,
    and yet your hands are marked with blood;
    transfixed by nails, they cling in pain
    to sorrow on a cross of wood.

5   Lord Jesus, come to me anew;
    your hands, your eyes, your thoughts be mine,
    until I learn to love like you
    and live on earth the life divine.

© Michael Perry (born 1942)†

Alternative tune: GIDEON (131)

134

NUN DANKET ALL   8 6 8 6 (CM)   J. Crüger (1598–1662)

1   O dearest Lord, your sacred head
    with thorns was pierced for me:
    pour out your blessing on my head,
    that yours my thoughts may be.

2   O dearest Lord, your sacred hands
    with nails were pierced for me:
    pour out your blessing on my hands
    that yours my work may be.

3   O dearest Lord, your sacred feet
    with nails were pierced for me:
    pour out your blessing on my feet
    that yours my path may be.

4   O dearest Lord, your sacred heart
    with spear was pierced for me:
    pour out your Spirit in my heart
    that yours my life may be.

from *Poems of Father Andrew*
© A. R. Mowbray and Company,
after H. E. Hardy (1869–1946)
and in this version Jubilate Hymns†

Alternative tune: ALBANO (135)

135

ALBANO   8 6 8 6 (CM)   F. V. Novello (1781–1861)

1   O Christ, the Master Carpenter,
    high on a cross you died;
    a wooden cross, with iron nails,
    a spear thrust in your side.

2   O Christ, upon that Friday cross
    your work on earth was done;
    yet, truly, in my life today
    your work has just begun.

3   O Christ, take up your workman's tools
    and shape my life anew,
    that I who now appear rough-hewn
    may be restored by you.

4   O Christ, the Master Carpenter,
    let beauty gently shine
    within the workshop of my life –
    the praise be yours, not mine.

after H. Pink
© David Mowbray (born 1938)†

136

1 My song is love unknown,
   my saviour's love for me;
   love to the loveless shown
   that they might lovely be:
   but who am I, that for my sake
   my Lord should take frail flesh and die?

2 He came from heaven's throne
   salvation to bestow;
   but they refused, and none
   the longed-for Christ would know:
   this is my friend, my friend indeed,
   who at my need his life did spend.

3 Sometimes they crowd his way
   and his sweet praises sing,
   resounding all the day
   hosannas to their king:
   then 'crucify' is all their breath,
   and for his death they thirst and cry.

4 Why, what has my Lord done
to cause this rage and spite?
he made the lame to run,
and gave the blind their sight:
what injuries! yet these are why
the Lord most high so cruelly dies.

5 With angry shouts, they have
my dear Lord done away;
a murderer they save,
the prince of life they slay!
yet willingly he bears the shame
that through his name all might be free.

6 Here might I stay and sing
of him my soul adores;
never was love, dear King,
never was grief like yours! –
this is my friend in whose sweet praise
I all my days could gladly spend.

S. Crossman (1624–1683)
© in this version Jubilate Hymns†

Descant and arrangement © Noël Tredinnick (born 1949)†

3 Some-times they crowd his way and his sweet prais-es
6 Here might I stay and sing of him my soul a -

sing, re - sound - ing all the day ho - san - nas
- dores; nev - er was love, dear King, nev - er was

to___ their king: then 'cru - ci - fy' is
grief___ like yours! — this is my friend in

all their breath, and for his death they thirst___ and cry.
whose sweet praise I all my days could glad - ly spend.

137

HAWKHURST 8 8 8 8 (LM)   H. J. Gauntlett (1805–1876)

1 See, Christ was wounded for our sake,
   and bruised and beaten for our sin,
   so by his sufferings we are healed,
   for God has laid our guilt on him.

2 Look on his face, come close to him –
   see, you will find no beauty there:
   despised, rejected, who can tell
   the grief and sorrow he must bear?

3 Like sheep that stray we leave God's path,
   to choose our own and not his will;
   like sheep to slaughter he has gone,
   obedient to his Father's will.

4 Cast out to die by those he loved,
   reviled by those he died to save,
   see how sin's pride has sought his death,
   see how sin's hate has made his grave.

5 For on his shoulders God has laid
   the weight of sin that we should bear;
   so by his passion we have peace,
   through his obedience and his prayer.

from Isaiah 53
Brian Foley (born 1919)
© Faber Music Ltd

138(i)

ARGENT 7 6 7 6 D

© Noël Tredinnick (born 1949)†

138(ii)

MORDEN PARK   7 6 7 6 © Norman Warren (born 1934)†

1 *mf* No weight of gold or silver
      can measure human worth;
      no soul secures its ransom
      with all the wealth of earth:
      no sinners find their freedom
      but by the gift unpriced,
      the Lamb of God unblemished,
      the precious blood of Christ.

2 *p* Our sins, our griefs and troubles
      he bore and made his own;
      we hid our faces from him,
      rejected and alone;
      his wounds are for our healing,
      our peace is by his pain –
      behold, the Man of sorrows,
      the Lamb for sinners slain!

3 *mf* In Christ the past is over,
      a new world now begins;
      with him we rise to freedom
      who saves us from our sins:
  f we live by faith in Jesus
      to make his glory known –
      behold, the Man of sorrows,
      the Lamb upon his throne!

© Timothy Dudley-Smith (born 1926)

Alternative tune: EWING (573)

139

PASSION CHORALE 7 6 7 6 D

Melody from H. L. Hassler (1564–1612)
arranged J. S. Bach (1685–1750)

1 O sacred head surrounded
   by crown of piercing thorn;
   O royal head so wounded,
   reviled and put to scorn:
   death's shadows rise before you,
   the glow of life decays,
   yet angel hosts adore you
   and tremble as they gaze!

2 Your youthfulness and vigour
   are spent, your strength is gone,
   and in your tortured figure
   I see death drawing on:
   what agony of dying,
   what love, to sinners free!
   My Lord, all grace supplying,
   O turn your face on me!

3 Your sinless soul's oppression
   was all for sinners' gain;
   mine, mine was the transgression,
   but yours the deadly pain:
   I bow my head, my Saviour,
   for I deserve your place;
   O grant to me your favour,
   and heal me by your grace.

4 What language shall I borrow
   to thank you, dearest Friend,
   for this your dying sorrow,
   your mercy without end?
   Lord, make me yours for ever:
   your servant let me be;
   and may I never, never
   betray your love for me.

   after Bernard of Clairvaux (1091–1153)
   and P. Gerhardt (1607–1676);
   J. W. Alexander (1804–1859) and
   H. W. Baker (1821–1877)
   © in this version Jubilate Hymns†

140(i)

CHORUS ANGELORUM 8 6 8 6 (CM)   A. Somervell (1863–1937)

(ii)

GERONTIUS 8 6 8 6 (CM)   J. B. Dykes (1823–1876)

1 *f* Praise to the Holiest in the height,
     and in the depth be praise;
     in all his words most wonderful,
     most sure in all his ways!

2 *mf* O loving wisdom of our God!
     when all was sin and shame,
     a second Adam to the fight
     and to the rescue came.

3   O wisest love! that flesh and blood,
     which did in Adam fail,
     should strive afresh against the foe,
     should strive and should prevail;

4   And that the highest gift of grace
     should flesh and blood refine:
     God's presence and his very self,
     and essence all-divine.

5 *mp* O generous love! that he who came
     as man to smite our foe,
     the double agony for us
     as man should undergo:

6 *p* And in the garden secretly,
     and on the cross on high,
     should teach his brethren, and inspire
     to suffer and to die.

7 *f* Praise to the Holiest in the height,
     and in the depth be praise;
     in all his words most wonderful,
     most sure in all his ways!

J. H. Newman (1801–1890)

A third tune (RICHMOND) is printed overleaf.

140(iii)

RICHMOND   8 6 8 6 (CM)

Adapted from T. Haweis (1734–1820)
by S. Webbe (c. 1770–1843)

1 *f* Praise to the Holiest in the height,
        and in the depth be praise;
        in all his words most wonderful,
        most sure in all his ways!

2 *mf* O loving wisdom of our God!
        when all was sin and shame,
        a second Adam to the fight
        and to the rescue came.

3   O wisest love! that flesh and blood,
        which did in Adam fail,
        should strive afresh against the foe,
        should strive and should prevail;

4   And that the highest gift of grace
        should flesh and blood refine:
        God's presence and his very self,
        and essence all-divine.

5 *mp* O generous love! that he who came
　　　　as man to smite our foe,
　　　　the double agony for us
　　　　as man should undergo:

6 *p* And in the garden secretly,
　　　　and on the cross on high,
　　　　should teach his brethren, and inspire
　　　　to suffer and to die.

7 *f* Praise to the Holiest in the height,
　　　　and in the depth be praise;
　　　　in all his words most wonderful,
　　　　most sure in all his ways!

J. H. Newman (1801–1890)

Arrangement by David Willcocks (born 1919)
© Oxford University Press

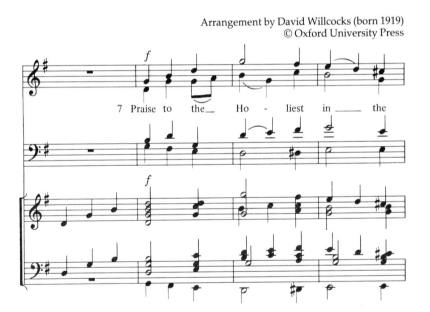

141

MEDFIELD STREET 88884

© Simon Beckley (born 1938)†
© arranged John Barnard (born 1948)†

This melody is particularly effective when sung unaccompanied. Pianists are recommended to make sparing use of the optional bass, perhaps only for verses 2 and 4.

1 *mp* The hands of Christ, the caring hands,
   they nailed them to a cross of wood;
   the feet that climbed the desert road
   and brought the news of peace with God,
    they pierced them through.

2 The kingly Christ, the saviour-king,
   they ringed his head with briars woven;
   the lips that freely spoke of heaven,
   that told the world of sins forgiven,
    they mocked with wine.

3 Too late for life, in death too late
   they tried to maim him with a spear;
   for sacrilege they could not bear –
   the sabbath comes, so they must tear
    the heart from God.

4 *mf* To him be praise, all praise to him
   who died upon the cross of pain;
   whose agonies were not in vain –
  f for Christ the Lord is risen again
    and brings us joy!

© Michael Perry (born 1942)†

142(i)

GRAFTON 8 7 8 7 8 7

French church melody from
Chants Ordinaires de l'Office Divin Paris 1881
arranged S. H. Nicholson (1875–1947)
arrangement © Hymns Ancient & Modern Ltd

1 Sing, my tongue, the glorious battle,
   sing the final, fierce affray!
   how the cross became a triumph
   where our sin was borne away;
   how, the pains of death enduring,
   earth's Redeemer won the day.

2 When at last the appointed fulness
   of the sacred time had come,
   he was sent, the world's Creator,
   from the Father's heavenly home;
   and he came in truest manhood
   from a humble virgin's womb.

3 Now the thirty years are ended
   which on earth he willed to see;
   willingly he goes to suffer,
   born to set his people free;
   on the cross the Lamb is lifted,
   there the sacrifice to be.

142(ii)

PANGE LINGUA 8 7 8 7 8 7

Sarum Plainsong Mode iii
arranged J. H. Arnold (1887–1956)
arrangement © Oxford University Press

A - men.

4 Gall and vinegar they offer,
   mocking him with thorns and reed;
   nails and spear, the Saviour piercing,
   make his sacred body bleed:
   by that blood the whole creation
   from the stain of sin is freed.

5 Praise and honour to the Father,
   praise and honour to the Son,
   praise and honour to the Spirit,
   ever Three and ever One:
   one in triumph, one in glory
   while eternal ages run!   (Amen)

after the Latin by Venantius Fortunatus (c.535–600)
J. M. Neale (1818–1866)
© in this version Jubilate Hymns†

Alternative tune: PICARDY (195)

143(i)

THE HOLY SON   8 8 8 8 (LM)

Peter Hurford (born 1930)

1 The Lord made man, the scriptures tell,
   to bear his image and his sign;
   yet we by nature share as well
   the ancient mark of Adam's line.

2 In Adam's fall falls every man,
   with every gift the Father gave:
   the crown of all creation's plan
   becomes a rebel and a slave.

3 Herein all woes are brought to birth,
   all aching hearts and sunless skies:
   brightness is gone from all the earth,
   the innocence of nature dies.

4 Yet Adam's children, born to pain,
   by self enslaved, by sin enticed,
   still may by grace be born again,
   children of God, beloved in Christ.

5 In Christ is Adam's ransom met,
   earth, by his cross, is holy ground;
   Eden indeed is with us yet –
   in Christ are life and freedom found!

143(ii)

BIRLING   8 8 8 8 (LM)

Eighteenth- or nineteenth-century melody
arranged G. T. Shaw (1879–1943)
arrangement © Oxford University Press

1   The Lord made man, the scriptures tell,
    to bear his image and his sign;
    yet we by nature share as well
    the ancient mark of Adam's line.

2   In Adam's fall falls every man,
    with every gift the Father gave:
    the crown of all creation's plan
    becomes a rebel and a slave.

3   Herein all woes are brought to birth,
    all aching hearts and sunless skies:
    brightness is gone from all the earth,
    the innocence of nature dies.

4   Yet Adam's children, born to pain,
    by self enslaved, by sin enticed,
    still may by grace be born again,
    children of God, beloved in Christ.

5   In Christ is Adam's ransom met,
    earth, by his cross, is holy ground;
    Eden indeed is with us yet –
    in Christ are life and freedom found!

© Timothy Dudley-Smith (born 1926)

144(i)

STRACATHRO 8 6 8 6 (CM)

Melody C. Hutcheson (1792–1860)
arranged D. Evans (1874–1948)
arrangement © Oxford University Press

1 There is a fountain opened wide
   where life and hope begin;
   for Christ the Lord was crucified
   to cleanse us from our sin.

2 The dying thief rejoiced to see
   that fountain in his day;
   and there have I, as vile as he,
   washed all my sins away.

3 O Lamb of God, your precious blood
   shall never lose its power,
   till all the ransomed church of God
   be saved to sin no more.

4 And since, by faith, I saw the stream
   your flowing wounds supply,
   redeeming love has been my theme,
   and shall be till I die.

5 When this poor, lisping, stammering tongue
   lies silent in the grave,
   then in a nobler, sweeter song
   I'll sing your power to save.

W. Cowper (1731–1800)
© in this version Jubilate Hymns†

144(ii)

BELMONT 8 6 8 6 (CM)

W. Gardiner (1770–1853)

1   There is a fountain opened wide
    where life and hope begin;
    for Christ the Lord was crucified
    to cleanse us from our sin.

2   The dying thief rejoiced to see
    that fountain in his day;
    and there have I, as vile as he,
    washed all my sins away.

3   O Lamb of God, your precious blood
    shall never lose its power,
    till all the ransomed church of God
    be saved to sin no more.

4   And since, by faith, I saw the stream
    your flowing wounds supply,
    redeeming love has been my theme,
    and shall be till I die.

5   When this poor, lisping, stammering tongue
    lies silent in the grave,
    then in a nobler, sweeter song
    I'll sing your power to save.

W. Cowper (1731–1800)
© in this version Jubilate Hymns†

145

English melody before 1642

1   Through all our days we'll sing the praise
    of Christ, the resurrected;
    who, though divine, did not decline
    to be by men afflicted:
    pain, pain and suffering –
    he knew its taste, he bore its sting;
    peace, peace has come to earth
    through Christ our king and saviour.

2   His birth obscure, his family poor,
    he owned no crown, no kingdom;
    yet those who grope in darkness, hope
    since he brought light and freedom:
    shame, shame and agony –
    though guiltless he of felony;
    shout, shout his sinless name,
    our Jesus, king and saviour.

3   At fearful cost his life he lost
    that death might be defeated;
    the Man of Love, now risen above,
    in majesty is seated:
    low, low was his descent
    to those by sin and sorrow bent;
    life, life to all who trust
    the Lord, our king and saviour.

4   And all who trust will find they must
    obey the will of heaven;
    for grief intense can make some sense
    to those who are forgiven:
    hard, hard the road he trod –
    the Son of Man, the Son of God;
    hope, hope in Christ alone,
    our reigning king and saviour.

© Michael Saward (born 1932)†

146(i)

BOW BRICKHILL 8 8 8 8 (LM)

S. H. Nicholson (1875–1947)
© Hymns Ancient & Modern Ltd

(ii)

OMBERSLEY 8 8 8 8 (LM)

W. H. Gladstone (1840–1891)

146(iii)

BRESLAU   8 8 8 8 (LM)   Melody in *As Hymnodus Sacer* Leipzig 1625

1 We sing the praise of him who died,
   of him who died upon the cross;
   the sinner's hope let none deride –
   for this we count the world but loss.

2 Inscribed upon the cross we see
   in shining letters, 'God is Love';
   he bears our sins upon the tree,
   he brings us mercy from above.

3 The cross – it takes our guilt away,
   it holds the fainting spirit up;
   it cheers with hope the gloomy day
   and sweetens every bitter cup:

4 It makes the coward spirit brave
   and nerves the feeble arm for fight;
   it takes the terror from the grave
   and gilds the bed of death with light:

5 The balm of life, the cure of woe,
   the measure and the pledge of love;
   the sinner's refuge here below,
   the angels' theme in heaven above.

                    T. Kelly (1769–1855)

147(i)

ROCKINGHAM 8 8 8 8 (LM)   Adapted E. Miller (1735–1807)

1 *mf* When I survey the wondrous cross
   on which the prince of glory died,
   my richest gain I count as loss,
   and pour contempt on all my pride.

2 Forbid it, Lord, that I should boast
   save in the cross of Christ my God;
   the very things that charm me most –
   I sacrifice them to his blood.

3 *p* See from his head, his hands, his feet,
   sorrow and love flow mingled down:
   when did such love and sorrow meet,
   or thorns compose so rich a crown?

4 *mf* Were the whole realm of nature mine,
   that were an offering far too small;
   f love so amazing, so divine,
   demands my soul, my life, my all!

I. Watts (1674–1748)

147(ii)

O WALY WALY 8 8 8 8 (LM)

English traditional melody
© arranged Noël Tredinnick (born 1949)†

1 *mf* When I survey the wondrous cross
 on which the prince of glory died,
 my richest gain I count as loss,
 and pour contempt on all my pride.

2 Forbid it, Lord, that I should boast
 save in the cross of Christ my God;
 the very things that charm me most –
 I sacrifice them to his blood.

3 *p* See from his head, his hands, his feet,
 sorrow and love flow mingled down:
 when did such love and sorrow meet,
 or thorns compose so rich a crown?

4 *mf* Were the whole realm of nature mine,
 that were an offering far too small;
 f love so amazing, so divine,
 demands my soul, my life, my all!

I. Watts (1674–1748)

148

HORSLEY   8 6 8 6 (CM)   W. Horsley (1774–1858)

1   There is a green hill far away
    outside a city wall,
    where our dear Lord was crucified,
    who died to save us all.

2   We may not know, we cannot tell
    what pains he had to bear,
    but we believe it was for us
    he hung and suffered there.

3   He died that we might be forgiven,
    he died to make us good;
    that we might go at last to heaven,
    saved by his precious blood.

4   There was no other good enough
    to pay the price of sin;
    he, only, could unlock the gate
    of heaven – and let us in.

5   Lord Jesus, dearly you have loved;
    and we must love you too,
    and trust in your redeeming blood
    and learn to follow you.

                            Cecil F. Alexander (1818–1895)

For other hymns on this theme, see:
Sunday Themes index
    Section 25, The Victory of the Cross (p. xi)
    Section 26, The Way of the Cross (p. xi)

GOD: LORD AND SAVIOUR

Risen and Victorious

149(i) SONG 46 10 10   Orlando Gibbons (1583–1625)

(ii) EASTER SKIES 10 10   © John Marsh (born 1947)

1 All shall be well!
   for on our Easter skies
   see Christ the sun
      of righteousness arise.

2 All shall be well!
   the sacrifice is made;
   the sinner freed,
      the price of pardon paid.

3 All shall be well!
   the cross and passion past;
   dark night is done,
      bright morning come at last.

4 All shall be well!
   within our Father's plan
   death has no more
      dominion over man.

5 Jesus alive!
   rejoice and sing again,
   'All shall be well
      for evermore, Amen!'

© Timothy Dudley-Smith (born 1926)

150(i)

WÜRTTEMBERG 7 7 7 7 4   *Hundert Arien* Dresden 1694

Al - le - lu - ia!

(ii)

SAVANNAH 7 7 7 7   J. Wesley's *Foundery Collection* 1742

The tune SAVANNAH is only to be used when the hymn is started at verse 2 and the Alleluias are omitted.

1   All creation join to say:
     Christ the Lord is risen today!
     raise your joys and triumphs high;
     sing, you heavens, and earth reply:
        Alleluia!

2   Love's redeeming work is done;
     fought the fight, the battle won:
     see, our Sun's eclipse has passed;
     see, the dawn has come at last!
     Alleluia!

3   Vain the stone, the watch, the seal:
     Christ has burst the gates of hell;
     death in vain forbids his rise –
     Christ has opened paradise:
        Alleluia!

4   Now he lives, our glorious king;
     now, O death, where is your sting?
     Once he died, our souls to save –
     where's your victory, boasting grave?
        Alleluia!

5   So we rise where Christ has led,
     following our exalted head;
     made like him, like him we rise –
     ours the cross, the grave, the skies:
        Alleluia!

6   Hail the Lord of earth and heaven!
     praise to you by both be given;
     every knee to you shall bow,
     risen Christ, triumphant now:
        Alleluia!

C. Wesley (1707–1788)
© in this version Jubilate Hymns†

151

LUX EOI 8 7 8 7 D

A. Sullivan (1842–1900)
descant © John Barnard (born 1948)†

4 Al - le - lu - ia,   al - le - lu - ia!   glo - ry be to   God on high:

al - le - lu - ia to the Sa - viour   who has gained the__ vic - to - ry;

al - le - lu - ia   to the Spi - rit, fount   of love and sanc - ti - ty:

al - le - lu - ia, al - le - lu - ia   to   the Tri - une Ma - jes - ty!

1   Alleluia, alleluia!
        hearts to heaven and voices raise:
    sing to God a hymn of gladness,
        sing to God a hymn of praise;
    he who on the cross a victim
        for the world's salvation bled –
    Jesus Christ, the king of glory,
        now is risen from the dead.

2   Alleluia, Christ is risen!
        death at last has met defeat:
    see the ancient powers of evil
        in confusion and retreat;
    once he died, and once was buried:
        now he lives for evermore,
    Jesus Christ, the world's redeemer,
        whom we worship and adore.

3   Christ is risen, we are risen!
        set your hearts on things above:
    there in all the Father's glory
        lives and reigns our king of love;
    hear the word of peace he brings us,
        see his wounded hands and side!
    now let every wrong be ended,
        every sin be crucified.

4   Alleluia, alleluia!
        glory be to God on high:
    alleluia to the Saviour
        who has gained the victory;
    alleluia to the Spirit,
        fount of love and sanctity:
    alleluia, alleluia
        to the Triune Majesty!

after C. Wordsworth (1807–1885)
verses 2 and 3 © Jubilate Hymns†

152(i)

CHURCH CLOSE 6 7 7 11   © David Iliff (born 1939)†

1   *p*   Comes Mary to the grave:
no singing bird has spoken,
nor has the world awoken,
and in her grief all love lies lost
     and broken.

2   Says Jesus at her side,
no longer Jesus dying,
'Why, Mary, are you crying?'
mf She turns, with joy, 'My Lord! my love!'
     replying.

3   *f*   With Mary on this day
we join our voices praising
the God of Jesus' raising,
and sing the triumph of his love
     amazing.

from John 20
© Michael Perry (born 1942)†

(ii)

EASTER MORNING 6 7 7 11   © Norman Warren (born 1934)†

152(iii)

PASCHAL DAWN   6 7 7 11   © John Barnard (born 1948)†

Descant

3 With Ma - ry we join our voi-ces prais - ing

the God of Je - sus' rais - ing, and sing the

tri - umph of his love a - maz - ing.

153

WÜRTTEMBERG   7 7 7 7 4   *Hundert Arien* Dresden 1694

1 *f* Christ the Lord is risen again,
    Christ has broken every chain;
    hear the angel voices cry,
    singing evermore on high:
      Alleluia!

2 *mf* He who gave for us his life,
    who for us endured the strife,
    is our paschal lamb today;
 f we too sing for joy and say:
      Alleluia!

3 *mp* He who bore all pain and loss
    comfortless upon the cross
 mf lives in glory now on high,
    pleads for us and hears our cry:
      Alleluia!

4 *mp* He who slumbered in the grave
 f is exalted now to save;
    through the universe it rings
    that the lamb is King of kings:
      Alleluia!

5 *mf* Now he bids us tell abroad
    how the lost may be restored,
    how the penitent forgiven,
    how we too may enter heaven:
      Alleluia!

6 *f* Christ, our paschal lamb indeed,
    all your ransomed people feed!
    take our sins and guilt away;
    let us sing by night and day:
      Alleluia!

after M. Weisse (1480–1534)
Catherine Winkworth (1827–1878)

154

VULPIUS 8 8 8 4

Melody M. Vulpius (c. 1560–1616)

Al - le - lu - ia, al - le - lu - ia, al - le - lu - ia!

1 Good Christians all, rejoice and sing!
   now is the triumph of our king;
   to all the world glad news we bring:
   Alleluia, alleluia, alleluia!

2 The Lord of life is risen today;
   death's mighty stone is rolled away:
   let every tongue rejoice and say,
   'Alleluia, alleluia, alleluia!'

3 We praise in songs of victory
   that love, that life, which cannot die,
   and sing with hearts uplifted high,
   'Alleluia, alleluia, alleluia!'

4 Your name we bless, O risen Lord,
   and sing today with one accord
   the life laid down, the life restored:
   Alleluia, alleluia, alleluia!

C. A. Alington (1872–1955)
© Hymns Ancient & Modern Ltd

155

EASTER HYMN 7 7 7 7 and Alleluias

Lyra Davidica 1708
arranged W. H. Monk (1823–1889)
descant © John Barnard (born 1948)†

3 But the pains which he — en - dured Al - le - lu - ia,

our — sal - va - tion have pro-cured; al - le - lu - ia,

now a-bove — the sky — he's king al - le - lu - ia,

where the an-gels e - ver sing.— al - le - lu - ia!

1 Jesus Christ is risen today,   Alleluia,
   our triumphant holy day;   alleluia,
   who did once upon the cross   alleluia,
   suffer to redeem our loss.   alleluia!

2 Hymns of joy then let us sing   Alleluia,
   praising Christ our heavenly king;   alleluia,
   who endured the cross and grave   alleluia,
   sinners to redeem and save!   alleluia!

3 But the pains which he endured   Alleluia,
   our salvation have procured;   alleluia,
   now above the sky he's king   alleluia,
   where the angels ever sing.   alleluia!

after a fourteenth-century author
unknown (eighteenth century)

156

ST. ALBINUS 7 8 7 8 4 H. J. Gauntlett (1805–1876)

Al - le - lu - ia!

1 Jesus lives! Your terrors now
can, O death, no more appal us:
Jesus lives! – by this we know
you, O grave, cannot enthral us:
  Alleluia!

2 Jesus lives! – henceforth is death
but the gate of life immortal;
this shall calm our trembling breath
when we pass its gloomy portal:
  Alleluia!

3 Jesus lives! – for us he died:
then, alone to Jesus living,
pure in heart may we abide,
glory to our saviour giving:
  Alleluia!

4 Jesus lives! – this bond of love
neither life nor death shall sever,
powers in hell or heaven above
tear us from his keeping never:
  Alleluia!

5 Jesus lives! – to him the throne
over all the world is given;
may we go where he is gone,
rest and reign with him in heaven:
  Alleluia!

after C. F. Gellert (1715–1769)
Frances E. Cox (1812–1897)
© in this version Jubilate Hymns†

Descant and arrangement by G. T. Shaw (1879–1943)

5 Je - sus lives! — to him the throne o - ver all the —
world is giv - en; may we go — where he — is — gone,
rest and reign with — him in hea - ven: Al - le - lu - ia!

157

EASTER SONG   8 8 4 4 8 8 and Alleluias

Geistliche Kirchengesang
Cologne 1623
arranged R. Vaughan Williams (1872–1958)
arrangement © Oxford University Press

Al - le - lu - ia, al - le - lu - ia!

Al - le - lu - ia, al - le -

-lu - ia, al - le - lu - ia, al - le - lu - ia, al - le - lu - ia!

1 Light's glittering morning fills the sky,
   heaven thunders out its victor cry;
        Alleluia, alleluia!
   earth shouts her Easter triumph high,
   and groaning hell makes wild reply.
        Alleluia, alleluia,
        alleluia, alleluia, alleluia!

2 For Christ the Lord, the mighty king,
   closes with death and draws its sting;
        Alleluia, alleluia!
   he tramples down the powers of night,
   brings out his ransomed saints to light.
        Alleluia . . .

3 His rocky tomb the threefold guard
   of watch and stone and seal had barred,
        Alleluia, alleluia!
   but now in royal triumph high
   he comes from death to victory!
        Alleluia . . .

4 Hell's gates are broken down at last,
   our days of mourning now are past;
        Alleluia, alleluia!
   'Weep not,' an angel voice has said,
   'Jesus is risen from the dead!'
        Alleluia . . .

5 All praise be yours, O risen Lord,
   from death to endless life restored;
        Alleluia, alleluia!
   to Father, Son and Spirit be
   all power and praise eternally!
        Alleluia . . .

from the Latin
J. M. Neale (1818–1866)
© in this version Jubilate Hymns†

158

CHRIST AROSE   6 5 6 4 and refrain   R. Lowry (1826–1899)

Up from the grave he a - rose____ as the vic - tor o - ver all his

foes; _____ he a - rose in tri - umph from the

dark do-main, and he lives for ev- er with his saints to reign— he a-

-rose, _____ he a - rose, Al - le - lu - ia— Christ a - rose!

1 Low in the grave he lay,
   Jesus my saviour,
   waiting the coming day,
   Jesus my Lord!
         Up from the grave he arose
         as the victor over all his foes;
         he arose in triumph from the dark domain,
         and he lives for ever with his saints to reign –
         he arose, he arose, Alleluia – Christ arose!

2 Vainly they guard his bed,
   Jesus my saviour;
   vainly they seal the dead,
   Jesus my Lord!
         Up from the grave he arose . . .

3 Death cannot keep his prey,
   Jesus my saviour;
   he tore the bars away,
   Jesus my Lord!
         Up from the grave he arose . . .

R. Lowry (1826–1899)

159

CROFT'S 136th   666688

W. Croft (1678–1727)

1 Now lives the Lamb of God,
   our Passover, the Christ,
   who once with nails and wood
   for us was sacrificed:
       Come, keep the feast, the anthem sing
       that Christ indeed is Lord and king!

2 Now risen from the dead
   Christ never dies again;
   in us, with Christ as head,
   sin nevermore shall reign:
       Come, keep the feast . . .

3 In Adam all must die,
   forlorn and unforgiven;
   in Christ all come alive,
   the second Man from heaven.
       Come, keep the feast . . .

4 Give praise to God alone
   who life from death can bring;
   whose mighty power can turn
   the winter into spring:
       Come, keep the feast . . .

from *The Easter Anthems*
© David Mowbray (born 1938)†

Alternative tune: CHRISTCHURCH (565)

160

TEMPUS ADEST FLORIDUM 7 6 7 6 D

English carol tune
arranged J. Stainer (1840–1901)

1 Spring has come for us today!
  Christ has burst his prison,
  and from three days' sleep in death
  like the sun has risen.
  All the winter of our sins,
  long and dark, is dying:
  welcome now the light of Christ,
  life and joy supplying!

2 Alleluia! let us sing
  to our king immortal
  who in triumph broke the bars
  of the tomb's dark portal.
  Alleluia! to our God,
  Father, Son, and Spirit:
  to your holy name be praise,
  honour, power, and merit.

after John of Damascus (c.675–749)
J. M. Neale (1818–1866)

161

ELLACOMBE 7 6 7 6 D

Württemberg Gesangbuch 1784
as in *The Australian Hymn Book* 1977

1 The day of resurrection!
   come, spread the news abroad;
   the passover of gladness,
   the passover of God:
   from death to life eternal,
   from earth up to the sky,
   our Christ has brought us over
   with hymns of victory.

2 Now let the skies be joyful
   and earth sing back her praise;
   let all the nations worship
   the God of endless days:
   let all things seen and unseen
   their joyful music blend,
   for Christ the Lord has risen—
   our triumph knows no end!

after John of Damascus (c.675–749)
J. M. Neale (1818–1866)

162

YVONNE   10 10 11 10   © Norman Warren (born 1934)†

1   These are the facts as we have received them,
    these are the truths that the Christian believes,
    this is the basis of all of our preaching:
    Christ died for sinners and rose from the tomb.

2   These are the facts as we have received them:
    Christ has fulfilled what the scriptures foretold,
    Adam's whole family in death had been sleeping,
    Christ through his rising restores us to life.

3   These are the facts as we have received them:
    we, with our saviour, have died on the cross;
    now, having risen, our Jesus lives in us,
    gives us his Spirit and makes us his home.

4   These are the facts as we have received them:
    we shall be changed in the blink of an eye,
    trumpets shall sound as we face life immortal,
    this is the victory through Jesus our Lord.

5   These are the facts as we have received them,
    these are the truths that the Christian believes,
    this is the basis of all of our preaching:
    Christ died for sinners and rose from the tomb.

                                from 1 Corinthians 15 etc.
                                © Michael Saward (born 1932)†

Alternative tune: EPIPHANY HYMN (338)

163(i)

VICTORY 8 8 8 4

First three lines adapted from
G. P. da Palestrina (1525–1594)
Alleluia added by W. H. Monk (1823–1889)

Al -le - lu - ia!

1 The strife is past, the battle done;
   now is the victor's triumph won –
   O let the song of praise be sung,
      Alleluia!

2 Death's mightiest powers have done their worst;
   and Jesus has his foes dispersed –
   let shouts of praise and joy outburst,
      Alleluia!

3 On the third day he rose again,
   glorious in majesty to reign –
   sing out with joy the glad refrain,
      Alleluia!

4 Lord over death, our wounded king,
   save us from Satan's deadly sting
   that we may live for you and sing,
      Alleluia!

from the Latin
F. Pott (1832–1909)
© in this version Jubilate Hymns†

163(ii)

VULPIUS 8 8 8 4

Melody M. Vulpius (c. 1560–1616)

Al - le - lu - ia, al - le - lu - ia, al -le-lu - ia!

164(i)

VINEYARD HAVEN 668666

Richard Dirksen (born 1921)
© Harold Flammer Inc.

With majesty (♩ = c. 72)

1   This day above all days
glad hymns of triumph bring;
lift every heart to love and praise
and every voice to sing:
    for Jesus is risen,
our glorious Lord and king!

164(ii)

CARDINGTON 668666   © Paul Edwards (born 1955)†

2 Christ keeps his Eastertide!
   The Father's power descends;
   the shuttered tomb he opens wide,
   the rock-hewn grave he rends:
       for Jesus is risen,
   and death's dominion ends!

3 What sovereign grace is found
   in Christ for all our need!
   The powers of sin and death are bound,
   the ransomed captives freed:
       for Jesus is risen,
   the prince of life indeed!

4 So lift your joyful songs
   with all the hosts on high,
   where angel and archangel throngs
   his ceaseless praises cry:
       for Jesus is risen,
   and lives no more to die!

© Timothy Dudley-Smith (born 1926)

165

VRUECHTEN 6 7 6 7 D   Dutch melody from *David's Psalmen* Amsterdam 1685
arranged C. Wood (1866–1926)

Had Christ, who once was slain, not burst his three-day pri - son

our faith would be in vain— but now has Christ a - ris - en, a-

-ris - en, a - ris - en, a - ris - - - en!

1 This joyful Eastertide
   away with sin and sadness!
   our Lord, the crucified,
   has filled our hearts with gladness:
        Had Christ, who once was slain,
        not burst his three-day prison
        our faith would be in vain –
        but now has Christ arisen,
        arisen, arisen, arisen!

2 My being shall rejoice
   secure within God's keeping,
   until the trumpet voice
   shall wake us from our sleeping:
        Had Christ . . .

3 Death's waters lost their chill
   when Jesus crossed the river;
   his love shall reach me still,
   his mercy is for ever:
        Had Christ . . .

after G. R. Woodward (1848–1934)
© in this version Jubilate Hymns†

166

NOËL NOUVELET   6 5 6 5 D

French melody
arranged M. E. F. Shaw (1875–1958)
arrangement © Oxford University Press

1 Welcome, happy morning!
age to age shall say;
hell today is conquered,
heaven is won today:
come then, True and Faithful,
now fulfil your word;
this is your third morning:
rise, O buried Lord!

2 Earth with joyful welcome
clothes herself for spring;
greets with life reviving
her returning king:
flowers in every pasture,
leaves on every bough,
speak of sorrows ended;
Jesus triumphs now!

3 Author and sustainer,
source of life and breath;
you for our salvation
trod the path of death:
Jesus Christ is living,
God for evermore!
Now let all creation
hail him and adore.

4 Loose our souls imprisoned
bound with Satan's chain;
all that now is fallen,
raise to life again!
show your face in brightness,
shine the whole world through;
hope returns with daybreak,
life returns with you.

after Venantius Fortunatus (c.535–600)
J. Ellerton (1826–1893)
© in this version Jubilate Hymns†

167

MACCABAEUS   10 11 11 11 and refrain   Adapted from G. F. Handel (1685–1759)

Yours be the glo - ry! ris - en, con-quering Son: end-less is the vic-tory o-ver death you won.

1 Yours be the glory! risen, conquering Son;
  endless is the victory over death you won;
  angels robed in splendour rolled the stone away,
  kept the folded grave clothes
              where your body lay:
        Yours be the glory! risen, conquering Son:
        endless is the victory over death you won.

2 See! Jesus meets us, risen from the tomb,
  lovingly he greets us, scatters fear and gloom;
  let the church with gladness
              hymns of triumph sing!
  for her Lord is living, death has lost its sting:
        Yours be the glory . . .

3 No more we doubt you, glorious prince of life:
  what is life without you? aid us in our strife;
  make us more than conquerors
              through your deathless love,
  bring us safe through Jordan to your home above:
        Yours be the glory . . .

after E. L. Budry (1854–1932)
R. B. Hoyle (1875–1939)
© World Student Christian Federation,
and in this version Jubilate Hymns†

168

ST. FULBERT 8 6 8 6 (CM)   H. J. Gauntlett (1805–1876)

1 You choirs of new Jerusalem,
   your sweetest notes employ
   the paschal victory to hymn
   in songs of holy joy!

2 For Judah's Lion burst his chains
   and crushed the serpent's head;
   he cries aloud through death's domains
   to wake the imprisoned dead.

3 Devouring depths of hell their prey
   at his command restore;
   his ransomed hosts pursue their way
   where Jesus goes before.

4 Triumphant in his glory now –
   to him all power is given;
   to him in one communion bow
   all saints in earth and heaven.

5 All glory to the Father be,
   the Spirit and the Son:
   all glory to the One-in-Three
   while endless ages run.

after Fulbert of Chartres (c.975–1028)
R. Campbell (1814–1868)

For other hymns on this theme, see:
Sunday Themes index
    Section 27, The Resurrection of Christ (p. xi)
    Section 30 (2), The Resurrection and the Life (p. xiii)
Song Section
    Alleluia, alleluia! give thanks (S.3)
    He is Lord (S.7)

GOD: LORD AND SAVIOUR
Ascended and Reigning

169

CHURCH TRIUMPHANT   8 8 8 8 (LM)   J. W. Elliott (1833–1915)

1 I know that my redeemer lives –
   what comfort this assurance gives!
   he lives, he lives, who once was dead,
   he lives, my everlasting Head.

2 He lives, triumphant from the grave,
   he lives, eternally to save;
   he lives, to bless me with his love,
   and intercedes for me above.

3 He lives to help in time of need,
   he lives, my hungry soul to feed;
   he lives, and grants me daily breath,
   he lives, and I shall conquer death.

4 He lives, my kind, wise, constant friend,
   who still will guard me to the end;
   he lives, and while he lives I'll sing,
   Jesus, my prophet, priest, and king.

5 He lives, my saviour, to prepare
   a place in heaven, and lead me there;
   he lives, all glory to his name,
   Jesus, unchangeably the same.

S. Medley (1738–1799)

Alternative tune: EASTER SONG (157) adding Alleluias as appropriate.

170

HYFRYDOL   8 7 8 7 D

R. H. Prichard (1811–1887)
as in *The Australian Hymn Book* 1977

1 Alleluia, sing to Jesus!
   his the sceptre, his the throne:
   Alleluia! – his the triumph,
   his the victory alone.
   Hear the songs of holy Zion
   thunder like a mighty flood:
   'Jesus out of every nation
   has redeemed us by his blood!'

2 Alleluia! – not as orphans
   are we left in sorrow now:
   Alleluia! – he is near us;
   faith believes, nor questions how.
   Though the cloud from sight received him
   whom the angels now adore,
   shall our hearts forget his promise,
   'I am with you evermore'?

3 Alleluia! – bread of heaven,
   here on earth our food, our stay:
   Alleluia! – here the sinful
   come to you from day to day.
   Intercessor, friend of sinners,
   earth's redeemer, plead for me,
   where the songs of all the sinless
   sweep across the crystal sea.

4 Alleluia, sing to Jesus!
   his the sceptre, his the throne:
   Alleluia! his the triumph,
   his the victory alone.
   Hear the songs of holy Zion
   thunder like a mighty flood:
   'Jesus out of every nation
   has redeemed us by his blood!'

W. C. Dix (1837–1898)

Alternative tune: ALLELUIA (428)

171

DARWALL'S 148th   666688

J. Darwall (1731–1789)
descant S. H. Nicholson (1875–1947)
descant © Hymns Ancient & Modern Ltd

5 All strength is in your hand, all power to you is given; — all
wis-dom to _____ com-mand in earth and hell and heaven: be-yond all
words cre - a - tion sings the King of kings and Lord of lords.

1 Ascended Christ, who gained
   the glory that we sing,
   anointed and ordained,
   our prophet, priest, and king:
       by many tongues
       the church displays
       your power and praise
       in all her songs.

2 No titles, thrones, or powers
   can ever rival yours;
   no passing mood of ours
   can turn aside your laws:
       you reign above
       each other name
       of worth or fame,
       the Lord of love.

3 Now from the Father's side
   you make your people new;
   since for our sins you died
   our lives belong to you:
       from our distress
       you set us free
       for purity
       and holiness.

4 You call us to belong
   within one body here;
   in weakness we are strong
   and all your gifts we share:
       in you alone
       we are complete
       and at your feet
       with joy bow down.

5 All strength is in your hand,
   all power to you is given;
   all wisdom to command
   in earth and hell and heaven:
       beyond all words
       creation sings
       the King of kings
       and Lord of lords.

© Christopher Idle (born 1938)✝

Alternative tune: CHRISTCHURCH (565)

172(i)

CAMBERWELL 6 5 6 5 D

Michael Brierley (born 1932)
© Josef Weinberger Ltd

A version of this tune in four-part harmony is printed overleaf.

1 *f* At the name of Jesus every knee shall bow,
every tongue confess him king of glory now;
this the Father's pleasure,
    that we call him Lord,
who from the beginning was the mighty word.

2 *mf* At his voice creation sprang at once to sight,
all the angel faces, all the hosts of light;
thrones and dominations, stars upon their way,
all the heavenly orders, in their great array.

3   Humbled for a season, to receive a name
from the lips of sinners unto whom he came;
faithfully he bore it spotless to the last,
brought it back victorious
    when from death he passed.

4   Bore it up triumphant with its human light,
through all ranks of creatures
    to the central height;
to the eternal Godhead, to the Father's throne,
filled it with the glory of his triumph won.

5 *mp* Name him, Christians, name him,
    with love strong as death,
but with awe and wonder, and with bated breath;
he is God the saviour, he is Christ the Lord,
ever to be worshipped, trusted and adored.

6   In your hearts enthrone him; there let him subdue
all that is not holy, all that is not true;
 mf crown him as your captain in temptation's hour,
let his will enfold you in its light and power.

7 *f* With his Father's glory Jesus comes again,
angel hosts attend him and announce his reign;
for all wreaths of empire meet upon his brow,
and our hearts confess him king of glory now.

Caroline M. Noel (1817–1877)
© in this version Jubilate Hymns†

Harmony

vv. 1-6

v. 7

The unison and harmony versions are harmonically compatible.

1 *f* At the name of Jesus every knee shall bow,
   every tongue confess him king of glory now;
   this the Father's pleasure,
       that we call him Lord,
   who from the beginning was the mighty word.

2 *mf* At his voice creation sprang at once to sight,
   all the angel faces, all the hosts of light;
   thrones and dominations, stars upon their way,
   all the heavenly orders, in their great array.

3 Humbled for a season, to receive a name
   from the lips of sinners unto whom he came;
   faithfully he bore it spotless to the last,
   brought it back victorious
       when from death he passed.

4 Bore it up triumphant with its human light,
   through all ranks of creatures
       to the central height;
   to the eternal Godhead, to the Father's throne,
   filled it with the glory of his triumph won.

172(ii)

EVELYNS 6 5 6 5 D

W. H. Monk (1823–1889)

5 *mp* Name him, Christians, name him,
           with love strong as death,
    but with awe and wonder, and with bated breath;
    he is God the saviour, he is Christ the Lord,
    ever to be worshipped, trusted and adored.

6   In your hearts enthrone him; there let him subdue
    all that is not holy, all that is not true;
  mf crown him as your captain in temptation's hour,
    let his will enfold you in its light and power.

7 *f* With his Father's glory Jesus comes again,
    angel hosts attend him and announce his reign;
    for all wreaths of empire meet upon his brow,
    and our hearts confess him king of glory now.

Caroline M. Noel (1817–1877)
© in this version Jubilate Hymns†

Alternative tune: CUDDESDON (582)

173(i)

CHRIST TRIUMPHANT   8 5 8 5 7 9

© Michael Baughen (born 1930)†
© arranged Noël Tredinnick (born 1949)†

Yours the glo-ry and the crown, ___ the high re -

- nown, ___ the e - ter - nal name. ___

1 *f* Christ triumphant, ever reigning,
Saviour, Master, King!
Lord of heaven, our lives sustaining,
hear us as we sing:
    Yours the glory and the crown,
    the high renown, the eternal name.

2 *mf* Word incarnate, truth revealing,
Son of Man on earth!
power and majesty concealing
by your humble birth:
f   Yours the glory . . .

3 *p* Suffering servant, scorned, ill-treated,
victim crucified!
f death is through the cross defeated,
sinners justified:
    Yours the glory . . .

4 *mf* Priestly king, enthroned for ever
high in heaven above!
sin and death and hell shall never
stifle hymns of love:
f   Yours the glory . . .

5   So, our hearts and voices raising
through the ages long,
ceaselessly upon you gazing,
this shall be our song:
    Yours the glory . . .

© Michael Saward (born 1932)†

173(ii)

GUITING POWER   858579

©John Barnard (born 1948)†

Descant

5 Our hearts and voi-ces rais-ing through the a - ges_ long,

Unison

upon you gaz - ing, this shall be_ our song: Yours the

Org.

glo-ry and the crown, the high re-nown, _____ the e-ter - nal name!

Yours the glo-ry and the crown, the high re-nown, the e-ter - nal name.

1 *f* Christ triumphant, ever reigning,
Saviour, Master, King!
Lord of heaven, our lives sustaining,
hear us as we sing:
Yours the glory and the crown,
the high renown, the eternal name.

2 *mf* Word incarnate, truth revealing,
Son of Man on earth!
power and majesty concealing
by your humble birth:
f   Yours the glory . . .

3 *p* Suffering servant, scorned, ill-treated,
victim crucified!
f death is through the cross defeated,
sinners justified:
Yours the glory . . .

4 *mf* Priestly king, enthroned for ever
high in heaven above!
sin and death and hell shall never
stifle hymns of love:
f   Yours the glory . . .

5 So, our hearts and voices raising
through the ages long,
ceaselessly upon you gazing,
this shall be our song:
Yours the glory . . .

174

1 *f* Crown him with many crowns,
the Lamb upon his throne,
while heaven's eternal anthem drowns
all music but its own!
Awake, my soul, and sing
of him who died to be
your saviour and your matchless king
through all eternity.

2 Crown him the Lord of life
triumphant from the grave,
who rose victorious from the strife
for those he came to save:
his glories now we sing
who died and reigns on high;
he died eternal life to bring
and lives that death may die.

3 *mf* Crown him the Lord of love,
who shows his hands and side –
those wounds yet visible above
in beauty glorified.
No angel in the sky
can fully bear that sight,
but downward bends his burning eye
at mysteries so bright.

4 Crown him the Lord of peace –
his kingdom is at hand;
from pole to pole let warfare cease
and Christ rule every land!
A city stands on high,
his glory it displays,
and there the nations 'Holy' cry
in joyful hymns of praise.

5 *f* Crown him the Lord of years,
the potentate of time,
creator of the rolling spheres
in majesty sublime:
all hail, Redeemer, hail,
for you have died for me;
your praise shall never, never fail
through all eternity!

M. Bridges (1800–1894) and
G. Thring (1823–1903)
© in this version Jubilate Hymns†

175

EBENEZER   8 7 8 7 D

T. J. Williams (1869–1944)
© representatives of the late Gwenlyn Evans

1 Hail, our once-rejected Jesus!
  Hail, our Galilean king!
  You have suffered to release us,
  hope and joy and peace to bring.
  Patient friend and holy saviour,
  bearer of our sin and shame;
  by your merits we find favour,
  life is given through your name.

2 Paschal Lamb, by God appointed,
  all our sins on you were laid;
  by almighty love anointed,
  full atonement you have made.
  All your people are forgiven
  through the virtue of your blood;
  opened is the gate of heaven,
  we are reconciled with God.

3 Jesus! Heavenly hosts adore you,
  seated at your Father's side;
  crucified, this world once saw you,
  now in glory you abide.
  There for sinners you are pleading,
  and our place you now prepare;
  always for us interceding,
  till in glory we appear.

4 Worship, honour, power and blessing
  you are worthy to receive;
  loudest praises, without ceasing,
  right it is for us to give.
  Help us, bright angelic spirits –
  joined with ours, your voices raise;
  help to show our saviour's merits,
  help to sing Emmanuel's praise.

J. Bakewell (1721–1819) and others
ⓒ in this version Jubilate Hymns†

176(i)

LLANFAIR   7 7 7 7 and Alleluias

R. Williams (1781–1821)

Unison

1 *f* Hail the day that sees him rise   Alleluia,
        to his throne beyond the skies,   alleluia,
        Christ, the Lamb for sinners given,   alleluia,
        enters now the highest heaven: alleluia!

2   There for him high triumph waits: Alleluia,
        Lift your heads, eternal gates,   alleluia,
        he has conquered death and sin,   alleluia,
        take the King of glory in: alleluia!

3   See! the heaven its Lord receives,   Alleluia,
        yet he loves the earth he leaves;   alleluia,
        though returning to his throne,   alleluia,
        still he calls mankind his own.   alleluia!

176(ii)

ASCENSION 7 7 7 7 and Alleluias   W. H. Monk (1823–1889)

4 *mf* Still for us he intercedes,   Alleluia,
       his prevailing death he pleads,   alleluia,
       near himself prepares our place,   alleluia,
       he the first-fruits of our race.   alleluia!

5   Lord, though parted from our sight Alleluia,
       far beyond the starry height,   alleluia,
       lift our hearts that we may rise   alleluia,
       one with you beyond the skies: alleluia!

6 *f* There with you we shall remain,   Alleluia,
       share the glory of your reign,   alleluia,
       there your face unclouded view,   alleluia,
       find our heaven of heavens in you.   alleluia!

                              C. Wesley (1707–1788) and
                              T. Cotterill (1779–1823)

176(iii)

CHISLEHURST   7 7 7 7 and Alleluias   S. H. Nicholson (1875–1947)
                                          © Hymns Ancient & Modern Ltd

1 *f* Hail the day that sees him rise   Alleluia,
    to his throne beyond the skies,   alleluia,
    Christ, the Lamb for sinners given,
    enters now the highest heaven: alleluia, alleluia, alleluia!

2   There for him high triumph waits: Alleluia,
    Lift your heads, eternal gates,   alleluia,
    he has conquered death and sin,
    take the King of glory in: alleluia, alleluia, alleluia!

3   See! the heaven its Lord receives,   Alleluia,
    yet he loves the earth he leaves;   alleluia,
    though returning to his throne,
    still he calls mankind his own.   alleluia, alleluia, alleluia!

4 *mf* Still for us he intercedes,   Alleluia,
    his prevailing death he pleads,   alleluia,
    near himself prepares our place,
    he the first-fruits of our race.   alleluia, alleluia, alleluia!

5   Lord, though parted from our sight   Alleluia,
    far beyond the starry height,   alleluia,
    lift our hearts that we may rise
    one with you beyond the skies: alleluia, alleluia, alleluia!

6 *f* There with you we shall remain,   Alleluia,
    share the glory of your reign,   alleluia,
    there your face unclouded view,
    find our heaven of heavens in you. alleluia, alleluia, alleluia!

C. Wesley (1707–1788) and
T. Cotterill (1779–1823)

177

REVELATION 8 6 8 8 8 6

1 He walks among the golden lamps
   on feet like burnished bronze:
   his hair as snows of winter white,
   his eyes with fire aflame, and bright
   his glorious robe of seamless light
   surpassing Solomon's.

2 And in his hand the seven stars,
   and from his mouth a sword:
   his voice the thunder of the seas;
   all creatures bow to his decrees
   who holds the everlasting keys
   and reigns as sovereign Lord.

3 More radiant than the sun at noon,
   who was, and is to be:
   who was, from everlasting days;
   who lives, the Lord of all our ways –
   to him be majesty and praise
   for all eternity.

from Revelation 1

178

METZLER 8 6 8 6 (CM)

R. Redhead (1820–1901)

1 *mf* Jesus our hope, our heart's desire,
        your work of grace we sing:
        you are the saviour of the world,
        its maker and its king.

2 *mp* How vast the mercy and the grace,
        how great the love must be,
        which led you to a cruel death
        to set your people free!

3 *f*   But now the chains of death are burst,
        the ransom has been paid,
        and you are at your Father's side
        in glorious robes arrayed.

4   All praise to you, triumphant Lord
        ascended high in heaven –
        to God, the Father, Spirit, Son,
        be praise and glory given!

                        from the Latin (seventh century)
                        J. Chandler (1806–1876)

179

REGENT SQUARE 8 7 8 7 8 7   H. T. Smart (1813–1879)

1 Look, you saints, the sight is glorious!
 see the man of sorrows now
 from the fight returned victorious –
 every knee to him shall bow:
  Crown him, crown him,
  crown him, crown him –
  crowns befit the victor's brow.

2 Crown the saviour, angels, crown him!
 rich the trophies Jesus brings;
 in the seat of power enthrone him
 while the vault of heaven rings:
  Crown him, crown him,
  crown him, crown him,
  crown the saviour King of kings.

3 Sinners in derision crowned him,
 mocked the dying saviour's claim;
 saints and angels crowd around him,
 sing his triumph, praise his name:
  Crown him, crown him,
  crown him, crown him;
  spread abroad the victor's fame.

4 Hear the shout as he _ is greet - ed, hear those loud tri - um-phant chords!

Je - sus Christ in glo - ry seat - ed – O what joy _ the _ sight af - fords!

Crown him, crown him, crown him, crown him; King of kings, and _ Lord of lords!

4   Hear the shout as he is greeted,
    hear those loud triumphant chords!
    Jesus Christ in glory seated –
    O what joy the sight affords!
    Crown him, crown him,
    crown him, crown him;
    King of kings, and Lord of lords!

T. Kelly (1769–1855)
© in this version Jubilate Hymns†

180

GOPSAL 666688

Melody and bass G. F. Handel (1685–1759)

Organ

1 Rejoice, the Lord is king!
  your Lord and king adore:
  mortals, give thanks and sing,
  and triumph evermore:
      Lift up your heart, lift up your voice:
      rejoice! – again I say, rejoice!

2 Jesus, the saviour, reigns,
  the God of truth and love;
  when he had purged our stains
  he took his seat above:
      Lift up your heart . . .

3 His kingdom cannot fail,
  he rules both earth and heaven;
  the keys of death and hell
  to Jesus now are given:
      Lift up your heart . . .

4 He sits at God's right hand,
  till all his foes submit
  and bow to his command
  and fall beneath his feet:
      Lift up your heart . . .

5 Rejoice in glorious hope!
  Jesus the judge shall come
  and take his servants up
  to their eternal home:
      We soon shall hear the archangel's voice:
      the trumpet sounds – rejoice, rejoice!

C. Wesley (1707–1788)

181

IN BABILONE   8 7 8 7 D

Dutch traditional melody

1   See, the conqueror mounts in triumph,
    see the king in royal state,
    riding on the clouds, his chariot,
    to his heavenly palace gate!
        hear the choirs of angel voices
        joyful alleluias sing!
        and the gates on high are opened
        to receive their mighty king.

2   He who on the cross has suffered,
    he who from the grave arose –
    he has conquered sin and Satan,
    he has overcome his foes:
        while he lifts his hands in blessing,
        he is parted from his friends;
        while their eager eyes behold him,
        in the clouds the Lord ascends.

3   You have raised our human nature
    on the clouds to God's right hand;
    there we sit in heavenly places,
    there with you in glory stand:
        mighty Lord, in your ascension
        we by faith can see our own:
        Jesus reigns, adored by angels;
        God with us is on the throne!

                          C. Wordsworth (1807–1885)

Alternative tune: EBENEZER (175)

182

ST. MAGNUS   8 6 8 6 (CM)   J. Clarke (c. 1674–1707)

1 *f* The head that once was crowned with thorns
    is crowned with glory now;
    a royal diadem adorns
    the mighty victor's brow.

2   The highest place that heaven affords
    is his, is his by right;
    the King of kings and Lord of lords
    and heaven's eternal light.

3 *mf* The joy of all who dwell above,
    the joy of all below;
    to whom he demonstrates his love
    and grants his name to know.

4 *mp* To them the cross with all its shame,
    with all its grace is given;
   mf their name, an everlasting name,
    their joy, the joy of heaven.

5 *mp* They suffer with their Lord below,
    f they reign with him above;
    their profit and their joy to know
    the mystery of his love.

6   The cross he bore is life and health,
    though shame and death to him;
    his people's hope, his people's wealth,
    their everlasting theme.

                                    T. Kelly (1769–1855)

183

CHURCH TRIUMPHANT   8 8 8 8 (LM)   J. W. Elliott (1833–1915)

1   The Lord is king! Lift up your voice,
    O earth, and all you heavens, rejoice;
    from world to world the song shall ring:
    'The Lord omnipotent is king!'

2   The Lord is king! Who then shall dare
    resist his will, distrust his care
    or quarrel with his wise decrees,
    or doubt his royal promises?

3   The Lord is king! Child of the dust,
    the judge of all the earth is just;
    holy and true are all his ways –
    let every creature sing his praise!

4   God reigns! He reigns with glory crowned:
    let Christians make a joyful sound!
    And Christ is seated at his side:
    the man of love, the crucified.

5   Come, make your needs, your burdens known:
    he will present them at the throne;
    and angel hosts are waiting there
    his messages of love to bear.

6   One Lord one kingdom all secures:
    he reigns, and life and death are yours;
    through earth and heaven one song shall ring:
    'The Lord omnipotent is king!'

                              J. Conder (1789–1855)

184

WARRINGTON 8 8 8 8 (LM)   R. Harrison (1748–1810)

1 Where high the heavenly temple stands,
the house of God not made with hands,
a great high priest our nature wears,
the guardian of our race appears.

2 He who for us as surety stood
and poured on earth his precious blood,
pursues in heaven his mighty will,
our saviour and our helper still.

3 Though now ascended up on high,
he sees us with a brother's eye;
he shares with us the human name
and knows the frailty of our frame.

4 Our fellow-sufferer yet retains
a fellow-feeling of our pains;
he still remembers in the skies
his tears, his agonies and cries.

5 With boldness therefore at his throne
let us make all our sorrows known:
to help us in the darkest hour,
we ask for Christ the saviour's power.

M. Bruce (1746–1767)
© in this version Jubilate Hymns†

185

VICTOR'S CROWN   5 5 5 5 D   © Noël Tredinnick (born 1949)†

1   Won, the victor's crown;
    run, the saviour's race;
    done, the Father's will –
    all the work of grace:
    praise adorns his brow,
    fire is in his eyes;
    honoured is his name;
    glory is his prize.

2   Gone, the devil's power;
    pierced, the gloomy night;
    torn, the temple veil –
    faith has turned to sight:
    death has been destroyed,
    gates of hell cast down;
    Jesus on his throne
    wears the victor's crown!

after D. T. Niles (1908–1970)
in © Christian Conference of Asia Hymnal,
revised and reprinted by permission.
© in this version Jubilate Hymns†

GOD: LORD AND SAVIOUR
Returning and Triumphant

186

PHILIP JAMES 6 6 11 D

1 Blow upon the trumpet!
   clap your hands together,
   sound aloud the praises of the Lord your king.
   He has kept his promise,
   granting us salvation:
   let his people jubilantly shout and sing!

2 Blow upon the trumpet!
   let the nations tremble;
   see his power obliterate the sun and moon.
   This is God's own army
   bringing all to judgement,
   for the day of Jesus Christ is coming soon.

3 Blow upon the trumpet!
   arrows in the lightning
   fly the storm of battle where he marches on.
   Glory to our shepherd
   keeping us through danger,
   setting us like jewels in his royal crown.

4 Blow upon the trumpet!
   Christ is surely coming,
   heaven's forces mobilizing at his word.
   We shall rise to meet him:
   death at last is conquered,
   God gives us the victory through Christ our Lord!

from Psalm 98, Joel 2 etc.
© Michael Perry (born 1942)†

187

BENSON   14 15 14 12 8

Millicent D. Kingham (1866–1927)

1 City of God, Jerusalem,
        where he has set his love;
   church of Christ that is one on earth
        with Jerusalem above:
   here as we walk this changing world
        our joys are mixed with tears,
   but the day will be soon
        when the Saviour returns
   and his voice will banish our fears.

2 Sing and be glad, Jerusalem,
        for God does not forget;
   he who said he would come to save
        never failed his people yet.
   Though we are tempted by despair
        and daunted by defeat,
   our invincible Lord
        will be seen in his strength,
   and his triumph will be complete.

3 Sorrow no more, Jerusalem,
        discard your rags of shame!
   take your crown as a gift from God
        who has called you by his name.
   Put off your sin, and wear the robe
        of glory in its place;
   you will shine in his light,
        you will share in his joy,
   you will praise his wonderful grace.

4 Look all around, Jerusalem,
        survey from west to east;
   sons and daughters of God the king
        are invited to his feast.
   Out of their exile far away
        his scattered family come,
   and the streets will resound
        with the songs of the saints
   when the Saviour welcomes us home.

from Baruch 4–5
© Christopher Idle (born 1938)†

188

MARCHING THROUGH GEORGIA
13 13 13 8 10 10 13 8

American traditional melody
© arranged David Wilson (born 1940)†

Unison

A - men, he comes! to bring his own re - ward! A - men, praise God! for just - ice now re - stored; king-doms of the world be - come the

king-doms of the Lord: Love has the vic-tory for ev - er!

1 Come and see the shining hope
        that Christ's apostle saw;
on the earth, confusion,
        but in heaven an open door,
where the living creatures
        praise the Lamb for evermore:
Love has the victory for ever!
    Amen, he comes! to bring his own reward!
    Amen, praise God! for justice now restored;
    kingdoms of the world
    become the kingdoms of the Lord:
    Love has the victory for ever!

2 All the gifts you send us, Lord,
        are faithful, good, and true;
holiness and righteousness
        are shown in all you do:
who can see your greatest Gift
        and fail to worship you?
Love has the victory for ever!
    Amen, he comes! . . .

3 Power and salvation
        all belong to God on high!
So the mighty multitudes of heaven
        make their cry,
singing Alleluia!
        where the echoes never die:
Love has the victory for ever!
    Amen, he comes! . . .

from Revelation 4–5 etc.
© Christopher Idle (born 1938)†

189(i)

LUTHER   8 7 8 7 8 8 7

Geistliche Lieder Wittenberg 1535

(ii)

PALACE GREEN   8 7 8 7 8 8 7

Michael Fleming (born 1928)
© Royal School of Church Music

1 Great God, what do I see and hear:
  the end of things created!
  the Judge of all the earth comes near
  on clouds of glory seated:
  the trumpet sounds, the graves restore
  the dead which they contained before –
  prepare, my soul, to meet him.

2 The dead in Christ shall first arise
  at that last trumpet's sounding,
  caught up to meet him in the skies,
  with joy their Lord surrounding:
  no gloomy fears their souls dismay;
  his presence brings eternal day
  for those prepared to meet him.

3 But sinners filled with guilty fears
  shall see his wrath prevailing;
  for they shall rise, and find their tears
  and sighs are unavailing:
  the day of grace is past and gone;
  they trembling stand before the throne
  all unprepared to meet him.

4 Great God, what do I see and hear:
  the end of things created!
  the Judge of all the earth comes near
  on clouds of glory seated:
  low at his cross I view the day
  when heaven and earth shall pass away,
  and thus prepare to meet him.

W. B. Collyer (1782–1854) and others
© in this version Jubilate Hymns†

190

CRÜGER 7676D

J. Crüger (1598–1662)

1   Hail to the Lord's anointed,
    great David's greater son!
    Hail, in the time appointed
    his reign on earth begun!
    He comes to break oppression,
    to set the captive free,
    to take away transgression
    and rule in equity.

2   He comes with comfort speedy
    to those who suffer wrong;
    to save the poor and needy
    and help the weak be strong:
    to give them songs for sighing,
    their darkness turn to light,
    whose souls, condemned and dying,
    are precious in his sight.

3   He shall come down like showers
    upon the fruitful earth;
    and love, joy, hope, like flowers
    spring in his path to birth:
    before him on the mountains
    shall peace, the herald, go;
    and righteousness in fountains
    from hill to valley flow.

4   Kings shall bow down before him
    and gold and incense bring;
    all nations shall adore him,
    his praise all people sing:
    to him shall prayer unceasing
    and daily vows ascend;
    his kingdom still increasing,
    a kingdom without end.

5   In all the world victorious,
    he on his throne shall rest;
    from age to age more glorious,
    all-blessing and all-blessed:
    the tide of time shall never
    his covenant remove;
    his name shall stand for ever,
    his changeless name of love.

J. Montgomery (1771–1854)

191

BENSON Irregular

Millicent D. Kingham (1866–1927)

vv. 2, 3

1 God is working his purpose out,
       as year succeeds to year:
   God is working his purpose out,
       and the time is drawing near:
   nearer and nearer draws the time,
       the time that shall surely be,
   when the earth shall be filled
       with the glory of God,
   as the waters cover the sea.

2 From utmost east to utmost west,
       wherever foot has trod,
   by the mouth of many messengers
       rings out the voice of God:
   Listen to me you continents,
       you islands look to me,
   that the earth may be filled . . .

3 We shall march in the strength of God,
       with the banner of Christ unfurled,
   that the light of the glorious gospel of truth
       may shine throughout the world;
   we shall fight with sorrow and sin
       to set their captives free,
   that the earth may be filled . . .

4 All we can do is nothing worth
       unless God blesses the deed;
   vainly we hope for the harvest-tide
       till God gives life to the seed:
   nearer and nearer draws the time,
       the time that shall surely be,
   when the earth shall be filled . . .

A. Ainger (1841–1919)
© in this version Jubilate Hymns†

192

MERTON 8 7 8 7

W. H. Monk (1823–1889)

1 *f* Hark! a trumpet call is sounding,
'Christ is near,' it seems to say:
'Cast away the dreams of darkness,
children of the dawning day!'

2 Wakened by the solemn warning,
let our earth-bound souls arise;
Christ, our sun, all harm dispelling,
shines upon the morning skies.

3 *mf* See! the Lamb, so long expected,
comes with pardon down from heaven;
let us haste, with tears of sorrow,
one and all to be forgiven:

4 That, when next he comes in glory
and the world is wrapped in fear
with his mercy he may shield us,
and with words of love draw near.

5 *f* Honour, glory, might and blessing
to the Father, and the Son,
with the everlasting Spirit,
while eternal ages run!

from the Latin (sixth century)
E. Caswall (1814–1878)

193

BRISTOL   8 6 8 6 (CM)

Ravenscroft's *Psalter* 1621
descant © David Iliff (born 1939)†

4 Our glad ho-san-nas, Prince of peace, your wel-come shall pro-claim;

and heaven's e-ter-nal arch-es ring with your be-lov-ed name.

1 *f* Hark the glad sound! – the Saviour comes,
the Saviour promised long;
let every heart prepare a throne
and every voice a song.

2 He comes the prisoners to release
in Satan's bondage held;
the gates of brass before him burst,
the iron fetters yield.

3 *mf* He comes the broken heart to bind,
the wounded soul to cure;
and with the treasures of his grace
to enrich the humble poor.

4 *f* Our glad hosannas, Prince of peace,
your welcome shall proclaim;
and heaven's eternal arches ring
with your beloved name.

P. Doddridge (1702–1751)

194

LONDONDERRY AIR   11 10 11 10 11 10 11 12   Irish traditional melody
© arranged John Barnard (born 1948)†

1 *mf* I cannot tell why he whom angels worship
    should set his love upon the sons of men,
    or why as shepherd
             he should seek the wanderers,
    to bring them back, they know not how nor when.
    But this I know, that he was born of Mary
    when Bethlehem's manger was his only home,
    and that he lived at Nazareth and laboured;
    and so the saviour, saviour of the world,
             has come.

2 *p* I cannot tell how silently he suffered
    as with his peace he graced this place of tears,
    nor how his heart upon the cross was broken,
    the crown of pain to three and thirty years.
  mf But this I know, he heals the broken-hearted
    and stays our sin and calms our lurking fear,
    and lifts the burden from the heavy-laden;
    for still the saviour, saviour of the world, is here.

3   I cannot tell how he will win the nations,
    how he will claim his earthly heritage,
    how satisfy the needs and aspirations
    of east and west, of sinner and of sage.
  f But this I know, all flesh shall see his glory,
    and he shall reap the harvest he has sown,
    and some glad day
             his sun will shine in splendour
    when he the saviour, saviour of the world,
             is known.

4 *mf* I cannot tell how all the lands shall worship,
    when at his bidding every storm is stilled,
    or who can say how great the jubilation
    when all our hearts with love for him are filled.
  f But this I know, the skies will sound his praises,
    ten thousand thousand human voices sing,
    and earth to heaven, and heaven to earth,
             will answer,
    'At last the saviour, saviour of the world, is king!'

W. Y. Fullerton (1857–1932)

195(i)

PICARDY   8 7 8 7 8 7

French traditional carol
as in *The English Hymnal* 1906

1 *mf* Jesus came – the heavens adoring –
    came with peace from realms on high;
    Jesus came for our redemption,
    humbly came on earth to die,
        Alleluia, alleluia!
    came in deep humility.

2   Jesus comes to us in mercy
    when our hearts are bowed with care;
    Jesus comes in power, to answer
    every earnest heartfelt prayer:
        Alleluia, alleluia!
    comes to save us from despair.

195(ii)

RHUDDLAN   878787

Welsh traditional melody from
Musical Relicks of the Welsh Bards 1800

3 *f* Jesus comes to hearts rejoicing –
all the past he now forgives;
Jesus comes to share his kingdom
with the sinners he receives:
    Alleluia, alleluia!
Death is conquered: Jesus lives!

4   Jesus comes on clouds triumphant
when the heavens shall pass away;
Jesus comes again in glory –
let us then our homage pay,
    Alleluia! ever singing
till the dawn of endless day.

G. Thring (1823–1903)
© in this version Jubilate Hymns†

196

HELMSLEY   8 7 8 7 4 7 extended

Adapted from an eighteenth-century
English melody

1 *f* Jesus comes with clouds descending –
see the Lamb for sinners slain!
thousand thousand saints attending
join to sing the glad refrain:
    Alleluia, alleluia, alleluia!
God appears on earth to reign.

2 *mf* Every eye shall then behold him
robed in awesome majesty;
those who jeered at him and sold him,
pierced and nailed him to the tree,
    shamed and grieving . . .
shall their true Messiah see.

3 All the wounds of cross and passion
still his glorious body bears;
cause of endless exultation
to his ransomed worshippers.
    With what gladness . . .
we shall see the Saviour's scars!

4 *f* Yes, Amen! let all adore you
high on your eternal throne;
crowns and empires fall before you –
claim the kingdom for your own.
    Come, Lord Jesus . . .
everlasting God, come down!

after J. Cennick (1718–1755)
C. Wesley (1707–1788) and
M. Madan (1726–1790)
© in this version Jubilate Hymns†

197

ANTIOCH 8 6 8 6 (CM)

G. F. Handel (1685–1759)
arranged L. Mason (1792–1872)

1 Joy   to   the world— the   Lord has come! let   earth   re - ceive   her
2 Joy   to   the earth— the   sav - iour reigns! let   songs   be heard   on
3 No more let sins   and   sor - rows grow nor thorns in - fest   the
4 He rules the world with truth   and   grace, and makes the   na - tions

king,   let   ev - ery__ heart__ pre - pare__ him __ room __ and
high,   while fields__ and__ streams__ and   hills __ and__ plains __ re -
ground: he   comes. to __ make__ his   bless - ings__ flow__ wher -
prove   the   glo - ries__ of ____ his   right - eous - ness, __ the

heaven and na - ture_sing,   and heaven and na - ture_sing,   and__
-peat the sound-ing joy,   re - peat the sound-ing joy,   re -
-ev - er guilt is_ found,   wher - ev - er guilt is_ found,   wher -
won - ders of his_ love,   the   won - ders of his_ love,   the __

and heaven and na-ture   sing,   and heaven and na-ture
re - peat   the sound-ing joy,   re - peat   the sound-ing
wher - ev - er guilt is found,   wher-ev - er guilt is
the   won - ders of his   love,   the won - ders of his

heaven,___	and	heaven _____	and	na - ture	sing!
-peat,___	re -	peat _____	the	sound - ing	joy.
-ev -	er,	ev -	er	guilt is	found.
won -	ders,	won -	ders	of his	love.

sing,	and heaven	and	na - ture	sing!
joy,	re - peat	the	sound - ing	joy.
found,	wher - ev -	er	guilt is	found.
love,	the won -	ders	of his	love.

I. Watts (1674–1748)
© in this version Jubilate Hymns†

198 ELMSDALE 10 11 11   © David Iliff (born 1939)†

1   Let the desert sing and the wasteland flower,
    for the glory of God in its light and power
    shall be seen on the hills where he comes to save!

2   Then the blind shall see and the deaf shall hear
    and the lame shall leap like the fallow deer
    and the voice of the dumb shall shout aloud.

3   When the ransomed walk with their Lord that day
    on the perfect road called the Sacred Way,
    every tear shall give place to a song of joy!

from Isaiah 35
© Michael Perry (born 1942)†

199

SLEEPERS, WAKE   898D66488

P. Nicolai (1556–1608)
arranged J. S. Bach (1685–1750)

1 Wake, O wake, and sleep no longer,
   for he who calls you is no stranger:
   awake, God's own Jerusalem!
   Hear, the midnight bells are chiming
   the signal for his royal coming:
   let voice to voice announce his name!
        We feel his footstep near,
        the Bridegroom at the door –
        Alleluia!
        The lamps will shine
        with light divine
   as Christ the saviour comes to reign.

2 Zion hears the sound of singing;
   her heart is thrilled with sudden longing:
   she stirs, and wakes, and stands prepared.
   Christ her friend, and lord, and lover,
   her star and sun and strong redeemer –
   at last his mighty voice is heard.
        The Son of God has come
        to make with us his home:
        sing Hosanna!
        The fight is won,
        the feast begun;
   we fix our eyes on Christ alone.

3 Glory, glory, sing the angels,
   while music sounds from strings and cymbals;
   all humankind, with songs arise!
   Twelve the gates into the city,
   each one a pearl of shining beauty;
   the streets of gold ring out with praise.
        All creatures round the throne
        adore the holy One
        with rejoicing:
        Amen be sung
        by every tongue
   to crown their welcome to the King.

after P. Nicolai (1556–1608)
© Christopher Idle (born 1938)†

200

AVE VIRGO   7 6 7 6 D

Medieval melody as given by J. Horn 1544

1 When the King shall come again
   all his power revealing,
   splendour shall announce his reign,
   life and joy and healing:
   earth no longer in decay,
   hope no more frustrated;
   this is God's redemption day
   longingly awaited.

2 In the desert trees take root
   fresh from his creation;
   plants and flowers and sweetest fruit
   join the celebration:
   rivers spring up from the earth,
   barren lands adorning;
   valleys, this is your new birth,
   mountains, greet the morning!

3 Strengthen feeble hands and knees,
   fainting hearts, be cheerful!
   God who comes for such as these
   seeks and saves the fearful:
   now the deaf can hear the dumb
   sing away their weeping;
   blind eyes see the injured come
   walking, running, leaping.

4 There God's highway shall be seen
   where no roaring lion,
   nothing evil or unclean
   walks the road to Zion:
   ransomed people homeward bound
   all your praises voicing,
   see your Lord with glory crowned,
   share in his rejoicing!

from Isaiah 35
© Christopher Idle (born 1938)†

Alternative tune: TEMPUS ADEST FLORIDUM (160)

201

GLORIOUS COMING   7 7 7 7 Triple

1 When the Lord in glory comes,
   not the trumpets, not the drums,
   not the anthem, not the psalm,
   not the thunder, not the calm,
   not the shout the heavens raise,
   not the chorus, not the praise,
   not the silences sublime,
   not the sounds of space and time,
   but his voice when he appears
   shall be music to my ears;
       but his voice when he appears
       shall be music to my ears.

2 When the Lord is seen again,
   not the glories of his reign,
   not the lightnings through the storm,
   not the radiance of his form,
   not his pomp and power alone,
   not the splendours of his throne,
   not his robe and diadems,
   not the gold and not the gems,
   but his face upon my sight
   shall be darkness into light;
       but his face upon my sight
       shall be darkness into light.

3 When the Lord to human eyes
   shall bestride our narrow skies,
   not the child of humble birth,
   not the carpenter of earth,
   not the man by all denied,
   not the victim crucified,
   but the God who died to save,
   but the victor of the grave,
   he it is to whom I fall,
   Jesus Christ, my all in all;
       he it is to whom I fall,
       Jesus Christ, my all in all.

202

BEVERLEY   8 7 8 8 7 7 7 7 7

W. H. Monk (1823–1889)

1 You are coming, O my Saviour,
  you are coming, O my King,
  in your beauty all-resplendent,
  in your glory all-transcendent –
  well may we rejoice and sing:
  coming! – in the opening east
  brighter shines your heavenly light;
  coming! – O my glorious Priest:
  come in all your power and might!

2 You are coming, great Redeemer,
  we shall meet you on your way;
  we shall see you, we shall know you,
  we shall bless you, we shall show you
  all our hearts could never say:
  there, enraptured by the view,
  hearts and voices we will raise,
  pouring out our love to you
  in thanksgiving, worship, praise.

3 You are coming – at your table
  we are witnesses for this;
  with your love and grace you greet us,
  in communion, Lord, you meet us –
  foretaste of our coming bliss:
  showing not your death alone,
  and your love so rich and great,
  but your coming and your throne,
  all for which we long and wait.

4 O the joy to see you reigning,
  you, my own belovèd Lord;
  every tongue your name confessing –
  worship, honour, glory, blessing
  brought to you with one accord:
  you, my Master and my Friend,
  vindicated and renowned;
  to the earth's remotest end
  glorified, adored and crowned!

Frances R. Havergal (1836–1879)
© in this version Jubilate Hymns†

For other hymns on this theme, see:
Sunday Themes index
  Section 6, The Advent Hope (p. viii)
Additional hymns
  You servants of the Lord (598)

GOD: LORD AND SAVIOUR
Praised and Worshipped

203(i)

MILES LANE   8 6 8 6 (CM) extended

Later form of melody by W. Shrubsole
(c. 1759–1806)
as in *The Australian Hymn Book* 1977

and crown him, crown him, crown him, crown him Lord of   all.

1   All hail the power of Jesus' name!
    let kings before him fall,
    his power and majesty proclaim
    and crown him Lord of all.

2   Come, crown him, moon and stars of night;
    he made you, great and small:
    bright sun, praise him who gave you light
    and crown him Lord of all.

3   Crown him, you martyrs spurning pain,
    who witnessed to his call;
    now sing your victory-song again
    and crown him Lord of all.

4   Let all who trust in Christ exclaim
    in wonder, to recall
    the one who bore our sin and shame,
    and crown him Lord of all.

5   Then in that final judgement hour
    when all rebellions fall,
    we'll rise in his triumphant power
    and crown him Lord of all.

after E. Perronet (1725–1792) and
J. Rippon (1751–1836)
© Jubilate Hymns†

(see also traditional version, 587)

203(ii)

DIADEM   8 6 8 6 (CM) extended   J. Ellor (1819–1899)

crown _____ him,

crown him,   crown him,   crown him,   crown _____

crown him,   crown him,   crown him, and   crown him Lord of   all.

204(i) CREATION 10 10 10 4 © Beryl Matthews (born 1926)

Al - le - lu - ia!

1 *mf* All praise to Christ, our Lord and king divine,
yielding your glory in your love's design,
that in our darkened hearts
          your grace might shine:
Alleluia!

2 *mp* You came to us in lowliness of thought;
by you the outcast and the poor were sought,
and by your death was our redemption bought:
Alleluia!

3 The mind of Christ is as our mind should be –
he was a servant, that we might be free;
humbling himself to death on Calvary:
Alleluia!

4 *mf* And so we see in God's great purpose, how
Christ has been raised above all creatures now;
and at his name shall every nation bow:
Alleluia!

5 *f* Let every tongue confess with one accord,
in heaven and earth, that Jesus Christ is Lord,
and God the Father be by all adored:
Alleluia! (Amen.)

from *The Song of Christ's Glory* (Philippians 2)
F. Bland Tucker (1895–1984)
and Jubilee Hymns
© The Church Pension Fund. Used by permission

204(ii) ENGELBERG 10 10 10 4   C. V. Stanford (1852–1924)

205

UNSER HERRSCHER 8 7 8 7 8 7

J. Neander (1650–1680)

A descant to this tune may be found at 324.

1 *f* Alleluia! raise the anthem,
let the skies resound with praise;
sing to Christ who brought salvation,
wonderful his works and ways:
God eternal, Word incarnate,
whom the heaven of heavens obeys.

2 *mp* Long before he formed the mountains,
spread the seas or made the sky,
love eternal, free and boundless,
moved the Lord of life to die;
fore-ordained the Prince of princes
for the throne of Calvary.

3 There for us and our redemption
see him all his life-blood pour:
there he wins our full salvation,
dies that we may die no more –
then arising lives for ever,
f King of kings, whom we adore.

4 Praise and honour to the Father,
praise and honour to the Son,
praise and honour to the Spirit,
ever Three and ever One:
one in grace and one in glory
while eternal ages run!

J. Hupton (1762–1849) and
J. M. Neale (1818–1866)
© in this version Jubilate Hymns†

206

NATIVITY   8 6 8 6 (CM)   H. Lahee (1826–1912)

1   Come let us join our cheerful songs
    with angels round the throne;
    ten thousand thousand are their tongues,
    but all their joys are one.

2   Worthy the Lamb who died, they cry,
    to be exalted thus!
    Worthy the Lamb, our lips reply,
    for he was slain for us!

3   Jesus is worthy to receive
    all praise and power divine;
    and all the blessings we can give
    with songs of heaven combine.

4   Let all who live beyond the sky,
    the air and earth and seas
    unite to lift his glory high
    and sing his endless praise!

5   Let all creation join in one
    to bless the sacred name
    of him who reigns upon the throne,
    and to adore the Lamb!

I. Watts (1674–1748)

207(i)

BARNARD GATE   11 10 11 10   © John Barnard (born 1948)†

1 Come, let us worship the Christ of creation!
  he set the numberless stars in their flight,
  guiding the planets in accurate orbit:
  King of the universe, rule us in might!

2 He is the image, the clear revelation;
  in him there glows all the glory divine,
  radiant in splendour, dispersing the shadows:
  Light of the world, in our hearts ever shine!

3 He is our brother, the true incarnation;
  unknown to many, disowned by his race;
  he was forsaken, despised and rejected:
  suffering Servant, we share your disgrace.

4 He is our saviour, our hope of redemption;
  he won our freedom, the victim who died;
  spotless and perfect, his life-blood he yielded:
  Lamb of atonement, dispel all our pride!

207(ii)

SPEAN 11 10 11 10

J. F. Bridge (1844–1924)

5 He is our victor in whose resurrection
  death is defeated, that we may receive
  life for eternity, hope and forgiveness:
  Lord of the grave, help us now to believe!

6 He is the giver who, since his ascension,
  comes by his Spirit with gifts from above;
  fills and renews us and gives us his kingdom:
  Jesus, we long for the fruits of your love.

7 He is our monarch, enthroned in the heavens,
  coming in triumph; yes, coming again!
  Sin will be banished and we shall be with him:
  come, then, in majesty! – come, Lord, and reign!

© Frank Allred (born 1923)
and Michael Saward (born 1932)†

208

BATTLE HYMN   7 7 8 7 8 7 6 8 8 8 6

American traditional melody
© arranged Noël Tredinnick (born 1949)†

Praise and glo-ry be to Je - sus,   praise and glo-ry be to Je - sus,

praise _ and glo-ry be to Je - sus, for Je-sus Christ is king!

Fine

1 Come sing the praise of Jesus,
   sing his love with hearts aflame,
   sing his wondrous birth of Mary,
   when to save the world he came;
   tell the life he lived for others,
   and his mighty deeds proclaim,
   for Jesus Christ is king.
       Praise and glory be to Jesus,
       praise and glory be to Jesus,
       praise and glory be to Jesus,
       for Jesus Christ is king!

2 When foes arose and slew him,
   he was victor in the fight;
   over death and hell he triumphed
   in his resurrection-might;
   he has raised our fallen manhood
   and enthroned it in the height,
   for Jesus Christ is king.
       Praise and glory be to Jesus . . .

3 There's joy for all who serve him,
   more than human tongue can say;
   there is pardon for the sinner,
   and the night is turned to day;
   there is healing for our sorrows,
   there is music all the way,
   for Jesus Christ is king.
       Praise and glory be to Jesus . . .

4 We witness to his beauty,
   and we spread his love abroad;
   and we cleave the hosts of darkness,
   with the Spirit's piercing sword;
   we will lead the souls in prison
   to the freedom of the Lord,
   for Jesus Christ is king.
       Praise and glory be to Jesus . . .

5 To Jesus be the glory,
   the dominion, and the praise;
   he is Lord of all creation,
   he is guide of all our ways;
   and the world shall be his empire
   in the fulness of the days,
   for Jesus Christ is king.
       Praise and glory be to Jesus . . .

J. C. Winslow (1882–1974)
© Mrs. J. Tyrrell

209(i)

SCHÖNSTER HERR JESU   558 D   *Silesian Folk Songs* Leipzig 1842

1   Fairest Lord Jesus,
    Lord of all creation,
    Jesus, of God and man the Son;
    you will I cherish,
    you will I honour,
    you are my soul's delight and crown.

2   Fair are the rivers,
    meadows and forests
    clothed in the fresh green robes of spring;
    Jesus is fairer,
    Jesus is purer,
    he makes the saddest heart to sing.

209(ii)

SILCHESTER 5 5 8 D

W. K. Stanton (1891–1978)
© Oxford University Press

3 Fair is the sunrise,
   starlight and moonlight
   spreading their glory across the sky;
   Jesus shines brighter,
   Jesus shines clearer,
   than all the heavenly host on high.

4 All fairest beauty,
   heavenly and earthly,
   Jesus, my Lord, in you I see;
   none can be nearer,
   fairer or dearer,
   than you, my Saviour, are to me.

from the German (seventeenth century)
Lilian Stevenson (1870–1960)
© Oxford University Press
and in this version Jubilate Hymns

210

KING DIVINE   7 7 7 7 and refrain

C. W. Rigby (1901–1962)
© information sought

An-gels, saints and na-tions sing, 'Praise to Je-sus Christ our__king,__

Lord   of earth and__sky and sea,__ king of love on__ Cal - va-ry!'

1   Hail Redeemer! king divine,
    priest and Lamb, by God's design;
    king whose reign shall never cease,
    prince of everlasting peace:
        Angels, saints and nations sing,
        'Praise to Jesus Christ our king,
        Lord of earth and sky and sea,
        king of love on Calvary!'

2   King whose name creation thrills,
    rule our minds, our hearts and wills,
    till in peace each nation rings
    with your praises, King of kings:
        Angels, saints and nations . . .

3   King most holy, king of truth,
    guide the lowly, guide the youth;
    Christ, the king of glory bright,
    be to us eternal light:
        Angels, saints and nations . . .

P. Brennan (1877–1952)
© Search Press

211(i)

ST. PETER   8 6 8 6 (CM)   A. R. Reinagle (1799–1877)

1 How sweet the name of Jesus sounds
   in a believer's ear!
   it soothes our sorrows, heals our wounds
   and drives away our fear.

2 It makes the wounded spirit whole,
   and calms the troubled breast;
   it satisfies the hungry soul,
   and gives the weary rest.

3 Dear name, the rock on which I build,
   my shield and hiding-place;
   my never-failing treasury, filled
   with boundless stores of grace!

4 Jesus, my shepherd, brother, friend,
   my prophet, priest and king;
   my Lord, my life, my way, my end –
   accept the praise I bring.

5 Weak is the effort of my heart,
   and cold my warmest thought;
   but when I see you as you are,
   I'll praise you as I ought.

6 Till then I would your love proclaim
   with every fleeting breath;
   and may the music of your name
   refresh my soul in death.

                              J. Newton (1725–1807)

211(ii)

RACHEL   8 6 8 6 D (DCM)

212

HYFRYDOL 8 7 8 7 D

R. H. Prichard (1811–1887)
as in *The Australian Hymn Book* 1977

Yes, I'll sing the won-drous sto - ry of the Christ who died for me,___

sing _ it with _ his saints _ in glo - ry gath - ered by _ the cry - stal sea.

1   I will sing the wondrous story
    of the Christ who died for me;
    how he left the realms of glory
    for the cross of Calvary:
        Yes, I'll sing the wondrous story
        of the Christ who died for me,
        sing it with his saints in glory
        gathered by the crystal sea.

2   I was lost, but Jesus found me,
    found the sheep that went astray;
    raised me up and gently led me
    back into the narrow way:
        Yes, I'll sing . . .

3   I was faint and fears possessed me,
    I was bruised from many a fall;
    hope was gone, and shame distressed me,
    but his love has pardoned all:
        Yes, I'll sing . . .

4   Days of darkness still may meet me,
    sorrow's path I often tread;
    but his presence still is with me,
    by his guiding hand I'm led:
        Yes, I'll sing . . .

5   He will keep me till the river
    rolls its waters at my feet;
    then at last he'll bring me over
    saved by grace and made complete.
        Yes, I'll sing . . .

F. H. Rowley (1854–1952)
© Marshall, Morgan and Scott Ltd

213

LYDIA   8 6 8 6 (CM) extended   T. Phillips (1735–1807)

1 Jesus! the name high over all
in hell or earth or sky;
angels again before it fall
and devils fear and fly,
and devils fear and fly.

2 Jesus! the name to sinners dear,
the name to sinners given;
it scatters all their guilty fear,
it turns their hell to heaven,
it turns their hell to heaven.

3 Jesus the prisoner's fetters breaks
and bruises Satan's head;
power into strengthless souls he speaks
and life into the dead,
and life into the dead.

4 O that the world might taste and see
the riches of his grace!
the arms of love that welcome me
would all mankind embrace,
would all mankind embrace.

5 His righteousness alone I show,
his saving grace proclaim;
this is my work on earth below,
to cry 'Behold the Lamb!'
to cry 'Behold the Lamb!'

6 Happy if with my final breath
I may but gasp his name,
preach him to all, and cry in death,
'Christ Jesus is the Lamb!'
'Christ Jesus is the Lamb!'

C. Wesley (1707–1788)

214(i)

EASTVIEW 666688

J. V. Lee (1892–1959)
© The United Reformed Church

1   Join all the glorious names
    of wisdom, love and power,
    that ever mortals knew,
    that angels ever bore;
    all are too poor to speak his worth,
    too poor to set my Saviour forth!

2   Great Prophet of my God,
    my tongue shall bless your name:
    by you the joyful news
    of our salvation came;
    the joyful news of sins forgiven,
    of hell subdued and peace with heaven.

3   Jesus, my great High Priest,
    the Lamb of God who died!
    my guilty conscience seeks
    no sacrifice beside:
    the power of your atoning blood
    has won acceptance with my God.

214(ii)

CROFT'S 136th   666688

W. Croft (1678–1727)

4 Divine almighty Lord,
   my Conqueror and my King:
   your sceptre and your sword,
   your reigning grace I sing;
   yours is the power – and so I sit
   in willing service at your feet.

5 Now let my soul arise,
   and tread the tempter down:
   my Captain leads me on
   to conquest and a crown;
   the child of God shall win the day,
   though death and hell obstruct the way.

                    I. Watts (1674–1748)

215

ALL SAINTS   8 7 8 7 7 7

Later form of melody from
Geistreiches Gesangbuch Darmstadt 1698

1 Let us love and sing and wonder;
   let us praise the saviour's name!
   he has hushed the law's loud thunder;
   he has quenched Mount Sinai's flame:
   he has freed us by his blood;
   he has brought us near to God.

2 Let us love the Lord who bought us,
   dying for our rebel race;
   called us by his word and taught us
   by the Spirit of his grace:
   he has freed us by his blood;
   he presents our souls to God.

3 Let us sing, though fierce temptation
   threatens hard to drag us down;
   for the Lord, our strong salvation,
   holds in view the conqueror's crown:
   he who freed us by his blood,
   soon will bring us home to God.

4 Let us praise, and join the chorus
of the saints enthroned on high;
here they trusted him before us –
now their praises fill the sky:
'You have freed us by your blood,
you are worthy, Lamb of God!'

J. Newton (1725–1807)

216

SAVIOUR CHRIST   3 5 3 3   © Norman Warren (born 1934)†

Ev - er - more   a - dore   him!

1 *mf* Saviour Christ,
    in praise we name him;
    all his deeds
    proclaim him:

2 *mp* Lamb of God
    for sinners dying;
    all our need
    supplying:

3 *mf* Risen Lord
    in glory seated;
    all his work
    completed:

4   King of kings
    ascended, reigning;
    all the world
    sustaining:

5 *f* Christ is all!
    Rejoice before him:
    evermore
    adore him!

    Evermore
    adore him!

© Timothy Dudley-Smith (born 1926)

217(i)

BLAENWERN   8 7 8 7 D   W. P. Rowlands (1860–1937)

217(ii)

LOVE DIVINE 8 7 8 7   J. Stainer (1840–1901)

1 *mf* Love divine, all loves excelling,
        joy of heaven, to earth come down:
        fix in us your humble dwelling,
        all your faithful mercies crown.

2   Jesus, you are all compassion,
        boundless love that makes us whole:
        visit us with your salvation,
        enter every trembling soul.

3 *f* Come, almighty to deliver,
        let us all your grace receive;
        suddenly return, and never,
        never more your temple leave.

4 *mf* You we would be always blessing,
        serve you as your hosts above,
        pray, and praise you without ceasing,
        glory in your perfect love.

5   Finish then your new creation:
        pure and sinless let us be;
        let us see your great salvation,
        perfect in eternity:

6 *f* Changed from glory into glory
        till in heaven we take our place,
        there to cast our crowns before you,
        lost in wonder, love and praise!

C. Wesley (1707–1788)

218(i)

ALL MAJESTY 66556664 © Norman Warren (born 1934)†

1 Name of all majesty,
   fathomless mystery,
   king of the ages
   by angels adored;
        power and authority,
        splendour and dignity,
        bow to his mastery –
   Jesus is Lord!

2 Child of our destiny,
   God from eternity,
   love of the Father
   on sinners outpoured;
        see now what God has done
        sending his only Son,
        Christ the beloved One –
   Jesus is Lord!

218(ii)

MAJESTAS 6 6 5 5 6 6 6 4

© Michael Baughen (born 1930)†
© arranged Noël Tredinnick (born 1949)†

3 Saviour of Calvary,
  costliest victory,
  darkness defeated
  and Eden restored;
     born as a man to die,
     nailed to a cross on high,
     cold in the grave to lie –
  Jesus is Lord!

4 Source of all sovereignty,
  light, immortality,
  life everlasting
  and heaven assured;
     so with the ransomed, we
     praise him eternally,
     Christ in his majesty –
  Jesus is Lord!

© Timothy Dudley-Smith (born 1926)

219(i)

UNIVERSITY   8 6 8 6 (CM)   C. Collignon (1725–1785)

1   O for a thousand tongues to sing
    my great redeemer's praise,
    the glories of my God and king,
    the triumphs of his grace!

2   Jesus, the name that charms our fears
    and bids our sorrows cease;
    this music in the sinner's ears
    is life and health and peace.

3   He breaks the power of cancelled sin,
    he sets the prisoner free;
    his blood can make the foulest clean,
    his blood availed for me.

4   He speaks – and, listening to his voice,
    new life the dead receive,
    the mournful broken hearts rejoice,
    the humble poor believe.

5   Hear him, you deaf! his praise, you dumb,
    your loosened tongues employ;
    you blind, now see your saviour come,
    and leap, you lame, for joy!

6   My gracious Master and my God,
    assist me to proclaim
    and spread through all the earth abroad
    the honours of your name.

C. Wesley (1707–1788)

219(ii)

LYNGHAM   8 6 8 6 extended

T. Jarman (1782–1862)

1 O for a thou - sand tongues to sing my great re-deem-er's praise, my great re-deem - er's praise, the glo -ries of my God and king, the the tri-umphs of his grace, the tri-umphs of his tri-umphs of his grace, the tri-umphs of his grace, the grace, the tri - umphs of his grace! tri - umphs of his grace, the tri-umphs of his grace!

220

YE BANKS AND BRAES 8 8 8 8 D (DLM)

Scottish melody
© arranged Norman Warren (born 1934)†

1 Praise be to Christ in whom we see
   the image of the Father shown,
   the first-born Son revealed and known,
   the truth and grace of deity;
   through whom creation came to birth,
   whose fingers set the stars in place,
   the unseen powers, and this small earth,
   the furthest bounds of time and space.

2 Praise be to him whose sovereign sway
   and will upholds creation's plan;
   who is, before all worlds began
   and when our world has passed away:
   Lord of the church, its life and head,
   redemption's price and source and theme,
   alive, the first-born from the dead,
   to reign as all-in-all supreme.

3 Praise be to him who, Lord most high,
   the fulness of the Godhead shares;
   and yet our human nature bears,
   who came as man to bleed and die:
   and from his cross there flows our peace
   who chose for us the path he trod,
   that so might sins and sorrows cease
   and all be reconciled to God.

from Colossians 1
© Timothy Dudley-Smith (born 1926)

221

ROOTHAM'S GREEN   15 14 15 14   © Paul Edwards (born 1955)†

1 The brightness of God's glory
    and the image of his being,
the heir of richest majesty,
    the arm of regal might;
creator of the universe
    all-knowing and all-seeing
is Christ who brings forgiveness
    and the lifting of our night.

2 Far greater than the angels
    is the author of salvation,
begotten of his Father's love
    before all time began;
our offering of righteousness,
    our refuge from temptation,
one hope in all our sufferings
    is Christ, the Son of Man.

3 How awesome is his perfect life
    unending and unbroken,
how faultless are his judgements
    and how faithful is his word!
Then hear, repent and worship him,
    obey, for God has spoken,
receive his Holy Spirit
    and acknowledge him as Lord!

from Hebrews 1
© Michael Perry (born 1942)†

222

ORIEL 878787

C. Ett's *Cantica Sacra* Munich 1840
arranged W. H. Monk (1823–1889)
descant A. Gray (1855–1935)

Descant

5 Je-sus!—name of all our prais-ing in this world to which you came;

here we sing of love a - maz-ing, and _ your sav - ing power pro- claim;

hearts and voi - ces heaven-ward rais-ing, all our hope is in your name!

1 To the name of our salvation
  honour, worship, let us pay;
  which for many a generation
  deep in God's foreknowledge lay:
  saints of every race and nation
  sing aloud that name today.

2 Jesus is the name we treasure
  more than words can ever tell;
  name of grace beyond all measure,
  ear and heart delighting well:
  this our refuge and our treasure
  conquering sin and death and hell.

3 Highest name for adoration,
  strongest name of victory,
  sweetest name for meditation
  in our pain and misery:
  name for greatest veneration
  by the citizens on high.

4 Name of love, whoever preaches
  speaks like music to the ear;
  who in prayer this name beseeches
  finds its comfort ever near:
  who its perfect wisdom reaches
  heavenly joy possesses here.

5 Jesus! – name of all our praising
  in this world to which you came;
  here we sing of love amazing,
  and your saving power proclaim;
  hearts and voices heavenward raising,
  all our hope is in your name!

from the Latin (1496)
J. M. Neale (1818–1866)
© in this version Jubilate Hymns†

223

LAUDES DOMINI   6 6 6 D   J. Barnby (1838–1896)

1 When morning gilds the skies,
  my heart awakening cries:
      May Jesus Christ be praised;
  alike at work and prayer
  I know my Lord is there:
      may Jesus Christ be praised!

2 When sadness fills my mind
  my strength in him I find:
      may Jesus Christ be praised;
  when earthly hopes grow dim
  my comfort is in him:
      may Jesus Christ be praised!

3 The night becomes as day
  when from the heart we say:
      May Jesus Christ be praised;
  the powers of darkness fear
  when this glad song they hear:
      May Jesus Christ be praised!

4 Be this, while life is mine,
  my canticle divine:
      May Jesus Christ be praised;
  be this the eternal song
  through all the ages long:
      May Jesus Christ be praised!

from the German (nineteenth century)
E. Caswall (1814–1878)
© in this version Jubilate Hymns†

For other hymns on this theme, see:
Sunday Themes index
  Section 33, The Ascension of Christ (p. xiii)
Song Section
  Come and praise the Lord our king (S.8)
  Jesus is Lord (S.17)
  Sing alleluia to the Lord (S.22)
  Sovereign Lord (S.9)
  There's no greater name than Jesus (S.27)
  Praise the Lord our God (S.31)
  Angels, praise him (S.32)

GOD: LORD AND SPIRIT
Breath of Life

224

ARDWICK   5 5 5 11

H. J. Gauntlett (1805–1876)

1 Away with our fears,
  our troubles and tears:
  the Spirit is come,
  the witness of Jesus returned to his home.

2 Our advocate there
  by his death and his prayer
  the gift has obtained,
  for us he has prayed, and the Comforter gained.

3 Our glorified Lord
  has given his word
  that his Spirit will stay,
  and never again will be taken away.

4 Our heavenly guide
  with us shall abide,
  his comforts impart,
  and set up his kingdom of love in our heart.

5 The heart that believes
  his kingdom receives,
  his power and his peace,
  his life, and his joy's everlasting increase.

C. Wesley (1707–1788)

225

WHITSUN PSALM   8 8 8 8 (LM)   © Noël Tredinnick (born 1949)†

1 Born by the Holy Spirit's breath,
   loosed from the law of sin and death,
   now cleared in Christ from every claim
   no judgement stands against our name.

2 In us the Spirit makes his home
   that we in him may overcome;
   Christ's risen life, in all its powers,
   its all-prevailing strength, is ours.

3 Children and heirs of God most high,
   we by his Spirit 'Father' cry;
   that Spirit with our spirit shares
   to frame and breathe our wordless prayers.

4 One is his love, his purpose one:
   to form the likeness of his Son
   in all who, called and justified,
   shall reign in glory at his side.

5 Nor death nor life, nor powers unseen,
   nor height nor depth can come between;
   we know through peril, pain and sword,
   the love of God in Christ our Lord.

from Romans 8
© Timothy Dudley-Smith (born 1926)

Alternative tune: FULDA (16)

226

CARLISLE 6 6 8 6 (SM)

C. Lockhart (1745–1815)
descant S. H. Nicholson (1875–1947)
descant © Oxford University Press

Descant

4 Breathe on me, breath of God; so shall I nev-er die,

but live with you the per - fect life of your e - ter-ni - ty.

1   Breathe on me, breath of God:
    fill me with life anew,
    that as you love, so I may love,
    and do what you would do.

2   Breathe on me, breath of God,
    until my heart is pure,
    until my will is one with yours
    to do and to endure.

3   Breathe on me, breath of God;
    fulfil my heart's desire,
    until this earthly part of me
    glows with your heavenly fire.

4   Breathe on me, breath of God;
    so shall I never die,
    but live with you the perfect life
    of your eternity.

E. Hatch (1835–1889)
© in this version Jubilate Hymns†

227

VENI, SANCTE SPIRITUS 7 7 7 D

Later form of melody by
S. Webbe the elder (1740–1816)

1 Come, most Holy Spirit, come!
  and from your celestial home
  shed a ray of light divine;
  come, O Father of the poor,
  faithful advocate and sure,
  let your radiance in us shine.

2 Heal our wounds, our strength renew;
  on our dryness send your dew,
  wash the stains of guilt away;
  bend the stubborn heart and will,
  melt the frozen, warm the chill,
  guide the steps that go astray.

3 Send upon us from above
  fruits of joy and peace and love,
  gentleness, humility:
  faithfulness and self-control,
  goodness, kindness fill the soul –
  give us true nobility.

4 On the faithful, who adore
  and confess you, evermore
  in your grace and power descend;
  grant your kingdom's sure reward,
  grant us your salvation, Lord,
  grant us joys that never end.

after S. Langton (c.1160–1228)
and E. Caswall (1814–1878)
© in this version Jubilate Hymns†

228(i)

MICHAEL 8787337

H. N. Howells (1892–1983)
© Novello & Co Ltd

1 Christ on whom the Spirit rested
  lived as one who cared for all;
  by the watching crowds attested:
  'This man has done all things well!'
       God's own grace
       on his face
  blessing us with heavenly peace.

2 Swift the promised Spirit filled them:
  rushing wind and tongues of flame;
  now the master's presence thrilled them,
  made them bold to preach his name,
       bringing light,
       day and night,
  helping them to judge aright.

228(ii)

MEINE HOFFNUNG   8 7 8 7 3 3 7   J. Neander's *Alpha and Omega* 1680

3 True and living God, your Spirit
   brought creation to its birth;
   with your help the meek inherit
   all the treasures of the earth:
          all things new
          flow from you,
   pure and beautiful and true.

4 Spirit of the Son and Father,
   come to us with power today!
   every life in fulness enter,
   all your gifts in us set free:
          all our days
          let us raise
   songs of gratitude and praise!

229

SALVE FESTA DIES Irregular

R. Vaughan Williams (1872–1958)

Christians, lift up your hearts, and make this a day of re-joi-cing;

God is our strength and song — glo-ry and praise to his name!

vv. 1,3,5

1 Praise for the Spi-rit of God, who came to the wait-ing dis-ci-ples;
3 Praise that his love ov-er-flowed in the hearts of all who re-ceived him,
5 Come, Ho-ly Spi-rit, to us, who live by your pre-sence with-in us,

there in the— wind and the fire — God gave new life to his own:
join - ing to - geth-er in peace— those once di - vid - ed by sin:
come to di - rect our— course, give us your life and your power:

Repeat refrain

vv. 2,4,6

2 God's might - y power was re - vealed when— those who—
4 Strength-ened by God's might - y power the dis - ci - ples went
6 Spi - rit of God, send us out to — live to your

once were so fear - ful now could be seen by the
out to all na - tions, preach-ing the gos - pel of
praise and your glo - ry; yours is the power and the

229 – Christians, lift up your hearts

world	wit - ness - ing	brave	-	ly	for	Christ: __
Christ,	laugh - ing	at	dan	-	ger	and	death: __
might,	ours	be	the	cour	-	age	and	faith: __

Repeat refrain

Christians, lift up your hearts,
and make this a day of rejoicing;
God is our strength and song –
glory and praise to his name!

1 Praise for the Spirit of God,
        who came to the waiting disciples;
    there in the wind and the fire
        God gave new life to his own:
    Christians, lift up your hearts . . .

2 God's mighty power was revealed
        when those who once were so fearful
    now could be seen by the world
        witnessing bravely for Christ:
    Christians, lift up your hearts . . .

3 Praise that his love overflowed
        in the hearts of all who received him,
    joining together in peace
        those once divided by sin:
    Christians, lift up your hearts . . .

4 Strengthened by God's mighty power
        the disciples went out to all nations,
    preaching the gospel of Christ,
        laughing at danger and death:
    Christians, lift up your hearts . . .

5 Come, Holy Spirit, to us,
        who live by your presence within us,
    come to direct our course,
        give us your life and your power:
    Christians, lift up your hearts . . .

6 Spirit of God, send us out
        to live to your praise and your glory;
    yours is the power and the might,
        ours be the courage and faith:
    Christians, lift up your hearts . . .

230

LUDGATE 666D

J. Dykes Bower (1905–1981)
© Royal School of Church Music

1 Let every Christian pray,
this day, and every day:
      Come, Holy Spirit, come!
Was not the Church we love
commissioned from above?
      Come, Holy Spirit, come!

2 The Spirit brought to birth
the church of Christ on earth
      to seek and save the lost:
never has he withdrawn,
since that tremendous dawn,
      his gifts at Pentecost.

3 Age after age, he strove
to teach her how to love:
      Come, Holy Spirit, come;
age after age, anew
she proved the gospel true:
      Come, Holy Spirit, come!

4 Only the Spirit's power
can fit us for this hour:
      Come, Holy Spirit, come;
instruct, inspire, unite,
and make us see the light:
      Come, Holy Spirit, come!

F. Pratt Green (born 1903)
© Stainer & Bell Ltd

Alternative tune: LAUDES DOMINI (223)

231

DOWN AMPNEY   6 6 11 D   R. Vaughan Williams (1872–1958)
© Oxford University Press

1 Come down, O Love divine!
  seek out this soul of mine
  and visit it
      with your own ardour glowing;
  O Comforter, draw near,
  within my heart appear,
  and kindle it,
      your holy flame bestowing.

2 O let it freely burn
  till earthly passions turn
  to dust and ashes
      in its heat consuming;
  and let your glorious light
  shine ever on my sight,
  and make my pathway clear,
      by your illuming.

3 Let holy charity
  my outward vesture be,
  and lowliness
      become my inner clothing;
  true lowliness of heart
  which takes the humbler part,
  and for its own shortcomings
      weeps with loathing.

4 And so the yearning strong
  with which the soul will long
  shall far surpass
      the power of human telling;
  for none can guess its grace
  till we become the place
  in which the Holy Spirit
      makes his dwelling.

after Bianco da Siena (died 1434)
R. F. Littledale (1833–1890)
© in this version Jubilate Hymns†

Descant

4 And so the yearn-ing strong with which the soul — will —

long shall far sur-pass the power of hu-man tell - ing;

for none can guess its grace till we be - come the

place in which the Ho - ly Spi - rit makes his dwell-ing.

232

VENI CREATOR   8 8 8 8 (LM)   Mode viii (Mechelen version)

After v. 4

Praise — to your — e - ter - nal me-rit,   Fa-ther, Son, and Ho - ly Spi-rit.

1 Creator Spirit, come, inspire
   our lives with light and heavenly fire;
   now make us willing to receive
   the sevenfold gifts you freely give.

2 Your pure anointing from above
   is comfort, life, and fire of love:
   so heal with your eternal light
   the blindness of our human sight.

3 Anoint and cheer our saddened face
   with all the fulness of your grace;
   remove our fears, give peace at home –
   where you are guide, no harm can come.

4 Teach us to know the Father, Son,
   and you with them the Three-in-One;
   that through the ages all along
   this shall be our endless song:
        Praise to your eternal merit,
        Father, Son, and Holy Spirit. Amen.

                    after R. Maurus (c.776–856)
                    and J. Cosin (1594–1671)
                    © in this version Jubilate Hymns†

(see also traditional version, 589)

A - men.

233

MALVERN HILLS   10 10 10 10   © David Iliff (born 1939)†

1   Filled with the Spirit's power, with one accord
    the infant church confessed its risen Lord:
    O Holy Spirit, in the church today
    no less your power of fellowship display.

2   Now with the mind of Christ set us on fire,
    that unity may be our great desire;
    give joy and peace, give faith to hear your call,
    and readiness in each to work for all.

3   Widen our love, good Spirit, to embrace
    the people of all lands and every race;
    like wind and fire with life among us move,
    till we are known as Christ's,
                and Christians prove.

                              J. R. Peacey (1896–1971)
                              © Mrs. M. E. Peacey

234

FIRE OF GOD 8 7 8 7 D   © David Wilson (born 1940)†

1   Fire of God, titanic Spirit,
    burn within our hearts today;
    cleanse our sin – may we exhibit
    holiness in every way:
    purge the squalidness that shames us,
    soils the body, taints the soul;
    and through Jesus Christ who claims us,
    purify us, make us whole.

2   Wind of God, dynamic Spirit,
    breathe upon our hearts today;
    that we may your power inherit
    hear us, Spirit, as we pray:
    fill the vacuum that enslaves us –
    emptiness of heart and soul;
    and, through Jesus Christ who saves us,
    give us life and make us whole.

3   Voice of God, prophetic Spirit,
    speak to every heart today
    to encourage or prohibit,
    urging action or delay:
    clear the vagueness which impedes us –
    come, enlighten mind and soul;
    and, through Jesus Christ who leads us,
    teach the truth that makes us whole.

© Michael Saward (born 1932)†

Alternative tune: ABBOT'S LEIGH (494)

235

SONG 13   7 7 7 7

Orlando Gibbons (1583–1625)
arranged C. H. Kitson (1874–1944)
arrangement copyright holder sought

1 *mf* Holy Spirit, truth divine,
        dawn upon this soul of mine:
        voice of God, and inward light,
        wake my spirit, clear my sight.

2   Holy Spirit, love divine,
        glow within this heart of mine:
        kindle every high desire,
        purify me with your fire.

3 *f*   Holy Spirit, power divine,
        fill and nerve this will of mine:
        boldly may I always live,
        bravely serve and gladly give.

4 *mf* Holy Spirit, law divine,
        reign within this soul of mine:
        be my law, and I shall be
        firmly bound, for ever free.

5 *mp* Holy Spirit, peace divine,
        still this restless heart of mine:
        speak to calm this tossing sea,
        grant me your tranquillity.

6 *f*   Holy Spirit, joy divine,
        gladden now this heart of mine:
        in the desert ways I sing –
        spring, O living water, spring!

S. Longfellow (1819–1892)

Alternative tune: LÜBECK (554)

236

LAVENDON   10 10 10 10   © Paul Edwards (born 1955)†

1 May we, O Holy Spirit, bear your fruit –
   your joy and peace pervade each word we say;
   may love become of life the very root,
   and grow more deep and strong with every day.

2 May patience stem the harmful word and deed,
   and kindness seek the good among the wrong;
   may goodness far beyond our lips proceed,
   as manifest in action as in song.

3 May faithfulness endure, yet as we grow
   may gentleness lend courage to the weak;
   and in our self-restraint help us to know
   the grace that made the King of Heaven meek.

© Paul Wigmore (born 1925)†

237

SPIRITUS VITAE 9 8 9 8

Mary Hammond (1878–1964)
© information sought

1 O Breath of life, come sweeping through us,
   revive your church with life and power;
   O Breath of life, come, cleanse, renew us
   and fit your church to meet this hour.

2 O Breath of love, come breathe within us,
   renewing thought and will and heart;
   come, love of Christ, afresh to win us,
   revive your church in every part!

3 O Wind of God, come bend us, break us
   till humbly we confess our need;
   then, in your tenderness remake us,
   revive, restore – for this we plead.

Elizabeth A. P. Head (1850–1936)

238

ST. COLUMBA 8 6 8 6 (CM)   Irish traditional melody

1   O Holy Spirit, come to bless
    your waiting church, we pray:
    we long to grow in holiness
    as children of the day.

2   Great Gift of our ascended king,
    his saving truth reveal,
    our tongues inspire his praise to sing,
    our hearts his love to feel.

3   O come, creator Spirit, move
    as on the formless deep;
    give life and order, light and love,
    where now is death or sleep.

4   We offer up to you, O Lord,
    ourselves to be your throne,
    our every thought and deed and word
    to make your glory known.

5   O Holy Spirit, Lord of might,
    through you all grace is given:
    grant us to know and serve aright
    one God in earth and heaven.

H. W. Baker (1821–1877)
© in this version Jubilate Hymns†

Alternative tune: ST. TIMOTHY (269)

239

SUSSEX CAROL   9 9 9 9 10 9

English traditional melody
arranged R. Vaughan Williams (1872–1958)
© Stainer & Bell Ltd

work out with-
-in us the Fa-ther's de-sign,   give to us   life, O Spi-rit di-vine.__

1 O Holy Spirit, giver of life,
   you bring our souls immortality;
   yet in our hearts are struggle and strife –
   we need your inward vitality:
       work out within us the Father's design,
       give to us life, O Spirit divine.

2 O Holy Spirit, giver of light
   to minds where all is obscurity;
   exchange for blindness, spiritual sight,
   that we may grow to maturity:
       work out . . .

3 O Holy Spirit, giver of love,
   and joy and peace and fidelity,
   the fruitfulness which comes from above –
   that self-control and humility:
       work out . . .

© Michael Saward (born 1932)†

240

BEATITUDO   8 6 8 6 (CM)   J. B. Dykes (1823–1876)

1 Spirit divine, inspire our prayers,
   and make our hearts your home;
   descend with all your gracious powers –
   O come, great Spirit, come!

2 Come as the light – reveal our need,
   our hidden failings show,
   and lead us in those paths of life
   in which the righteous go.

3 Come as the fire, and cleanse our hearts
   with purifying flame;
   let our whole life an offering be
   to our redeemer's name.

4 Come as the dew, and gently bless
   this consecrated hour;
   may barren souls rejoice to know
   your life-creating power.

5 Come as the dove, and spread your wings,
   the wings of peaceful love,
   and let your church on earth become
   blessed as the church above.

6 Come as the wind, with rushing sound
   and pentecostal grace,
   that all the world with joy may see
   the glory of your face.

A. Reed (1787–1862)
© in this version Jubilate Hymns†

Alternative tune: BILLING (362)

241(i)

ST. CUTHBERT   8 6 8 4   J. B. Dykes (1823–1876)

(ii)

WICKLOW   8 6 8 4   Irish traditional melody (slightly adapted)

1 Our great Redeemer, as he breathed
   his tender last farewell,
   a guide, a comforter, bequeathed
       with us to dwell.

2 He came in tongues of living flame
   to teach, convince, subdue;
   unseen as rushing wind he came –
       as powerful too.

3 He comes sweet influence to impart –
   a gracious, willing guest;
   when he can find one humble heart
       where he may rest.

4 And every virtue we possess,
   and every victory won,
   and every thought of holiness
       are his alone.

5 Spirit of purity and grace,
   our failing strength renew;
   and make our hearts a worthier place
       to welcome you.

Henriette Auber (1773–1862)
© in this version Jubilate Hymns†

242

LITTLE CORNARD 666688

M. E. F. Shaw (1875–1958)

1 Spirit of God most high,
 Lord of all power and might;
 source of our Easter joy,
 well-spring of life and light:
     strip from the church its cloak of pride,
     a stumbling-block to those outside.

2 Wind of God's Spirit, blow!
 into the valley sweep,
 bringing dry bones to life,
 wakening each from sleep:
     speak to the church your firm command,
     and bid a scattered army stand.

3 Fire of God's Spirit, melt
 every unbending heart;
 your people's love renew
 as at their journey's start:
     your reconciling grace release
     to bring the Christian family peace.

4 Spirit of Christ our Lord,
 send us to do your will;
 nothing need hold us back
 for you are with us still:
     forgetful of ourselves, may we
     receive your gift of unity!

© David Mowbray (born 1938)†

243

LIVING FLAME   76868686

1   Spirit of God within me,
    possess my human frame;
    fan the dull embers of my heart,
    stir up the living flame:
    strive till that image Adam lost,
    new minted and restored,
    in shining splendour brightly bears
    the likeness of the Lord.

2   Spirit of truth within me,
    possess my thought and mind;
    lighten anew the inward eye
    by Satan rendered blind:
    shine on the words that wisdom speaks
    and grant me power to see
    the truth made known to all in Christ,
    and in that truth be free.

3   Spirit of love within me,
    possess my hands and heart;
    break through the bonds of self-concern
    that seeks to stand apart:
    grant me the love that suffers long,
    that hopes, believes and bears;
    the love fulfilled in sacrifice,
    that cares as Jesus cares.

4   Spirit of life within me,
    possess this life of mine;
    come as the wind of heaven's breath,
    come as the fire divine!
    Spirit of Christ, the living Lord,
    reign in this house of clay,
    till from its dust with Christ I rise
    to everlasting day.

244

ELLACOMBE 7 6 7 6 D

Württemberg Gesangbuch 1784
as in *The Australian Hymn Book* 1977

1 The Spirit came, as promised,
in God's appointed hour;
and now to each believer
he comes in love and power:
and by his Holy Spirit,
God seals us as his own;
and through the Son and Spirit
makes access to his throne.

2 The Spirit makes our bodies
the temple of the Lord;
he binds us all together
in faith and true accord:
the Spirit in his greatness,
brings power from God above;
and with the Son and Father
dwells in our hearts in love.

3 He bids us live together
in unity and peace,
employ his gifts in blessing,
and let base passions cease:
we should not grieve the Spirit
by open sin or shame;
nor let our words and actions
deny his holy name.

4 The word, the Spirit's weapon,
will bring all sin to light;
and prayer, by his directing,
will add new joy and might:
be filled then with his Spirit,
live out God's will and word;
rejoice with hymns and singing,
make music to the Lord!

J. E. Seddon (1915–1983)
© Mrs. M. Seddon†

245

LAUDS 7777

John Wilson (born 1905)
© Oxford University Press

Descant

7 Praise __ the love, _____ praise __ the love! _____ Al - le - lu - ia, al - - le - lu - ia!__

Org.

1   There's a spirit in the air,
    telling Christians everywhere:
    praise the love that Christ revealed,
    living, working, in our world.

2   Lose your shyness, find your tongue,
    tell the world what God has done:
    God in Christ has come to stay;
    we can see his power today.

3   When believers break the bread,
    when a hungry child is fed,
    praise the love that Christ revealed,
    living, working, in our world.

4   Still his Spirit leads the fight,
    seeing wrong and setting right:
    God in Christ has come to stay;
    we can see his power today.

5   When a stranger's not alone,
    where the homeless find a home,
    praise the love that Christ revealed,
    living, working, in our world.

6   May his Spirit fill our praise,
    guide our thoughts and change our ways:
    God in Christ has come to stay;
    we can see his power today.

7   There's a Spirit in the air,
    calling people everywhere:
    praise the love that Christ revealed,
    living, working, in our world.

Brian Wren (born 1936)
© Oxford University Press

Alternative tune: MONKLAND (23)

246

BLOW THE WIND SOUTHERLY   12 10 12 10 12 11 12 11   Traditional melody
© arranged John Barnard (born 1948)†

Spirit of holiness, wisdom and faithfulness,
wind of the Lord, blowing strongly and free:
strength of our serving
    and joy of our worshipping –
Spirit of God, bring your fulness to me!

1   You came to interpret and teach us effectively
    all that the Saviour has spoken and done;
    to glorify Jesus is all your activity –
    promise and gift of the Father and Son:
        Spirit of holiness . . .

2   You came with your gifts to supply all our poverty,
    pouring your love on the church in her need;
    you came with your fruit for our growth to maturity,
    richly refreshing the souls that you feed:
        Spirit of holiness . . .

© Christopher Idle (born 1938)†

For other hymns on this theme, see: Section 42, The Fruit of the Spirit (p. xv
Sunday Themes index   Song Section
    Section 34, The Holy Spirit (p. xiii)   Spirit of the living God, fall (S.23)
    Section 41, The More Excellent Way (p. xvii)   Spirit of the living God, move (S.24)

247

SOUTHWELL (IRONS)   8 6 8 6 (CM)   H. S. Irons (1834–1905)

1   Father of mercies, in your word
    what endless glory shines!
    For ever be your name adored
    for these celestial lines.

2   Here may the blind and hungry come
    and light and food receive;
    here shall the humble guest find room
    and taste and see and live.

3   Here the redeemer's welcome voice
    spreads heavenly peace around,
    and life and everlasting joys
    attend the glorious sound.

4   Here springs of consolation rise
    to cheer the fainting mind,
    and thirsty souls receive supplies
    and sweet refreshment find.

5   Divine instructor, gracious Lord,
    be now and always near:
    teach us to love your sacred word
    and view our saviour here.

Anne Steele (1717–1778)

248

EBENEZER 8 7 8 7 D

T. J. Williams (1869–1944)
© representatives of the late Gwenlyn Evans

1   God has spoken – by his prophets,
    spoken his unchanging word;
    each from age to age proclaiming
    God the one, the righteous Lord;
    in the world's despair and turmoil
    one firm anchor still holds fast:
    God is king, his throne eternal,
    God the first and God the last.

2   God has spoken – by Christ Jesus,
    Christ, the everlasting Son;
    brightness of the Father's glory,
    with the Father ever one:
    spoken by the Word incarnate,
    Life, before all time began,
    light of light, to earth descending,
    God, revealed as Son of Man.
    Man revealing God to man

3   God is speaking – by his Spirit
    speaking to our hearts again;
    in the age-long word expounding
    God's own message, now as then.
    Through the rise and fall of nations
    one sure faith is standing fast:
    God abides, his word unchanging,
    God the first and God the last.

G. W. Briggs (1875–1959)
© 1953 by The Hymn Society of America/
Hope Publishing Co.
Used by permission

Alternative tune: MEAD HOUSE (489)

249

CROFT'S 136th   6 6 6 6 8 8   W. Croft (1678–1727)

1   How sure the Scriptures are!
    God's vital, urgent word,
    as true as steel, and far
    more sharp than any sword:
        So deep and fine,
        at his control
        they pierce where soul
        and spirit join.

2   They test each human thought,
    refining like a fire;
    they measure what we ought
    to do and to desire:
        For God knows all –
        exposed it lies
        before his eyes
        to whom we call.

3   Let those who hear his voice
    confronting them today,
    reject the tempting choice
    of doubting or delay:
        For God speaks still –
        his word is clear,
        so let us hear
        and do his will!

© Christopher Idle (born 1938)†

Alternative tune: DARWALL'S 148th (171)

250(i)

BEWELEY 6666

Cyril Taylor (born 1907)
© Oxford University Press

(ii)

IBSTONE 6666

Maria Tiddeman (1837–1915)

1 Lord, make your word my rule,
in it may I rejoice;
your glory be my aim,
your holy will, my choice:

2 Your promises my hope,
your providence my guard;
your arm my strong support,
yourself my great reward.

C. Wordsworth (1807–1885)

251(i)

RAVENSHAW 6 6 6 6   Melody from *Ave Hierarchia* M. Weisse (1480–1534)
adapted W. H. Monk (1823–1889)

1 Lord your word shall guide us
   and with truth provide us:
   teach us to receive it
   and with joy believe it.

2 When our foes are near us,
   then your word shall cheer us –
   word of consolation,
   message of salvation.

3 When the storms distress us
   and dark clouds oppress us,
   then your word protects us
   and its light directs us.

4 Who can tell the pleasure,
   who recount the treasure
   by your word imparted
   to the simple-hearted?

5 Word of mercy, giving
   courage to the living;
   word of life, supplying
   comfort to the dying.

6 O that we discerning
   its most holy learning,
   Lord, may love and fear you –
   evermore be near you!

H. W. Baker (1821–1877)
© in this version Jubilate Hymns†

251(ii)

CHESTERTON 6 6 6 6 D

G. P. Beaumont (1903–1970)
© Novello & Co Ltd

252(i)

LIVING WORD   11 10 11 10

(ii)

YVONNE   11 10 11 10

Unison

252(iii)

O QUANTA QUALIA   11 10 11 10   Melody from *Paris Antiphoner* 1681

1 Powerful in making us wise to salvation,
   witness to faith in Christ Jesus the Word;
   breathed out for all by the life-giving Father –
   these are the scriptures, and thus speaks the Lord.

2 Tool for employment and compass for travel,
   map in the desert and lamp in the dark;
   teaching, rebuking, correcting and training –
   these are the scriptures, and this is their work.

3 History, prophecy, song and commandment,
   gospel and letter and dream from on high;
   written by men borne along by the Spirit –
   these are the scriptures; on them we rely.

4 Gift for God's servants to fit them completely,
   fully equipping to walk in his ways;
   guide to good work and effective believing –
   these are the scriptures, for these we give praise!

© Christopher Idle (born 1938)†

253

QUIETUDE 6565

H. Green (1871–1930)

1 Speak, Lord, in the stillness,
   speak your word to me;
   help me now to listen
   in expectancy.

2 Speak, O gracious Master,
   in this quiet hour;
   let me see your face, Lord,
   feel your touch of power.

3 For the words you give me,
   they are life indeed;
   living Bread from heaven,
   now my spirit feed.

4 Speak, your servant listens –
   I await your word;
   let me know your presence,
   let your voice be heard!

5 Fill me with the knowledge
   of your glorious will;
   all your own good pleasure
   in my life fulfil.

Emily M. Crawford (1864–1927)
© in this version Jubilate Hymns†

254

CHURCH TRIUMPHANT   8 8 8 8 (LM)   J. W. Elliott (1833–1915)

1   The heavens declare your glory, Lord!
    in every star your wisdom shines;
    but when our eyes behold your word,
    we read your name in clearer lines.

2   Sun, moon, and stars convey your praise
    to all the earth, and never stand;
    so when your truth began its race,
    it touched and glanced on every land.

3   Nor shall your spreading gospel rest
    till through the world your truth has run;
    till Christ has all the nations blessed
    who see the light or feel the sun.

4   Great Sun of righteousness, arise
    and bless the world with heavenly light!
    your gospel makes the simple wise,
    your laws are pure, your judgements right.

5   Your noblest wonders here we view
    in souls renewed and sins forgiven:
    Lord, cleanse my sins, my soul renew,
    and make your word my guide to heaven.

I. Watts (1674–1748)

255(i)

PORCHESTER 878747 © Philip Humphreys (born 1935)

1 Thanks to God whose word was spoken
   in the deed that made the earth;
   his the voice that called a nation,
   his the fires that tried its worth.
       God has spoken:
   praise him for his open word!

2 Thanks to God whose Word incarnate
   heights and depths of life did share;
   deeds and words and death and rising
   grace in human form declare.
       God has spoken:
   praise him for his open word!

3 Thanks to God whose word was written
   in the Bible's sacred page,
   record of the revelation
   showing God to every age.
       God has spoken:
   praise him for his open word!

255(ii)

ST. HELEN   8 7 8 7 8 7   G. C. Martin (1844–1916)

In this tune, line 5 in each verse is repeated.

4 Thanks to God whose word is published
   in the tongues of every race;
   see its glory undiminished
   by the change of time or place.
       God has spoken:
   praise him for his open word!

5 Thanks to God whose word is answered
   by the Spirit's voice within;
   here we drink of joy unmeasured,
   life redeemed from death and sin.
       God is speaking:
   praise him for his open word!

R. T. Brooks (born 1918)
© 1954 by Agape, Carol Stream, IL 60187.
International copyright secured,
all rights reserved, used by permission

For other hymns on this theme, see:
Sunday Themes index
   Section 7, The Word of God in the Old Testament (p. viii)
   Section 17, Revelation: Parables (p. x)

GOD'S WORLD:
YEARS AND SEASONS

256

GATESCARTH 8 6 8 8 6   © Caryl Micklem (born 1925)

1 Christ be the Lord of all our days,
   the swiftly-passing years:
   Lord of our unremembered birth,
   heirs to the brightness of the earth;
   Lord of our griefs and fears.

2 Christ be the source of all our deeds,
   the life our living shares;
   the fount which flows from worlds above
   to never-failing springs of love;
   the ground of all our prayers.

3 Christ be the goal of all our hopes,
   the end to whom we come;
   guide of each pilgrim Christian soul
   which seeks, as compass seeks the pole,
   our many-mansioned home.

4 Christ be the vision of our lives,
   of all we think and are;
   to shine upon our spirits' sight
   as light of everlasting light –
   the bright and morning star.

© Timothy Dudley-Smith (born 1926)

257

DEDICATION 7 5 7 5 D

G. A. Macfarren (1813–1887)

1 Father, let us dedicate
   all this year to you,
   for the service small or great
   you would have us do;
   not from any painful thing
   freedom can we claim,
   but in all, that we may bring
      glory to your name.

2 Can a child presume to choose
   where or how to live?
   can a Father's love refuse
   all the best to give?
   More you give us every day
   than we dare to claim,
   and our grateful voices say,
      'Glory to your name!'

3 If you call us to a cross
   and its shadows come
   turning all our gain to loss,
   shrouding heart and home,
   let us think how your dear Son
   to his triumph came,
   then through pain and tears pray on,
      'Glory to your name!'

4 If in mercy you prepare
   joyful years ahead,
   if through days serene and fair
   peaceful paths we tread;
   then, whatever life may bring,
   let our lips proclaim
   and our glad hearts ever sing,
      'Glory to your name!'

L. Tuttiett (1825–1897)
© in this version Jubilate Hymns†

258

CULBACH 7 7 7 7

Adapted from a chorale in J. Scheffler's
Heilige Seelenlust Breslau 1657

1 For your mercy and your grace
faithful through another year,
hear our song of thankfulness,
Saviour and Redeemer, hear.

2 All our sins on you we cast,
you, our perfect Sacrifice;
and, forgetting what is past,
press towards our glorious prize.

3 Dark the future – let your light
guide us, bright and morning Star;
fierce the battles we must fight –
arm us, Saviour, for the war!

4 In our weakness and distress,
be our Rock, O Lord, we pray;
in the pathless wilderness,
be our true and living Way.

5 Keep us faithful, keep us pure,
keep us evermore your own;
help, O help us to endure,
make us fit to wear the crown!

H. Downton (1818–1885)
© in this version Jubilate Hymns†

259

LITTLE CORNARD 666688   M. E. F. Shaw (1875–1958)
© J. Curwen & Sons Ltd/William Elkin Music Services

1 Lord of our growing years,
   with us from infancy,
   laughter and quick-dried tears,
   freshness and energy:
        your grace surrounds us all our days –
        for all your gifts we bring our praise.

2 Lord of our strongest years,
   stretching our youthful powers,
   lovers and pioneers
   when all the world seems ours:
        your grace surrounds us . . .

3 Lord of our middle years,
   giver of steadfastness,
   courage that perseveres
   when there is small success:
        your grace surrounds us . . .

4 Lord of our older years,
   steep though the road may be,
   rid us of foolish fears,
   bring us serenity:
        your grace surrounds us . . .

5 Lord of our closing years,
   always your promise stands;
   hold us when death appears,
   safely within your hands:
        your grace surrounds us . . .

© David Mowbray (born 1938)†

Alternative tune: GOLDINGTON (261)

260

GREAT IS THY FAITHFULNESS
11 10 11 10 and refrain

W. M. Runyan (1870–1957)
© Hope Publishing Company

Great is your faith-ful-ness, great is your faith-ful-ness, morn-ing by

morn-ing new mer-cies I see; all I have need-ed your

hand has pro-vid-ed — great is your faith-ful-ness, Fa-ther, to me.

1 *mf* Great is your faithfulness, O God my Father,
   you have fulfilled all your promise to me;
   you never fail and your love is unchanging –
   all you have been you for ever will be.
   f   Great is your faithfulness,
        great is your faithfulness,
        morning by morning new mercies I see;
        all I have needed your hand has provided –
        great is your faithfulness, Father, to me.

2 *mf* Summer and winter, and springtime and harvest,
   sun, moon and stars in their courses above
   join with all nature in eloquent witness
   to your great faithfulness, mercy and love.
   f   Great is your faithfulness . . .

3 *mp* Pardon for sin, and a peace everlasting,
   your living presence to cheer and to guide;
   mf strength for today,
                and bright hope for tomorrow –
   these are the blessings your love will provide.
   f   Great is your faithfulness . . .

T. O. Chisholm (1866–1960)
in this version Jubilate Hymns
© 1925 and 1951 Hope Publishing Company,
Carol Stream, Illinois 60187.
All rights reserved, used by permission

261(i)

GOLDINGTON 666688

© David Peacock (born 1949)†

1 Lord of the changing year,
patterns and colours bright;
all that we see and hear,
sunrise and starlit night:
the seasons, Lord, in splendour shine,
your never-failing wise design.

2 Lord of the winter scene,
hard-frozen ice and snow;
death where once life has been,
nothing is seen to grow;
few creatures roam, few birds will fly
across the clouded Christmas sky:

3 Lord of unfolding spring,
promise of life to come;
nature begins to sing
where once her tongue was dumb;
the crocus blooms, the hedgerows wake,
and Easter day is soon to break:

261(ii)

LITTLE CORNARD 6 6 6 6 8 8

M. E. F. Shaw (1875–1958)

4 Lord of the summer days,
  spreading and green the trees;
  songthrush lifts high your praise,
  gulls light on deep-blue seas;
  the warmth and welcome of the sun
  brings happiness to everyone:

5 Lord of the autumn gold,
  reaping and harvest home,
  sheep safely in the fold,
  turn of the year has come:
  the seasons, Lord, in splendour shine,
  your never-failing wise design.

262(i)

BOW BRICKHILL   8 8 8 8 (LM)

S. H. Nicholson (1875–1947)
© Hymns Ancient & Modern Ltd

1 *mp* O Christ of all the ages, come!
  we fear to journey on our own;
  without you near we cannot face
  the future months, the years unknown.

2 Afflicted, tempted, tried like us,
  you match our moments of despair;
  with us you watch the desert hours,
  and in our sorrows you are there.

3 *p* O Saviour, fastened to a cross
  by tearing nails – our selfish ways;
  the grieving, caring Lord of love,
  you bear the sins of all our days.

262(ii)

GONFALON ROYAL 8 8 8 8 (LM)

P. C. Buck (1871–1947)

4 *f* Triumphant from the grave you rise –
the morning breaks upon our sight;
and with its dawning, future years
will shine with your unending light.

5 O Christ of all the ages, come!
the days and months and years go by:
accept our praise, redeem our lives –
our strength for all eternity! (Amen.)

263

SALVATOR MUNDI 11 10 11 10 D © Kenneth Coates (born 1917)

1 O Christ the same, through all our story's pages –
   our loves and hopes, our failures and our fears;
   eternal Lord, the king of all the ages,
   unchanging still amid the passing years:
   O living Word, the source of all creation,
   who spread the skies and set the stars ablaze;
   O Christ the same,
                  who wrought our whole salvation,
   we bring our thanks for all our yesterdays.

2 O Christ the same, the friend of sinners, sharing
   our inmost thoughts, the secrets none can hide;
   still as of old upon your body bearing
   the marks of love, in triumph glorified:
   O Son of Man, who stooped for us from heaven –
   O Prince of life, in all your saving power;
   O Christ the same, to whom our hearts are given:
   we bring our thanks for this the present hour.

3 O Christ the same, secure within whose keeping
   our lives and loves, our days and years remain;
   our work and rest, our waking and our sleeping,
   our calm and storm, our pleasure and our pain:
   O Lord of love, for all our joys and sorrows,
   for all our hopes, when earth shall fade and flee;
   O Christ the same, beyond our brief tomorrows,
   we bring our thanks for all that is to be.

© Timothy Dudley-Smith (born 1926)

Alternative tune: LONDONDERRY AIR (499)

GOD'S WORLD: DAYS AND NIGHTS
Morning

264

MORNING HYMN   8 8 8 8 (LM)   Melody by F. H. Barthélémon (1741–1808)

Part 1

1 Awake, my soul, and with the sun
   your daily stage of duty run;
   shake off your sleep, and joyful rise
   to make your morning sacrifice.

2 Redeem your mis-spent time that's past
   and live this day as if your last;
   improve your talent with due care,
   for God's great Day yourself prepare.

3 Let all your speaking be sincere,
   your conscience as the noonday clear;
   think how all-seeing God surveys
   your secret thoughts and all your ways.

Part 2

4 Give praise to God, who safely kept
   and well refreshed me while I slept:
   grant, Lord, that when from death I wake
   I may of endless life partake.

5 To you my vows I here renew:
   disperse my sins as morning dew;
   guard my first springs of thought and will,
   and with your love my spirit fill.

6 Direct, control, suggest this day
   all I desire or do or say;
   that all my powers with all their might
   for your sole glory may unite.

Doxology

7 Praise God, from whom all blessings flow
   in heaven above and earth below;
   one God, three persons, we adore –
   to him be praise for evermore!

T. Ken (1637–1710)
© in this version Jubilate Hymns†

265

BUNESSAN   10 9 10 9

Gaelic melody
© arranged Noël Tredinnick (born 1949)†

Unison

1 Morning has broken like the first morning;
   blackbird has spoken like the first bird:
   praise for the singing, praise for the morning,
   praise for them springing fresh from the word!

2 Sweet the rain's new fall, sunlit from heaven,
   like the first dew fall on the first grass:
   praise for the sweetness of the wet garden,
   sprung in completeness where his feet pass.

3 Mine is the sunlight, mine is the morning
   born of the one light Eden saw play:
   praise with elation, praise every morning,
   God's re-creation of the new day!

Eleanor Farjeon (1881–1965)
© David Higham Associates Ltd

266

RATISBON 7 7 7 7 7 7   Melody from J. G. Werner's *Choralbuch* Leipzig 1815
Harmony from W. H. Havergal (1793–1870)

1 *f* Christ whose glory fills the skies,
Christ the true, the only light;
Sun of righteousness, arise,
triumph over shades of night:
    Dayspring from on high, be near;
    Daystar, in my heart appear!

2 *mp* Dark and cheerless is the dawn
till your mercy's beams I see;
joyless is the day's return
till your glories shine on me:
    as they inward light impart,
    cheer my eyes and warm my heart.

3 *mf* Visit then this soul of mine,
pierce the gloom of sin and grief;
fill me, radiancy divine,
scatter all my unbelief:
  f   more and more yourself display,
    shining to the perfect day!

C. Wesley (1707–1788)

267

DANIEL 8 8 8 8 (LM)

Irish traditional melody
arranged M. E. F. Shaw (1875–1958)
arrangement © Oxford University Press

1 Lord, as I wake I turn to you,
  yourself the first thought of my day;
  my king, my God, whose help is sure,
  yourself the help for which I pray.

2 There is no blessing, Lord, from you
  for those who make their will their way,
  no praise for those who will not praise,
  no peace for those who will not pray.

3 Your loving gifts of grace to me,
  those favours I could never earn,
  call for my thanks in praise and prayer,
  call me to love you in return.

4 Lord, make my life a life of love,
  keep me from sin in all I do;
  Lord, make your law my only law,
  your will my will, for love of you.

from Psalm 5
Brian Foley (born 1919)
© Faber Music Ltd

268

SAMUEL 666688

A. Sullivan (1842–1900)

1 Lord, as the day begins
 lift up our hearts in praise;
 take from us all our sins,
 guard us in all our ways:
 our every step direct and guide
 that Christ in all be glorified!

2 Christ be in work and skill,
 serving each other's need;
 Christ be in thought and will,
 Christ be in word and deed:
 our minds be set on things above
 in joy and peace, in faith and love.

3 Grant us the Spirit's strength,
 teach us to walk his way;
 so bring us all at length
 safe to the close of day:
 from hour to hour sustain and bless,
 and let our song be thankfulness.

4   Now as the day begins
    make it the best of days;
    take from us all our sins,
    guard us in all our ways:
    our every step direct and guide
    that Christ in all be glorified!

269

ST. TIMOTHY   8 6 8 6 (CM)   H. W. Baker (1821–1877)

1   My Father, for another night
    of quiet sleep and rest;
    for all the joy of morning light,
    your holy name be blessed.

2   Now with the new-born day I give
    myself to you again;
    that gladly I for you may live,
    and you within me reign.

3   In every action, great or small,
    in every thought and aim;
    your glory may I seek in all,
    do all in Jesus' name.

4   My Father, for his sake, I pray,
    your child accept and bless;
    and lead me by your grace today
    in paths of righteousness.

270

MELCOMBE   8 8 8 8 (LM)   S. Webbe the elder (1740–1816)

1 New every morning is the love
   our waking and uprising prove:
   through sleep and darkness safely brought,
   restored to life and power and thought.

2 New mercies, each returning day,
   surround your people as they pray:
   new dangers past, new sins forgiven,
   new thoughts of God, new hopes of heaven.

3 If in our daily life our mind
   be set to honour all we find,
   new treasures still, of countless price,
   God will provide for sacrifice.

4 The trivial round, the common task,
   will give us all we ought to ask:
   room to deny ourselves, a road
   to bring us daily nearer God.

5 Prepare us, Lord, in your dear love
   for perfect rest with you above,
   and help us, this and every day,
   to grow more like you as we pray.

J. Keble (1792–1866)

271

PACHELBEL 88888

Adapted from a melody in the
Nürnberg Gesangbuch 1690

1   We share a new day's dawn with Christ,
     our lives refreshed and hopes restored:
     this is the day to serve our Lord!
     And with this new day's dawn we rise
     and lift our hearts up to the skies.

2   For heaven's grace we turn to prayer,
     for truth and strength we read Christ's word:
     here is the grace to serve our Lord!
     And so by heaven's grace this day
     we'll learn to walk in Jesus' way.

3   Our song shall be of perfect love –
     of Christ's redemption, faith's reward:
     this is love's service to our Lord!
     And perfect love shall be our song
     till all our days to Christ belong.

272(i)

HARVEY 7 4 7 4 D

G. P. Beaumont (1903–1970)
© Josef Weinberger Ltd

1 Welcome to another day!
  night is blinded:
  'Welcome', let creation say;
  darkness ended.
  Comes the sunshine after dew,
  time for labour;
  time to love my God anew
  and my neighbour.

2 Welcome to the day of prayer
  with God's people;
  welcome is the joy we share
  at his table.
  Bread and wine from heaven fall:
  come, receive it
  that the Christ may reign in all
  who believe it.

272(ii)

GWALCHMAI 7 4 7 4 D

J. D. Jones (1827–1870)

3 Welcome is the peace that's given,
   sure for ever;
   welcome is the hope of heaven
   when life's over.
   As we work and as we pray,
   trust God's story:
   come then, as the dawning day
   heralds glory!

© Michael Saward (born 1932)†

For other hymns on this theme, see:
 'The Lord's Day' (375–380)
 Holy, holy, holy, Lord God Almighty (7)
 Three-in-One and One-in-Three (12)

Who can measure heaven and earth (27)
When morning gilds the skies (223)
O joy of God, we seek you (422)

GOD'S WORLD: DAYS AND NIGHTS
Evening

273

MELITA 888888 J. B. Dykes (1823–1876)

1   Almighty Lord, the holy One
     whose reign in glory we await:
     look down from your eternal throne
     and our dark world illuminate;
     from sons and daughters of the light
     dispel the shameful deeds of night.

2   Defend us from all evil powers;
     our weakness and fatigue replace
     through all the silent sleeping hours
     with sweet refreshing by your grace;
     forgive our sins, our hope renew,
     that we may rest and rise with you.

from the Gelasian and Leonine
sacramentaries (eighth and seventh centuries)
© Christopher Idle (born 1938)†

Alternative tune: SURREY (117)

274

TALLIS' CANON   8 8 8 8 (LM)

Shortened form of melody by
Thomas Tallis (c.1505–1585)
from T. Ravenscroft's *Psalter* 1621

1   Glory to you, my God, this night
    for all the blessings of the light;
    keep me, O keep me, King of kings,
    beneath your own almighty wings.

2   Forgive me, Lord, through your dear Son,
    the wrong that I this day have done,
    that peace with God and man may be,
    before I sleep, restored to me.

3   Teach me to live, that I may dread
    the grave as little as my bed;
    teach me to die, that so I may
    rise glorious at the awesome day.

4   O may my soul on you repose
    and restful sleep my eyelids close;
    sleep that shall me more vigorous make
    to serve my God when I awake.

5   If in the night I sleepless lie,
    my mind with peaceful thoughts supply;
    let no dark dreams disturb my rest,
    no powers of evil me molest.

6   Praise God from whom all blessings flow
    in heaven above and earth below;
    one God, three persons, we adore –
    to him be praise for evermore!

T. Ken (1637–1710)
© in this version Jubilate Hymns†

275

SEBASTE   Irregular

J. Stainer (1840–1901)

1 Hail, gladdening Light, of his pure glo - ry poured
who is the immortal Fa - ther, heaven - ly, blessed,
Ho - li - est of ho - lies, Je - sus Christ our Lord.

2 Now we have come to the sun's hour of rest;
the lights of eve - ning round us shine; we hymn the Fa - ther,

Son, and Ho - ly Spi - rit di - vine.

3 Worthiest are you at all times to be sung with un - cor - rup - ted

tongue, Son of our God, gi - ver of life a - lone;

there-fore in all the world we make your glor - ies known.

from *Phos Hilaron* (Eastern vesper hymn)
J. Keble (1792–1866)
© in this version Jubilate Hymns†

276(i)

TE LUCIS   8 8 8 8 (LM)   Mode viii

(ii)

SOLOTHURN   8 8 8 8 (LM)

Swiss traditional melody
arranged C. H. Kitson (1874–1944)
arrangement copyright holder sought

1   Before the ending of the day,
     Creator of the world, we pray:
     protect us by your mighty grace,
     grant us your mercy and your peace:

2 Bless us in sleep, that we may find
   no terrors to disturb our mind;
   our cunning enemy restrain –
   guard us from sin and all its stain.

3 O Father, may your will be done
   through Jesus Christ your only Son;
   whom with the Spirit we adore,
   one God, both now and evermore.

from the Latin (pre-eighth century)
© in this version Jubilate Hymns†

277

QUEM PASTORES LAUDAVERE 8 8 8 7

German carol melody
fourteenth century
arranged R. Vaughan Williams (1872–1958)
arrangement © Oxford University Press

1 Light of gladness, Lord of glory,
   Jesus Christ our king most holy,
   shine among us in your mercy:
       earth and heaven join their hymn.

2 Let us sing at sun's descending
   as we see the lights of evening,
   Father, Son, and Spirit praising
       with the holy seraphim.

3 Son of God, through all the ages
   worthy of our holiest praises,
   yours the life that never ceases,
       light which never shall grow dim.

from *Phos Hilaron* (Eastern vesper hymn)
© Christopher Idle (born 1938)†

278

CHRISTE SANCTORUM 11 11 11 5

Melody from *Paris Antiphoner* 1681
© arranged David Iliff (born 1939)†

1 Lighten our darkness now the day is ended –
   Father in mercy, guard your children sleeping;
   from every evil, every harm defended,
   safe in your keeping:

2 To that last hour, when heaven's day is dawning,
   far spent the night that knows no earthly waking;
   keep us as watchmen, longing for the morning,
   till that day's breaking.

© Timothy Dudley-Smith (born 1926)

279

ARNSTADT   5 5 8 8 5 5

Melody A. Drese (1620–1701)

1 *mf* Round me falls the night –
Saviour, be my light:
through the hours in darkness shrouded
let me see your face unclouded;
let your glory shine
in this heart of mine.

2 *p* When my work is done
and my rest begun,
peaceful sleep and silence seeking
let me hear you softly speaking;
to my inward ear
whisper 'I am near.'

3 *mf* Holy, heavenly Light,
shining through earth's night,
joy and life and inspiration,
love enfolding every nation:
be with me tonight,
Saviour, be my light.

W. Romanis (1824–1899)
© in this version Jubilate Hymns†

280

ST. CLEMENT 9 8 9 8

C. C. Scholefield (1839–1904)

1 The day you gave us, Lord, is ended,
the sun is sinking in the west;
to you our morning hymns ascended,
your praise shall sanctify our rest.

2 We thank you that your church, unsleeping
while earth rolls onward into light,
through all the world her watch is keeping
and rests not now by day or night.

3 As to each continent and island
the dawn proclaims another day,
the voice of prayer is never silent,
nor dies the sound of praise away.

4 The sun that bids us rest is waking
   your church beneath the western sky;
   fresh voices hour by hour are making
   your mighty deeds resound on high.

5 So be it, Lord: your throne shall never,
   like earth's proud empires, pass away;
   your kingdom stands, and grows for ever,
   until there dawns that glorious day.

J. Ellerton (1826–1893)
© in this version Jubilate Hymns†

Descant and arrangement © John Barnard (born 1948)†

5 So be _ it, Lord:_your throne_shall ne - ver, like earth's _ proud

em - pires, pass _ a - way; your king - dom stands, and

grows_for ev - er, un - til_there dawns_that glor - ious day.

281

ELLERS   10 10 10 10

E. J. Hopkins (1818–1901)
arranged A. Sullivan (1842–1900)

1   Saviour, again to your dear name we raise
    with one accord our parting hymn of praise;
    we give you thanks before our worship cease –
    then, in the silence, hear your word of peace.

2   Give us your peace, Lord, on our homeward way:
    with you began, with you shall end the day;
    guard now the lips from sin, the hearts from shame,
    that in this house have called upon your name.

3   Give us your peace, Lord, through the coming night,
    turn all our darkness to your perfect light;
    then, through our sleep, our hope and strength renew,
    for dark and light are both alike to you.

4   Give us your peace throughout our earthly life:
    comfort in sorrow, courage in the strife;
    then, when your voice shall make our conflict cease,
    call us, O Lord, to your eternal peace.

J. Ellerton (1826–1893)

GOD'S WORLD:
LAND, SEA AND HARVEST

282

SHIPSTON 8 7 8 7

English traditional melody
arranged R. Vaughan Williams (1872–1958)
arrangement © Oxford University Press

1   God whose farm is all creation,
    take the gratitude we give;
    take the finest of our harvest,
    crops we grow that all may live.

2   Take our ploughing, seeding, reaping,
    hopes and fears of sun and rain,
    all our thinking, planning, waiting,
    ripened in this fruit and grain.

3   All our labour, all our watching,
    all our calendar of care
    in these crops of your creation,
    take, O God – they are our prayer.

© John Arlott (born 1914)

For other hymns on the theme GOD'S WORLD: DAYS AND NIGHTS: Evening (opposite), see:
Hymn Section
   Bless the Lord as day departs (608)
   Come, praise the Lord (609)

283(i)

ALL THINGS BRIGHT AND BEAUTIFUL   W. H. Monk (1823–1889)
7 6 7 6 and refrain

1   Each little flower that opens,
     each little bird that sings –
     he made their glowing colours,
     he made their tiny wings.
       All things bright . . .

2   The purple-headed mountain,
     the river running by,
     the sunset, and the morning
     that brightens up the sky:
       All things bright . . .

283(ii)

ROYAL OAK 7 6 7 6 and refrain

English traditional melody
seventeenth century
arranged M. E. F. Shaw (1875–1958)
arrangement © J. Curwen & Sons Ltd/William Elkin Music Services

3 The cold wind in the winter,
   the pleasant summer sun,
   the ripe fruits in the garden –
   he made them every one.
      All things bright . . .

4 He gave us eyes to see them,
   and lips that we might tell
   how great is God almighty,
   who has made all things well!
      All things bright . . .

Cecil F. Alexander (1818–1895)

284

ST GEORGE'S, WINDSOR   7 7 7 7 D

G. J. Elvey (1816–1893)
descant © John Barnard (born 1948)†

4 Ev - en so, Lord, quick-ly come – bring your fi - nal har-vest home!

ga - ther_all your peo - ple_ in   free from sor-row, free_ from sin,

there to-geth-er pur-i - fied, e - ver thank-ful   at   your   side –

come, with all your an-gels, come, bring that glor-ious har-vest home!

1 Come, you thankful people, come,
   raise the song of harvest home!
   fruit and crops are gathered in
   safe before the storms begin:
   God our maker will provide
   for our needs to be supplied;
   come, with all his people, come,
   raise the song of harvest home!

2 All the world is God's own field,
   harvests for his praise to yield;
   wheat and weeds together sown
   here for joy or sorrow grown:
   first the blade and then the ear,
   then the full corn shall appear –
   Lord of harvest, grant that we
   wholesome grain and pure may be.

3 For the Lord our God shall come
   and shall bring his harvest home;
   he himself on that great day,
   worthless things shall take away,
   give his angels charge at last
   in the fire the weeds to cast,
   but the fruitful ears to store
   in his care for evermore.

4 Even so, Lord, quickly come –
   bring your final harvest home!
   gather all your people in
   free from sorrow, free from sin,
   there together purified,
   ever thankful at your side –
   come, with all your angels, come,
   bring that glorious harvest home!

H. Alford (1810–1871)
© in this version Jubilate Hymns†

285

MELITA 888888

J. B. Dykes (1823–1876)

1 Eternal Father, strong to save,
  whose arm restrains the restless wave,
  who told the mighty ocean deep
  its own appointed bounds to keep:
    we cry, O God of majesty,
    for those in peril on the sea.

2 O Christ, whose voice the waters heard
  and hushed their raging at your word,
  who walked across the surging deep
  and in the storm lay calm in sleep:
    we cry, O Lord of Galilee,
    for those in peril on the sea.

3 Creator Spirit, by whose breath
  were fashioned sea and sky and earth;
  who made the stormy chaos cease
  and gave us life and light and peace:
    we cry, O Spirit strong and free,
    for those in peril on the sea.

4   O Trinity of love and power,
    preserve their lives in danger's hour;
    from rock and tempest, flood and flame,
    protect them by your holy name,
        and to your glory let there be
        glad hymns of praise from land and sea.

286

EAST ACKLAM 8 4 8 4 8 8 8 4   © Francis Jackson (born 1917)

1 For the fruits of his creation,
    thanks be to God;
for his gifts to every nation,
    thanks be to God;
for the ploughing, sowing, reaping,
silent growth while we are sleeping,
future needs in earth's safe-keeping,
    thanks be to God.

2 In the just reward of labour,
    God's will is done;
in the help we give our neighbour,
    God's will is done;
in our worldwide task of caring
for the hungry and despairing,
in the harvests we are sharing,
    God's will is done.

3 For the harvests of his Spirit,
    thanks be to God;
for the good we all inherit,
    thanks be to God;
for the wonders that astound us,
for the truths that still confound us,
most of all, that love has found us,
    thanks be to God.

F. Pratt Green (born 1903)
© Stainer & Bell Ltd

287

ALMSGIVING 8 8 8 4

J. B. Dykes (1823–1876)

1 O Lord of heaven and earth and sea,
  to you all praise and glory be,
  who loved us from eternity
      and gave us all.

2 The golden sunshine, gentle air,
  sweet flowers and fruit, your love declare;
  when harvests ripen you are there –
      you give us all.

3 For peaceful homes and healthful days,
  for all the blessings earth displays,
  we owe you thankfulness and praise –
      you give us all.

4 Freely you gave your only Son,
  who on the cross salvation won;
  and in the life through him begun
      you give us all.

5 You sent your Spirit from above
  as wind and fire and gentle dove;
  and in his gifts of power and love
      you gave us all.

6 For souls redeemed, for sins forgiven,
  for means of grace and hopes of heaven,
  to you, O Lord what can be given?
      you give us all.

7 We lose what on ourselves we spend;
  we have as treasure without end
  whatever, Lord, to you we lend –
      you give us all.

8 Father, from whom we all derive
  our life, our gifts, our power to give:
  O may we ever with you live;
      you give us all.

C. Wordsworth (1807–1885)
© in this version Jubilate Hymns†

288

STOWEY   11 11 11 11

English traditional melody
© arranged Norman Warren (born 1934)†

1 Praise God for the harvest of farm and of field,
  praise God for the people who gather their yield,
  the long hours of labour, the skills of a team,
  the patience of science, the power of machine.

2 Praise God for the harvest that's sent from afar,
  from market and harbour, from tropical shore:
  foods packed and transported,
                and planted and grown
  by God-given neighbours, unseen and unknown.

3 Praise God for the harvest
                that comes from the ground,
  by drill or by mineshaft, by opencast mound;
  for oil and for iron, for tinplate and coal,
  praise God, who in love has provided them all.

4 Praise God for the harvest of science and skill,
  the urge to discover, create and fulfil:
  for all new inventions that promise to gain
  a future more hopeful, a world more humane.

5 Praise God for the harvest of conflict and love,
  for leaders and peoples who struggle and serve
  to conquer oppression, earth's plenty increase,
  and gather God's harvest of justice and peace.

Brian Wren (born 1936)
© Oxford University Press

289

TRIUMPH 878787

H. J. Gauntlett (1805–1876)

1 Roar the waves, the waters praising
God who saves; and from beneath
creatures rise in shapes amazing
to our eyes – he gives them breath:
God who set the planets blazing
holds us yet in life or death.

2 Cries a bird at break of morning –
music heard when life began;
Christ was there at day's first dawning,
son to share a father's plan:
Jesus, born our hope and warning,
shall return – the Son of Man.

3 Sing the trees, the branches calling
in the breeze; the Spirit's song
sweeps the grass, the flowers falling.
Look! he passes all along:
wind of God whose strength appalling
mocks the proud and bends the strong.

4 Sound the praise of God the Father,
voices raise to Christ the Son;
in the Spirit Christians gather –
speak his merit everyone:
not in vain words glory – rather
tell again what God has done!

© Michael Perry (born 1942)†

Alternative tune: UNSER HERRSCHER (205)

290

ROSSLEIGH   6 6 8 6 (SM)

© Brian and Sheila Dunning
© arranged John Barnard (born 1948)†

1   The earth is yours, O God –
    you nourish it with rain;
    the streams and rivers overflow,
    the land bears seed again.

2   The soil is yours, O God –
    the shoots are moist with dew;
    and ripened by the burning sun
    the corn grows straight and true.

3   The hills are yours, O God –
    their grass is lush and green,
    providing pastures for the flocks
    which everywhere are seen.

4   The whole rich land is yours
    for fodder or for plough;
    and so, for rain, sun, soil and seed,
    O God, we thank you now.

from Psalm 65
© Michael Saward (born 1932)†

Alternative tune: FRANCONIA (110)

291

GOLDEN SHEAVES 8 7 8 7 D

A. Sullivan (1842–1900)

1 To you, O Lord, our hearts we raise
  in hymns of adoration:
  accept our sacrifice of praise,
  our shouts of exultation;
  for by your hand our souls are fed –
  what joys your love has given!
  You give to us our daily bread,
  so give us bread from heaven!

2 And now on this our festal day,
  your love to us expressing
  our gifts before you, Lord, we lay,
  the firstfruits of your blessing:
  bright robes of gold the fields adorn,
  the hills with joy are ringing;
  the valleys stand so thick with corn
  that even they are singing.

3 Yet in your presence we confess,
  O Lord of earth and heaven,
  our pride, our greed and selfishness –
  we ask to be forgiven:
  and where the hungry suffer still
  because of our ambition,
  there let our riches serve your will
  your love be our commission.

4 There is a country bright as day
  beyond the crystal river,
  where hunger will be done away
  and thirst be gone for ever;
  where praises ring out loud and strong
  that now with ours are blending;
  where we shall sing the harvest-song
  that never has an ending.

after W. C. Dix (1837–1898)
© in this version Word & Music✝

292

WIR PFLÜGEN   7 6 7 6 D and refrain

J. A. P. Schulz (1747–1800)

All good gifts a-round us are sent from heaven a - bove: then
thank the Lord, O thank the Lord for all ____ his love.

1 We plough the fields, and scatter
    the good seed on the land;
    but it is fed and watered
    by God's almighty hand:
    he sends the snow in winter,
    the warmth to swell the grain;
    the breezes and the sunshine
    and soft refreshing rain.
        All good gifts around us
        are sent from heaven above:
        then thank the Lord, O thank the Lord
        for all his love.

2 He only is the maker
    of all things near and far;
    he paints the wayside flower,
    he lights the evening star:
    the winds and waves obey him,
    by him the birds are fed;
    much more, to us his children
    he gives our daily bread.
        All good gifts . . .

3 We thank you, then, our Father,
    for all things bright and good;
    the seed-time and the harvest,
    our life, our health, our food:
    accept the gifts we offer
    for all your love imparts;
    and that which you most welcome
    our humble, thankful hearts!
        All good gifts . . .

after M. Claudius (1740–1815)
Jane M. Campbell (1817–1878)

293

HEATHLANDS 777777   H. T. Smart (1813–1879)

1 *mf* God of mercy, God of grace,
    show the brightness of your face:
    shine upon us, Saviour, shine,
    fill your church with light divine,
    and your saving health extend
    to the earth's remotest end.

2 *f* Let the people praise you, Lord!
    be by all who live adored:
    let the nations shout and sing
    glory to their saviour king,
mf at your feet their tribute pay,
    and your holy will obey.

3 *f* Let the people crown you king!
    then shall earth her harvest bring,
    God to us his blessing give,
    we to God devoted live;
    all below and all above,
    one in joy and light and love.

from *Deus Misereatur* (Psalm 67)
H. F. Lyte (1793–1847)

For other hymns on this theme, see:
Additional Hymns
    Bless the Lord, creation sings (604)

Song Section
    Angels, praise him (S.32)
    Praise the Lord our God (S.31)

GOD'S WORLD:
MARRIAGE, HOME AND CHILDREN

294

MARYTON   8 8 8 8 (LM)   H. P. Smith (1825–1898)

1   Jesus the Lord of love and life,
    draw near to bless this man and wife;
    as they are now in love made one,
    let your good will for them be done.

2   Give them each day your peace and joy,
    let no dark clouds these gifts destroy;
    in growing trust may love endure,
    to keep their marriage-bond secure.

3   As they have vowed to have and hold,
    each by the other be consoled;
    in wealth or want, in health or pain,
    till death shall part, let love remain.

4   Deepen, O Lord, their love for you,
    and in that love, their own renew;
    each in the other find delight,
    as lives and interests now unite.

5   Be to them both a guide and friend,
    through all the years their home defend;
    Jesus the Lord of love and life,
    stay near and bless this man and wife.

J. E. Seddon (1915–1983)
© Mrs. M. Seddon†

295

BISHOPGARTH   8 7 8 7 D

A. Sullivan (1842–1900)

1 *mf* Eternal Father, Lord of life,
you have in every nation
bestowed on loving man and wife
a share in your creation:
for this you formed the family,
the cradle of all living,
and that this wonder still should be,
today we make thanksgiving.

2 Help us to keep our sacred vow
of faithfulness, unbroken;
in all our words and works to show
each other love unspoken:
grant us your wisdom day by day;
through us may grace be flowing
to help our children on their way,
in truth and freedom growing.

3 *mp* And when the dangerous days come by
of doubt and fear and blindness,
then strengthen every family
with courage, faith and kindness;
mf that we, alert, your love may share
alike with friend and stranger,
and be the channels of your care,
and draw the sting of danger.

4 *f* May we with joy our tasks fulfil
as father, child, or mother,
that families may learn your will
in loving one another;
until at last that day may be
when all, the truth perceiving,
will know themselves your family,
in Jesus Christ believing.

H. C. A. Gaunt (1902–1983)
© Oxford University Press

Alternative tune: GOLDEN SHEAVES (291)

296

ST. MATTHIAS 8 8 8 8 8 8   W. H. Monk (1823–1889)

1 Father on high to whom we pray
   and lift our thankful hearts above,
   for all your mercies day by day,
   for gifts of hearth and home and love:
        protect them still beneath your care –
        Lord, in your mercy, hear our prayer.

2 O Christ who came as man to earth,
   and chose in Egypt's land to be
   a homeless child of alien birth,
   an exile and a refugee:
        for homeless people everywhere –
        Lord, in your mercy, hear our prayer.

3 Spirit divine, whose work is done
   in souls renewed and lives restored:
   strive in our hearts to make us one,
   one faith, one family, one Lord;
        till at the last one home we share –
        Lord, in your mercy, hear our prayer.

© Timothy Dudley-Smith (born 1926)

297

O PERFECT LOVE   11 10 11 10   J. Barnby (1838–1896)

1 Lord Jesus Christ, invited guest and saviour,
    with tender mercy hear us as we pray;
    grant our desire for those who seek your favour,
    come with your love and bless them both today.

2 Give them your strength
              for caring and for serving,
    give them your graces – faithfulness and prayer;
    make their resolve to follow you unswerving,
    make their reward your peace beyond compare.

3 Be their delight in joy, their hope in sorrow,
    be their true friend in pleasure as in pain;
    guest of today and guardian of tomorrow,
    turn humble water into wine again!

© Michael Perry (born 1942)†

298(i)

ENGLAND'S LANE 777777

English melody
arranged G. T. Shaw (1879–1943)
arrangement © Oxford University Press

1 For the beauty of the earth,
   for the beauty of the skies,
   for the love which from our birth
   over and around us lies,
       Christ our God, to you we raise
       this our sacrifice of praise.

2 For the beauty of each hour
   of the day and of the night,
   hill and vale, and tree and flower,
   sun and moon and stars of light,
       Christ our God . . .

3 For the joy of ear and eye,
   for the heart and mind's delight,
   for the mystic harmony
   linking sense to sound and sight,
       Christ our God . . .

298(ii)

ASHBURTON   777777   R. Jackson (1840–1914)

4 For the joy of human love,
   brother, sister, parent, child,
   friends on earth and friends above,
   pleasures pure and undefiled,
      Christ our God . . .

5 For each perfect gift divine
   to our race so freely given,
   joys bestowed by love's design,
   flowers of earth and fruits of heaven,
      Christ our God . . .

F. S. Pierpoint (1835–1917)

Alternative tunes: DIX (99)
          LUCERNA LAUDONIAE (27)
          NORICUM (27)

299

CORNWALL   886886   S. S. Wesley (1810–1876)

1   Great God, we praise the mighty love
     which urges us to rise above
     constricting doubts and fears;
     whose purpose is to set us free
     to live our lives creatively
     throughout the coming years.

2   We praise you for the love we see
     in man and wife and family,
     in friends and neighbours too;
     the love which nurtured us from birth,
     the love which teaches human worth
     and leads our minds to you.

3   We praise you most for love supreme
     which breaks through pain and death to stream
     in unrestricted light;
     which from Christ's resurrection dawn
     has shone, and never been withdrawn,
     to make our future bright.

4   For by your perfect love refined
     our own will not be undermined
     by futile guilt and shame;
     but through disaster, grief or strife
     we'll re-affirm the joy of life
     and glorify your name.

300

STRENGTH AND STAY   11 10 11 10

J. B. Dykes (1823–1876)

1 Happy the home that welcomes you, Lord Jesus,
   truest of friends, most honoured guest of all;
   where hearts and eyes are bright with joy
                   to greet you,
   your slightest wishes eager to fulfil.

2 Happy the home where man and wife together
   are of one mind, believing in your love;
   through love and pain, prosperity and hardship,
   through good and evil days your care they prove.

3 Happy the home, O loving friend of children,
   where they are given to you with hands of prayer;
   where at your feet they early learn to listen
   to your own words, and thank you for your care.

4 Happy the home where work is done
                   to please you,
   in tasks both great and small, that you may see
   each family doing all as you would wish them
   as members of your household, glad and free.

5 Happy the home that knows your healing comfort,
   where, unforgotten, every joy you share;
   until each one, their work on earth completed,
   comes to your Father's house to meet you there.

                   after K. P. J. Spitta (1801–1859)
                   © Honor Mary Thwaites (born 1914)

301

PENLAN 7 6 7 6 D

D. Jenkins (1848–1915)

1 His eyes will guide my footsteps
   when faltering age is near;
   his light will lift my darkness
   and help my ears to hear:
   in faith I claim the promise
   of Jesus' love for me;
   the Lord of hope and healing
   who made the blind to see.

2 When others fail or leave me,
   he comes to me in prayer;
   when life no longer needs me
   I find my comfort here:
   his promises are faithful –
   he lives, my closest friend;
   I know that he will keep me
   until my days shall end.

3 He comes when I am weary,
   in pain or in distress;
   with patient understanding
   and perfect gentleness:
   he was far more forsaken
   than I shall ever be;
   the presence of my saviour
   is everything to me.

302

ARNSTADT   5 5 8 8 5 5

Melody A. Drese (1620–1701)

1 Jesus, Lord, we pray,
   be our guest today!
   gospel story has recorded
   how your glory was afforded
   to a wedding day –
   be our guest, we pray.

2 Lord of love and life,
   blessing man and wife:
   as they stand, their need confessing,
   may your hand take theirs in blessing;
   you will share their life –
   bless this man and wife.

3 Lord of hope and faith,
   faithful unto death:
   let the ring serve as a token
   of a love sincere, unbroken,
   love more strong than death –
   Lord of hope and faith!

© Basil Bridge (born 1927)

303

JESUS LOVES ME   7 7 7 7 and refrain   Melody W. B. Bradbury (1816–1868)

1 Jesus loves me! – this I know,
   for the Bible tells me so;
   little ones to him belong –
   they are weak, but he is strong.
      Yes, Jesus loves me,
      yes, Jesus loves me,
      yes, Jesus loves me –
      the Bible tells me so.

2 Jesus loves me! – he who died,
   heaven's gate to open wide;
   he will wash away my sin,
   let his little child come in.
      Yes, Jesus loves me . . .

3 Jesus loves me! He will stay
   close beside me all the way,
   till he takes his little one
   to be with him near his throne.
      Yes, Jesus loves me . . .

Anna B. Warner (1824–1915)

304

IN MEMORIAM 86767676

J. Stainer (1840–1901)

1   There's a song for all the children
    that makes the heavens ring,
    a song that even angels
    can never, never sing;
    they praise the Lord their maker
    and see him glorified,
    but we can call him Saviour
    because for us he died.

2   There's a place for all the children
    where Jesus reigns in love,
    a place of joy and freedom
    that nothing can remove;
    a home that is more friendly
    than any home we know,
    where Jesus makes us welcome
    because he loves us so.

3   There's a friend for all the children
    to guide us every day,
    whose care is always faithful
    and never fades away;
    there's no-one else so loyal –
    his friendship stays the same;
    he knows us and he loves us,
    and Jesus is his name.

after A. Midlane (1825–1909)
© in this version Jubilate Hymns†

305

BUCKLAND 7 7 7 7   L. G. Hayne (1836–1883)

1 Loving Shepherd of your sheep,
keep your lamb, in safety keep;
nothing can your power withstand,
none can tear me from your hand.

2 Loving Lord, you chose to give
your own life that we might live;
and your hands outstretched to bless
bear the cruel nails' impress.

3 Help me praise you every day,
gladly serve you and obey;
like your glorious ones above,
happy in your precious love.

4 Loving Shepherd ever near,
teach your lamb your voice to hear;
let my footsteps never stray
from the true and narrow way.

5 Where you lead me I will go,
walking in your steps below;
till, before my Father's throne,
I shall know as I am known.

Jane Leeson (1809–1881)

For other hymns on this theme, see:
Sunday Themes index
  Section 48, The Family (p. xviii)

GOD'S WORLD:
WORK AND LEISURE:
ART AND SCIENCE

306

ANGELS' SONG   8 8 8 8 (LM)   Orlando Gibbons (1583–1625)

1   Forth in your name, O Lord, I go
    my daily labour to pursue;
    you, Lord, alone I choose to know
    in all I think or speak or do.

2   The task your wisdom has assigned
    here let me cheerfully fulfil;
    in all my work your presence find
    and prove your good and perfect will.

3   You I would set at my right hand
    whose eyes my inmost secrets view;
    and labour on at your command
    and offer all my work to you.

4   Help me to bear your easy yoke
    and every moment watch and pray;
    and still to things eternal look
    and hasten to that glorious day.

5   Gladly for you may I employ
    all that your generous grace has given;
    and run my earthly course with joy,
    and closely walk with you to heaven.

C. Wesley (1707–1788)
© in this version Jubilate Hymns†

Alternative tunes: DUKE STREET (542)
              DANIEL (133)

307

ANGEL VOICES   8 5 8 5 8 7

E. G. Monk (1819–1900)
descant © John Barnard (born 1948)†

Descant

5 Hon - our, glo - ry, might and me - rit for your works and

ways, — Fa - ther, Son — and Spi - rit,

God through _ end - less days; with the best that

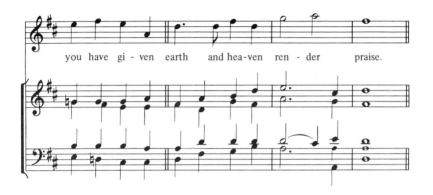

you have gi - ven earth and hea-ven ren - der praise.

1 *f* Angel voices ever singing
    round your throne of light,
angels' music ever ringing
    rests not day or night;
thousands only live to bless you
    and confess you Lord of might.

2 *mf* Lord beyond our mortal sight,
    in glory far away,
can it be that you delight
    in sinners' songs today;
may we know that you are near us
    and will hear us? Yes, we may!

3 Yes, we know your heart rejoices
    in each work divine,
using minds and hands and voices
    in your great design;
craftsman's art and music's measure
    for your pleasure all combine.

4 Here to you, great God, we offer
    praise in harmony,
and for your acceptance proffer
    all unworthily
hearts and minds and hands and voices
    in our choicest psalmody.

5 *f* Honour, glory, might and merit
    for your works and ways,
Father, Son and Holy Spirit,
    God through endless days;
with the best that you have given
    earth and heaven render praise.

F. Pott (1832–1909)
© in this version Jubilate Hymns†

308(i)

ARTHOG   8 5 8 5 8 7

G. Thalben-Ball (1896–1987)
© J. M. Thalben-Ball

1 Come to us, creative Spirit,
   in our Father's house;
   every human talent hallow,
   hidden skills arouse,
   that within your earthly temple,
   wise and simple,
   may rejoice.

2 Poet, painter, music-maker
   all your treasures bring;
   craftsman, actor, graceful dancer
   make your offering;
   join your hands in celebration:
   let creation
   shout and sing!

308(ii)

CREATIVE SPIRIT   8 5 8 5 8 7   © Norman Warren (born 1934)†

3 Word from God eternal springing
   fill our minds, we pray;
   and in all artistic vision
   give integrity:
   may the flame within us burning
   kindle yearning
   day by day.

4 In all places and forever
   glory be expressed
   to the Son, with God the Father
   and the Spirit blessed:
   in our worship and our living
   keep us striving
   for the best.

David Mowbray (born 1938)
© Stainer & Bell Ltd

Alternative tune: ANGEL VOICES (307)

309

COTTON WEAVER   8 7 8 7 8 7

Lancashire folk song
© arranged Robin Sheldon (born 1932)

small notes last verse.

1   Jesus is the Lord of living,
    all creation's bright array;
    hearts for loving and forgiving,
    ordered round of work and play –
        Jesus is the Lord of living,
        year by year and day by day.

2   Jesus is the man for others,
    love of God in man made plain;
    those whom God created brothers
    now in Christ are one again –
        Jesus is the man for others,
        ours the pardon, his the pain.

3   Jesus is the prince of glory,
    love and praise to him be shown:
    love for our salvation's story,
    praise for his eternal throne –
        Jesus is the prince of glory,
        glory be to him alone!

© Timothy Dudley-Smith (born 1926)

Alternative tune: ALLELUIA DULCE CARMEN (346)

310

BELMONT   8 6 8 6 (CM)   W. Gardiner (1770–1853)

1 From you all skill and science flow,
   all pity, care and love,
   all calm and courage, faith and hope –
   O pour them from above!

2 And share them, Lord, to each and all,
   as each and all have need;
   so let your gifts return to you
   in noble thought and deed.

3 And hasten, Lord, that perfect day
   when pain and death shall cease,
   and your just rule shall fill the earth
   with health and light and peace:

4 When ever green the grass shall be,
   and ever blue the skies,
   and our destruction shall no more
   deface your paradise.

C. Kingsley (1819–1875)
© in this version Word & Music†

Alternative tune: METZLER (178)

311

PERSONENT HODIE   6 6 6 6 6 5 5 3 9

Piae Cantiones 1582
arranged G. T. Holst (1874–1934)

Sing a-loud, loud, loud; sing a-loud,

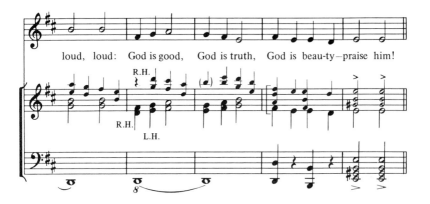

loud, loud: God is good, God is truth, God is beau-ty—praise him!

1 God is love – his the care,
 tending each, everywhere;
 God is love – all is there!
 Jesus came to show him,
 that we all might know him:
     Sing aloud, loud, loud;
     sing aloud, loud, loud:
     God is good,
     God is truth, God is beauty – praise him!

2 Jesus shared all our pain,
 lived and died, rose again,
 rules our hearts, now as then –
 for he came to save us
 by the truth he gave us:
     Sing aloud . . .

3 To our Lord praise we sing –
 light and life, friend and king,
 coming down love to bring,
 pattern for our duty,
 showing God in beauty:
     Sing aloud . . .

P. Dearmer (1867–1936)

312

RUSTINGTON   8 7 8 7 D

C. H. H. Parry (1848–1918)

1 Let creation bless the Father,
   glorify his name on high!
   In him all things have their being,
   live and move unceasingly:
   angels and archangels praise him,
   all the hosts of earth and heaven;
   power and might are his for ever
   who the Son to us has given.

2 Let creation greet in Jesus
   God the Father's promised Christ,
   seek and find in him salvation,
   Lamb of God once sacrificed;
   raised from death, in glory seated
   at the Father's side again:
   all God's children wait the moment
   for the coming of his reign.

3 Let creation bless the Spirit,
   present through all time and space
   in the work of life's unfolding,
   source of order, truth and grace:
   all the wealth of words and music,
   art and science, quest of faith –
   these are signs that God is with us,
   that his Spirit fills the earth.

4 Father, Son and Holy Spirit,
   undivided and supreme;
   filling all things, yet descending
   to our lives, to dwell within:
   through the church, let every creature
   learn to love and not destroy;
   let creation, reaching upward,
   scale the heights of peace and joy!

313

TALLIS' CANON   8 8 8 8 (LM)

Shortened form of melody by
Thomas Tallis (c. 1505–1585)
from T. Ravenscroft's *Psalter* 1621

1   O God, who gives to humankind
     a searching heart and questing mind:
     grant us to find your truth and laws,
     and wisdom to perceive their cause.

2   In all our learning give us grace
     to bow ourselves before your face;
     as knowledge grows, Lord, keep us free
     from self-destructive vanity.

3   Sometimes we think we understand
     all workings of your mighty hand;
     then through your Son help us to know
     those truths which you alone can show.

4   Teach us to joy in things revealed,
     to search with care all yet concealed;
     as through Christ's light your truth we find
     and worship you with heart and mind.

© Edward Burns (born 1938)

314(i)

PUTNEY   11 10 11 10

© Simon Beckley (born 1938)†
© arranged Noël Tredinnick (born 1949)†

1 O Lord of every shining constellation
   that wheels in splendour through the midnight sky:
   grant us your Spirit's true illumination
   to read the secrets of your work on high.

2 You, Lord, have made the atom's hidden forces;
   your laws its mighty energies fulfil:
   teach us, to whom you give such rich resources,
   in all we use, to serve your holy will.

3 O Life, awaking life in cell and tissue;
   from flower to bird, from beast to humankind:
   help us to trace, from birth to final issue,
   the sure unfolding purpose of your mind.

4 You, Lord, have stamped your image on your creatures
   and, though they mar that image, love them still:
   lift up our eyes to Christ, that in his features
   we may discern the beauty of your will.

5 Great Lord of nature, shaping and renewing,
   you made us more than nature's child to be;
   you help us tread, with grace our souls enduing,
   the road to life and immortality.

A. F. Bayly (1901–1984)
© Oxford University Press

314(ii)

HIGHWOOD   11 10 11 10

R. R. Terry (1865–1938)
© Oxford University Press

1   O Lord of every shining constellation
    that wheels in splendour through the midnight sky:
    grant us your Spirit's true illumination
    to read the secrets of your work on high.

2   You, Lord, have made the atom's hidden forces;
    your laws its mighty energies fulfil:
    teach us, to whom you give such rich resources,
    in all we use, to serve your holy will.

3   O Life, awaking life in cell and tissue;
    from flower to bird, from beast to humankind:
    help us to trace, from birth to final issue,
    the sure unfolding purpose of your mind.

4   You, Lord, have stamped your image on your creatures
    and, though they mar that image, love them still:
    lift up our eyes to Christ, that in his features
    we may discern the beauty of your will.

5   Great Lord of nature, shaping and renewing,
    you made us more than nature's child to be;
    you help us tread, with grace our souls enduing,
    the road to life and immortality.

A. F. Bayly (1901–1984)
© Oxford University Press

GOD'S WORLD:
HEALTH AND HEALING

ANGELUS   8 8 8 8 (LM)

Adapted from melody by G. Joseph
in *Heilige Seelenlust* Breslau 1657

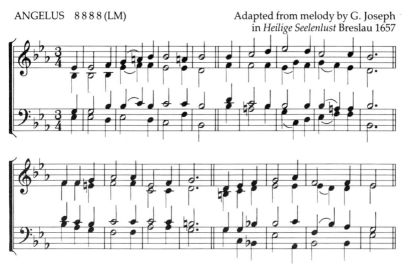

1 At evening, when the sun had set,
   the sick, O Lord, around you lay:
   in what distress and pain they met,
   but in what joy they went away!

2 Once more the evening comes, and we
   oppressed with various ills draw near;
   and though your form we cannot see,
   we know and feel that you are here.

3 O Saviour Christ, our fears dispel –
   for some are sick and some are sad,
   and some have never loved you well,
   and some have lost the love they had.

4 And none, O Lord, have perfect rest,
   for none are wholly free from sin;
   and those who long to serve you best
   are conscious most of wrong within.

5 O Saviour Christ, the Son of Man,
   you have been troubled, tested, tried;
   your kind but searching glance can scan
   the very wounds that shame would hide.

6 Your touch has still its ancient power;
   no word from you can fruitless fall:
   meet with us in this evening hour
   and in your mercy heal us all!

H. Twells (1823–1900)
© in this version Jubilate Hymns†

316(i)

ST. PAUL'S   6 6 8 6 (SM)   J. Stainer (1840–1901)

(ii)

MEMENTO   6 6 8 6 (SM)   G. P. Beaumont (1903–1970)

Unison

vv. 1-4   v. 5

316(iii)

SOUTHWELL (DAMON) 6 6 8 6 (SM)   W. Damon's *Psalmes* 1579

1 *mp* Lord Jesus, think of me
and take away my fear;
in my depression, may I be
assured that you are near.

2   Lord Jesus, think of me
by many cares oppressed;
in times of great anxiety
give me your promised rest.

3   Lord Jesus, think of me
when darker grows the day;
and in my sad perplexity
show me the heavenly way.

4   Lord Jesus, think of me
when night's dark shadows spread;
restore my lost serenity,
and show me light ahead.

5 *mf* Lord Jesus, think of me,
that when the night is past
I may the glorious morning see
and share your joy at last!

after Synesius (c.365–414)
A. W. Chatfield (1808–1896)
© in this version Jubilate Hymns†

317

THURLEIGH 848857

© Paul Edwards (born 1955)†

1 When Jesus walked upon this earth
his word was peace;
he spoke of fellowship with God,
he brought the prisoners release;
and all his caring
witnessed to his peaceful word.

2 When Jesus walked upon this earth
his touch was grace;
they came with stretcher, bandage, crutch
from east and west to seek his face;
and all his healing
witnessed to his gracious touch.

3 When Jesus walked upon this earth
his heart was love;
he came to take the humblest part,
among the penitent to move;
and all his serving
witnessed to his loving heart.

4 When Jesus walked upon this earth
   his name was king;
   to fight demonic powers he came
   and bring his glorious kingdom in:
   let all our praising
   witness to his kingly name!

318

MELCOMBE   8 8 8 8 (LM)   S. Webbe the elder (1740–1816)

1 We give God thanks for those who knew
   the touch of Jesus' healing love;
   they trusted him to make them whole,
   to give them peace, their guilt remove.

2 We offer prayer for all who go
   relying on his grace and power,
   to help the anxious and the ill,
   to heal their wounds, their lives restore.

3 We dedicate our skills and time
   to those who suffer where we live,
   to bring such comfort as we can
   to meet their need, their pain relieve.

4 So Jesus' touch of healing grace
   lives on within our willing care;
   by thought and prayer and gifts we prove
   his mercy still, his love we share.

319

SUTTON COMMON 6 6 8 6   © Norman Warren (born 1934)†

1   Heal me, hands of Jesus,
    and search out all my pain;
    restore my hope, remove my fear
    and bring me peace again.

2   Cleanse me, blood of Jesus,
    take bitterness away;
    let me forgive as one forgiven
    and bring me peace today.

3   Know me, mind of Jesus,
    and show me all my sin;
    dispel the memories of guilt
    and bring me peace within.

4   Fill me, joy of Jesus:
    anxiety shall cease
    and heaven's serenity be mine,
    for Jesus brings me peace!

© Michael Perry (born 1942)†

For other hymns on this theme, see:
Sunday Themes index
    Section 19, Christ the Healer (p. x)

GOD'S WORLD:
NATIONS, JUSTICE AND PEACE

320

IVYHATCH   8 8 8 8 (LM)   B. Luard-Selby (1853–1918)

1   Creator of the earth and skies,
    to whom all truth and power belong:
    grant us your truth to make us wise,
    grant us your power to make us strong.

2   We have not known you: to the skies
    our monuments of folly soar;
    and all our self-wrought miseries
    have made us trust ourselves the more.

3   We have not loved you: far and wide
    the wreckage of our hatred spreads;
    and evils wrought by human pride
    recoil on unrepentant heads.

4   We long to end this worldwide strife:
    how shall we follow in your way?
    Speak to us all your words of life
    until our darkness turns to day!

D. W. Hughes (1911–1967)
© Mary Hughes

Alternative tune: MELCOMBE (318)

321

CHRISTE SANCTORUM   10 11 11 6

Melody from *Paris Antiphoner* 1681
© arranged David Iliff (born 1939)†

1 Christ is the world's light, he and none other;
   born in our darkness, he became our brother –
   if we have seen him, we have seen the Father:
      Glory to God on high!

2 Christ is the world's peace, he and none other;
   no man can serve him and despise his brother –
   who else unites us, one in God the Father?
      Glory to God on high!

3 Christ is the world's life, he and none other;
   sold once for silver, murdered here, our brother –
   he, who redeems us, reigns with God the Father:
      Glory to God on high!

4 Give God the glory, God and none other;
   give God the glory, Spirit, Son and Father;
   give God the glory, God in man my brother:
      Glory to God on high!

F. Pratt Green (born 1903)
© Stainer & Bell Ltd

322

McKEE   8 6 8 6 (CM)

American melody
arranged H. T. Burleigh (1866–1949)
arrangement © sought

1   In Christ there is no east or west,
    in him no pride of birth;
    the chosen family God has blessed
    now spans the whole wide earth.

2   For God in Christ has made us one
    from every land and race;
    he reconciled us through his Son
    and met us with his grace.

3   It is by grace we are assured
    that we belong to him:
    the love we share in Christ our Lord,
    the Spirit's work within.

4   So brothers, sisters, praise his name
    who died to set us free
    from sin, division, hate and shame,
    from spite and enmity!

5   In Christ there is no east or west –
    he breaks all barriers down;
    by Christ redeemed, by Christ possessed,
    in Christ we live as one.

from a line by W. A. Dunkerley (1852–1941)
© Michael Perry (born 1942)†

Alternative tunes: ST. BERNARD (484)
                     ST. STEPHEN (483)

323

RINKART 67676666   Melody and bass J. S. Bach (1685–1750)

1   Christ is the world's true light,
     its captain of salvation,
     our daystar clear and bright,
     desire of every nation:
     new life, new hope awakes
     where we accept his way;
     freedom her bondage breaks
     and night is turned to day.

2   In Christ all races meet,
     their ancient feuds forgetting,
     the whole round world complete
     from sunrise to its setting:
     when Christ is known as Lord
     all shall forsake their fear,
     to ploughshare beat the sword,
     to pruning-hook the spear.

3   One Lord, in one great name
     unite all who have known you,
     cast out our pride and shame
     that hinder to enthrone you:
     the world has waited long,
     has laboured long in pain;
     to heal its ancient wrong
     come, Prince of peace, and reign!

G. W. Briggs (1875–1959)
© Oxford University Press

Alternative tune: NUN DANKET (33)

324

UNSER HERRSCHER   878787

J. Neander (1650–1680)
descant J. Dykes Bower (1905–1981)
descant © Hymns Ancient & Modern Ltd

4 Heal your chil-dren's war-ring mad-ness, bend our pride to your con-trol;

shame our wan-ton, self-ish glad-ness, rich in things and poor in soul.

Grant us wis-dom, grant us cour-age lest we miss your king-dom's goal.

1 God of grace and God of glory,
   come among us in your power;
   crown your ancient church's story,
   bring her bud to glorious flower.
        Grant us wisdom,
        grant us courage
   for the facing of this hour.

2 See the hosts of evil round us
   scorn your Christ, attack his ways!
   Fears and doubts too long have bound us –
   free our hearts to work and praise.
        Grant us wisdom,
        grant us courage
   for the living of these days.

3 Save us from weak resignation
   to the evils we deplore;
   let the search for your salvation
   be our glory evermore.
        Grant us wisdom,
        grant us courage
   serving you whom we adore.

4 Heal your children's warring madness,
   bend our pride to your control;
   shame our wanton, selfish gladness,
   rich in things and poor in soul.
        Grant us wisdom,
        grant us courage
   lest we miss your kingdom's goal.

H. E. Fosdick (1878–1969)
© Elinor F. Downs

325

ROXETH 7 7 7 4 D

© John Barnard (born 1948)†

1 God save and bless our nation,
    be all our inspiration;
in every generation
    make hatred cease:
let love and justice guide us,
    nor fear nor greed divide us;
come, Lord, and walk beside us –
    grant us your peace!

2 Lord, be our true confession,
    our hope, our faith's possession;
so hear our intercession,
    help us to stand:
not by the strength you gave us,
    nor pride that you forgave us,
but for your glory save us –
    God bless our land!

© Michael Perry (born 1942)†

326

NATIONAL ANTHEM 6 6 4 6 6 6 4

Melody from *Thesaurus Musicus*
London 1745

1 God save our gracious Queen,
  God bless and guard our Queen,
      long live the Queen!
  Guard us in liberty,
  bless us with unity,
  save us from tyranny:
      God save the Queen!

2 Lord be our nation's light,
  guide us in truth and right:
      in you we stand;
  give us your faithfulness,
  keep us from selfishness,
  raise us to godliness:
      God save our land!

3 Spirit of love and life,
  healing our nation's strife,
      on you we call:
  teach us your better way,
  grant us your peace today;
  God bless our Queen, we pray,
      God save us all!

unknown (c.1745)
© in this version Jubilate Hymns†

(see also traditional version, 592)

327

WINGS OF JOY   6 4 4 4 6

Descant

6 Help   us   to   do   your   will, ____   stir

Unison

heart and mind, and through our   grate-ful lives your world re - new.

1   Here, Lord, we come to you,
    the fount of life,
    eternal love:
    so in this faithless world
    our faith renew.

2   Lord, all things come from you
    for every life
    in every land:
    that we may share your gifts,
    our love renew.

3   Here, Lord, we bring to you
    each lonely life,
    each hungry child:
    in all who want and wait,
    their hope renew.

4   Lord, we confess to you
    our selfish ease,
    our lack of love:
    now through your Spirit's touch
    your church renew.

5   So, Lord, we come to you,
    we are all one,
    of humankind:
    so in our common need
    our life renew –

6   Help us to do your will,
    turn prayer to deed,
    stir heart and mind,
    and through our grateful lives
    your world renew.

J. E. Seddon (1915–1983)
© Mrs. M. Seddon†

328

LORD OF THE YEARS   11 10 11 10

© Michael Baughen (born 1930)†
© arranged David Iliff (born 1939)†

1   Lord, for the years your love has kept and guided,
    urged and inspired us, cheered us on our way,
    sought us and saved us, pardoned and provided:
    Lord of the years, we bring our thanks today.

2   Lord, for that word,
              the word of life which fires us,
    speaks to our hearts and sets our souls ablaze,
    teaches and trains, rebukes us and inspires us:
    Lord of the word, receive your people's praise.

3   Lord, for our land in this our generation,
    spirits oppressed by pleasure, wealth and care:
    for young and old, for commonwealth and nation,
    Lord of our land, be pleased to hear our prayer,

4   Lord, for our world;
              when we disown and doubt him,
    loveless in strength, and comfortless in pain,
    hungry and helpless, lost indeed without him:
    Lord of the world, we pray that Christ may reign.

5 Lord, in liv-ing power re - make us — self on the cross and Christ up-on the throne, for the fu - ture take us: Lord of our lives, to live for Christ a - lone.

5   Lord for ourselves; in living power remake us –
    self on the cross and Christ upon the throne,
    past put behind us, for the future take us:
    Lord of our lives, to live for Christ alone.

329

RHUDDLAN 8 7 8 7 8 7

Welsh traditional melody from
Musical Relicks of the Welsh Bards 1800

1 *mf* Judge eternal, throned in splendour,
Lord of lords and King of kings,
with your living fire of judgement
purge this realm of bitter things;
comfort all its wide dominion
with the healing of your wings.

2 *mp* Weary people still are longing
for the hour that brings release,
and the city's crowded clamour
cries aloud for sin to cease;
and the countryside and woodlands
plead in silence for their peace.

3 *mf* Crown, O Lord, your own endeavour,
cleave our darkness with your sword,
cheer the faint and feed the hungry
with the richness of your word;
cleanse the body of this nation
through the glory of the Lord.

H. S. Holland (1847–1918)
© in this version Jubilate Hymns†

330

GRACIOUS GOD   7 9 9 8 7

© Noël Tredinnick (born 1949)†

Let the peo - ples praise you, O God, let all the peo - ples praise you!

1 May God be gracious to us!
   that your way may be known upon earth
   and your power to save among nations:
       Let the peoples praise you, O God,
       let all the peoples praise you!

2 Let nations sing with gladness
   for your judgement of peoples is fair
   and you guide the earth's many nations:
       Let the peoples praise you . . .

3 See how the earth is fruitful,
   for the blessing of God has been given:
   may the whole wide world now revere him!
       Let the peoples praise you . . .

from *Deus Misereatur* (Psalm 67)
© Michael Baughen (born 1930)†

331

WAREHAM   8 8 8 8 (LM)

W. Knapp (1698–1768)
descant S. H. Nicholson (1875–1947)
descant © Hymns Ancient & Modern Ltd

3 He shall for-give your sins_un - told— re - mem-ber now his love_of old;

walk in his way, his word_a - dore, and_keep_his truth for ev - er-more.

1 Rejoice, O land, in God your Lord,
   obey his will and keep his word;
   for you the saints lift up their voice:
   fear not, O land, in God rejoice!

2 Glad shall you be, with blessing crowned,
   and joy and peace shall clothe you round;
   yes, love with you shall make a home
   until you see God's kingdom come.

3 He shall forgive your sins untold –
   remember now his love of old;
   walk in his way, his word adore,
   and keep his truth for evermore.

R. Bridges (1844–1930)
© in this version Jubilate Hymns†

332

LONDON NEW   8 6 8 6 (CM)   *Scottish Psalter* Edinburgh 1635

1 Remember, Lord, the world you made,
  for Adam's race to find
  the life of heaven on earth displayed,
  a home for humankind.

2 A home of peace: but war and strife
  and hatred we confess;
  where death is in the midst of life
  and children fatherless.

3 A home of freedom: yet the flame
  burns low for liberty;
  and few will serve in Jesus' name
  that all men may be free.

4 A home of plenty: clothed and fed
  our sturdy children play;
  while other children cry for bread
  not half the world away.

5 Renew our love, O Lord, and touch
  our hearts to feel and care
  that we who seem to have so much
  so little seem to share.

6 For those who have no prayers to say,
  who in despair are dumb,
  teach us to live as well as pray
  'O Lord, your kingdom come!'

© Timothy Dudley-Smith (born 1926)

333

HANOVER   10 10 11 11

A Supplement to the New Version 1708
probably by W. Croft (1678–1727)
descant A. Gray (1855–1935)

Descant

4 God's king-dom is come, the gift and the_ goal; in Je-sus be-

-gun, in hea-ven made whole. The heirs of the king-dom shall_

ans-wer his call; and_ all_things cry_'Glo-ry!' to God all_ in all.

1   The kingdom of God
        is justice and joy;
   for Jesus restores
        what sin would destroy.
   God's power and glory
        in Jesus we know;
   and here and hereafter
        the kingdom shall grow.

2   The kingdom of God
        is mercy and grace;
   the captives are freed,
        the sinners find place,
   the outcast are welcomed
        God's banquet to share;
   and hope is awakened
        in place of despair.

3   The kingdom of God
        is challenge and choice:
   believe the good news,
        repent and rejoice!
   His love for us sinners
        brought Christ to his cross:
   our crisis of judgement
        for gain or for loss.

4   God's kingdom is come,
        the gift and the goal;
   in Jesus begun,
        in heaven made whole.
   The heirs of the kingdom
        shall answer his call;
   and all things cry 'Glory!'
        to God all in all.

B. Rees (1911–1983)
© Mrs. M. E. Rees

334

ST. CECILIA 6 6 6 6   L. G. Hayne (1836–1883)

1 *mf* Your kingdom come, O God!
     your rule, O Christ, begin;
     break with your iron rod
     the tyrannies of sin.

2   Where is your reign of peace
     and purity and love?
     When shall all hatred cease
     as in the realms above?

3   When comes the promised time,
     the end of strife and war;
     when lust, oppression, crime
     and greed shall be no more?

4 *f*   O Lord our God, arise
     and come in your great might!
     revive our longing eyes
     which languish for your sight.

5 *mp* As rebels scorn your name
     and wolves devour your fold,
     by many deeds of shame
     we learn that love grows cold.

6 *mf* On nations near and far
     thick darkness gathers yet:
 f   arise, O Morning Star,
     arise and never set!

L. Hensley (1824–1905)

335

SAN ROCCO   8 6 8 6 (CM)   © Derek Williams (born 1945)

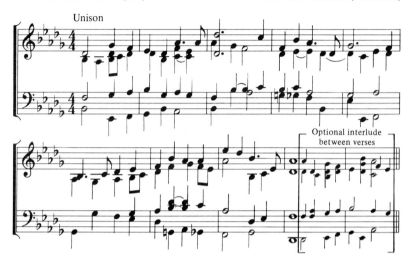

1 When Christ was lifted from the earth,
   his arms stretched out above,
   through every culture, every birth,
   to draw an answering love.

2 Still east and west his love extends,
   and always, near or far,
   he calls and claims us as his friends
   and loves us as we are.

3 Where generation, class or race
   divide us to our shame,
   he sees not labels but a face,
   a person and a name.

4 Thus freely loved, though fully known,
   may I in Christ be free
   to welcome and accept his own
   as Christ accepted me.

Brian Wren (born 1936)
© Oxford University Press

For other hymns on this theme, see:
Sunday Themes index
   Section 49, Those in Authority (p. xviii)

GOD'S CHURCH:
PRAISE AND ADORATION

336

JERUSALEM   8 8 8 8 D (DLM)   C. H. H. Parry (1848–1918)

Slow but with animation

Bring to the Lord a glad new song, chil-dren of
grace ex-tol your king; wor-ship and praise to God be -

crea - ture praise the Lord!

ff

1   Bring to the Lord a glad new song,
    children of grace extol your king;
    worship and praise to God belong –
    to instruments of music, sing!
    Let those be warned who spurn his name,
    nations and kings attend his word;
    God's justice shall bring tyrants shame:
    let every creature praise the Lord!

2   Praise him within these hallowed walls,
    praise him beneath the dome of heaven;
    by cymbals' sounds and trumpets' calls
    let praises fit for God be given:
    with strings and brass and wind rejoice –
    then, join his praise with full accord
    all living things with breath and voice:
    let every creature praise the Lord!

from Psalms 149 and 150
© Michael Perry (born 1942)†

337

SICILIAN MARINERS   8 7 8 7   Eighteenth-century Italian melody

1 Come, O Fount of every blessing,
   tune my heart to sing your grace:
   streams of mercy never ceasing
   call for songs of loudest praise.

2 Jesus sought me when a stranger
   wandering far away from God,
   and, to rescue me from danger,
   he redeemed me by his blood.

3 Prone to wander – Lord, I feel it;
   prone to leave the God I love!
   take my heart; in mercy seal it,
   guard it for the realms above.

4 Lord, my joy, my consolation,
   all my days to you belong;
   as your grace is my salvation,
   so your grace shall be my song.

R. Robinson (1735–1790)
© in this version Jubilate Hymns†

Alternative tune: HALTON HOLGATE (370)

338(i)

EPIPHANY HYMN   11 10 11 10   J. F. Thrupp (1827–1867)

1 *f* Brightest and best of the suns of the morning,
dawn on our darkness and come to our aid;
star of the east, the horizon adorning,
guide where our infant redeemer is laid!

2 *mf* What shall we give him, in costly devotion?
Shall we bring incense and offerings divine,
gems of the mountain and pearls of the ocean,
myrrh from the forest or gold from the mine?

3 Vainly we offer each lavish oblation,
vainly with gifts would his favour secure;
richer by far is the heart's adoration,
dearer to God are the prayers of the poor.

4 *f* Brightest and best of the suns of the morning,
dawn on our darkness and come to our aid;
star of the east, the horizon adorning,
guide where our infant redeemer is laid!

R. Heber (1783–1826)
© in this version Jubilate Hymns†

Alternative tune: SPEAN (207)

338(ii)

EPIPHANY   11 10 11 10 D

S. S. Wesley (1810–1876)

339(i)

SEVEN SEAS   8 8 8 8 (LM)   © David Peacock (born 1949)†

Unison

1 E - ter - nal light, __ shine __ in my heart, __ e -
2 E - ter - nal life, __ raise __ me from death, __ e -
3 Un - til by your most cost - ly __ grace, __ in -

- ter - nal hope, lift up my __ eyes; e - ter - nal power, be
- ter - nal bright-ness, help me __ see; e - ter - nal Spir - it,
- vi - ted by your ho - ly __ word, at last I come be -

my sup - port, __ e - ter - nal wis - dom, make me wise. __
give me breath, __ e - ter - nal Sa - viour, come to me: __
- fore your face __ to know you, my e - ter - nal God. __

339(ii)

SARAH RACHEL   8 8 8 8 (LM)   © Norman Warren (born 1934)†

1   Eternal light, shine in my heart,
      eternal hope, lift up my eyes;
      eternal power, be my support,
      eternal wisdom, make me wise.

2   Eternal life, raise me from death,
      eternal brightness, help me see;
      eternal Spirit, give me breath,
      eternal Saviour, come to me:

3   Until by your most costly grace,
      invited by your holy word,
      at last I come before your face
      to know you, my eternal God.

after Alcuin (c.735–804)
© Christopher Idle (born 1938)†

Alternative tune: O WALY WALY (82)

340

GOD OF GODS   87878887   © Christian Strover (born 1932)†

1 God of gods, we sound his praises,
  highest heaven its homage brings;
  earth and all creation raises
  glory to the King of kings:
  holy, holy, holy, name him,
  Lord of all his hosts proclaim him;
  to the everlasting Father
  every tongue in triumph sings.

2 Christians in their hearts enthrone him,
  tell his praises wide abroad;
  prophets, priests, apostles own him
  martyrs' crown and saints' reward.
  Three-in-One his glory sharing,
  earth and heaven his praise declaring,
  praise the high majestic Father,
  praise the everlasting Lord!

3 Hail the Christ, the king of glory,
  he whose praise the angels cry;
  born to share our human story,
  love and labour, grieve and die:
  by his cross his work completed,
  sinners ransomed, death defeated;
  in the glory of the Father
  Christ ascended reigns on high.

4 Lord, we look for your returning;
  teach us so to walk your ways,
  hearts and minds your will discerning,
  lives alight with joy and praise:
  in your love and care enfold us,
  by your constancy uphold us;
  may your mercy, Lord and Father,
  keep us now and all our days!

from *Te Deum*
© Timothy Dudley-Smith (born 1926)

341

RUSTINGTON 8787D

C. H. H. Parry (1848–1918)

1 *f* God, we praise you! God, we bless you!
God, we name you sovereign Lord!
Mighty King whom angels worship,
Father, by your church adored:
all creation shows your glory,
heaven and earth draw near your throne
singing 'Holy, holy, holy,'
Lord of hosts, and God alone!

2 *mf* True apostles, faithful prophets,
saints who set their world ablaze,
martyrs, once unknown, unheeded,
join one growing song of praise,
while your church on earth confesses
one majestic Trinity:
Father, Son, and Holy Spirit,
God, our hope eternally.

3 Jesus Christ, the king of glory,
everlasting Son of God,
mp humble was your virgin mother,
hard the lonely path you trod:
mf by your cross is sin defeated,
hell confronted face to face,
heaven opened to believers,
sinners justified by grace.

4 *f* Christ, at God's right hand victorious,
you will judge the world you made;
Lord, in mercy help your servants
for whose freedom you have paid:
raise us up from dust to glory,
guard us from all sin today;
King enthroned above all praises,
save your people, God, we pray.

from *Te Deum*
© Christopher Idle (born 1938)†

342(i)

LUCKINGTON 10 4 6 6 6 6 10 4

B. Harwood (1859–1949)
© Executors of the late B. Harwood

1 Let all the world in every corner sing,
    'My God and King!'
The heavens are not too high,
his praise may thither fly;
the earth is not too low,
his praises there may grow:
let all the world in every corner sing,
    'My God and King!'

342(ii)

HERBERT 10 4 6 6 6 6 10 4

H. A. Dyer (1878–1917)

2 Let all the world in every corner sing,
    'My God and King!'
The church with psalms must shout –
no door can keep them out;
but above all, the heart
must bear the longest part:
let all the world in every corner sing,
    'My God and King!'

G. Herbert (1593–1632)

343

RENDEZ À DIEU 9 8 9 8 D

L. Bourgeois (c. 1510–c. 1561)
Genevan Psalter 1551

1   New songs of celebration render
    to him who has great wonders done:
    Love sits enthroned in ageless splendour –
    come and adore the mighty one!
    He has made known his great salvation
    which all his friends with joy confess;
    he has revealed to every nation
    his everlasting righteousness.

2   Joyfully, heartily resounding,
    let every instrument and voice
    peal out the praise of grace abounding,
    calling the whole world to rejoice.
    Trumpets and organs, set in motion
    such sounds as make the heavens ring;
    all things that live in earth and ocean,
    make music for your mighty king.

3   Rivers and seas and torrents roaring,
    honour the Lord with wild acclaim;
    mountains and stones look up adoring
    and find a voice to praise his name.
    Righteous, commanding, ever-glorious,
    praises be his that never cease:
    just is our God, whose truth victorious
    establishes the world in peace.

from *Cantate Domino* (Psalm 98)
E. R. Routley (1917–1982)
© 1974 by Agape, Carol Stream, IL 60187.
International copyright secured,
all rights reserved, used by permission

344

WAS LEBET   12 10 12 10

Melody from MS by
J. H. Rheinhardt, Üttingen 1754

* Verses 1 and 5 only.

1   O worship the Lord in the beauty of holiness,
     bow down before him, his glory proclaim;
     with gold of obedience and incense of lowliness,
     kneel and adore him – the Lord is his name.

2   Low at his feet lay your burden of carefulness,
     high on his heart he will bear it for you,
     comfort your sorrows
              and answer your prayerfulness,
     guiding your steps in the way that is true.

3   Fear not to enter his courts in the slenderness
     of the poor wealth you would count as your own;
     truth in its beauty and love in its tenderness –
     these are the offerings to bring to his throne.

4   These, though we bring them
              in trembling and fearfulness,
     he will accept for the name that is dear;
     mornings of joy give for evenings of tearfulness,
     trust for our trembling and hope for our fear.

5   O worship the Lord in the beauty of holiness,
     bow down before him, his glory proclaim;
     with gold of obedience and incense of lowliness,
     kneel and adore him – the Lord is his name.

J. S. B. Monsell (1811–1875)

345

LLANFAIR   7 7 7 7 and Alleluias

R. Williams (1781–1821)

Unison

1 Praise the Lord, his glories show,   Alleluia,
  all that lives on earth below;   alleluia,
  angels round his throne above,   alleluia,
  all who see and share his love.   alleluia!

2 Earth to heaven and heaven to earth   Alleluia,
  tell his wonders, sing his worth;   alleluia,
  age to age, and shore to shore,   alleluia,
  praise him, praise him evermore.   alleluia!

3 Praise the Lord, his mercies trace,   Alleluia,
  praise his providence and grace;   alleluia,
  all that he for us has done,   alleluia,
  all he gives us in his Son!   alleluia!

H. F. Lyte (1793–1847)

346

ALLELUIA, DULCE CARMEN   8 7 8 7 8 7

S. Webbe the elder's
Essay on the Church Plain Chant 1782

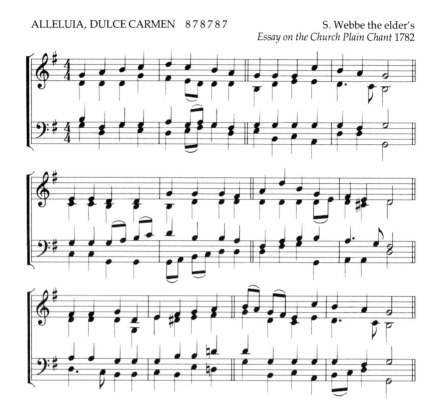

1 Praise we offer, Lord of glory,
  for your coming to our earth;
  called to be the child of Mary,
  taking manhood by your birth:
  praise we offer, Lord of glory
  for your coming to our earth.

2 Praise we offer, Lord of glory,
  for your passion and your death;
  called to suffer for us sinners,
  faithful till your final breath:
  praise we offer, Lord of glory
  for your passion and your death.

3 Praise we offer, Lord of glory,
  for your conquest of the grave;
  called to break the chains which bound us,
  rising, faithful souls to save:
  praise we offer, Lord of glory
  for your conquest of the grave.

4 Praise we offer, Lord of glory,
  for your Spirit's touch of power;
  called to give our lives new radiance,
  filling us from hour to hour;
  praise we offer, Lord of glory
  for your Spirit's touch of power.

5 Praise we offer, Lord of glory,
  for the hope which all our days,
  called to being by your labours,
  turns our thought to endless praise:
  praise we offer, Lord of glory –
  endless songs of joyful praise!

          after N. F. S. Grundtvig (1783–1872)
          © Michael Saward (born 1932)†

347

EIN' FESTE BURG   8 7 8 7 6 6 6 6 7

Later form of melody by
Martin Luther (1483–1546)

A more elaborate arrangement of this tune may be found at 522.

1 Rejoice today with one accord,
  sing out with jubilation;
  rejoice, and praise our mighty Lord –
  his arm has brought salvation:
  his works of love proclaim
  the greatness of his name;
  for he is God alone,
  his mercy he has shown –
  let all his saints adore him!

2 When in distress to him we cried,
  he heard our sad complaining:
  O trust in him, our faithful guide –
  his love is all-sustaining:
  to him our hearts shall raise
  triumphant songs of praise;
  now every voice shall sing,
  'O praise our God and king!'
  let all his saints adore him!

H. W. Baker (1821–1877)

348

PERSONENT HODIE 666665539

Piae Cantiones 1582
arranged G. T. Holst (1874–1934)

Shout for joy, joy, joy; shout for joy,

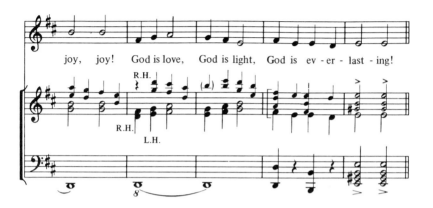

joy, joy! God is love, God is light, God is ev - er - last - ing!

1 Shout for joy, loud and long,
   God be praised with a song!
   to the Lord we belong –
   children of the Father,
   God the great life-giver!
        Shout for joy, joy, joy;
        shout for joy, joy, joy!
        God is love, God is light,
        God is everlasting!

2 By God's word all was made,
   heaven and earth, light and shade,
   nature's wonders displayed,
   man to rule creation
   from its first foundation.
        Shout for joy . . .

3 Yet our pride makes us fall!
   so Christ came for us all –
   not the righteous to call –
   by his cross and passion,
   bringing us salvation!
        Shout for joy . . .

4 Now has Christ truly risen
   and his Spirit is given
   to all those under heaven
   who will walk beside him,
   though they once denied him!
        Shout for joy . . .

349(i)

ONSLOW SQUARE   7 7 11 8   © David Wilson (born 1940)†

1 Sing a new song to the Lord, he to whom wonders be-long; re-joice in his tri-umph and tell of his power O sing to the Lord a new song!

vv. 1-3   v. 4

1 Sing a new song to the Lord,
   he to whom wonders belong;
   rejoice in his triumph and tell of his power –
   O sing to the Lord a new song!

2 Now to the ends of the earth
   see his salvation is shown;
   and still he remembers his mercy and truth,
   unchanging in love to his own.

3 Sing a new song and rejoice,
   publish his praises abroad;
   let voices in chorus, with trumpet and horn,
   resound for the joy of the Lord!

349(ii)

LITTLEBOURNE 7 7 11 8   © John Barnard (born 1948)†

4 Join with the hills and the
sea thunders of praise to prolong:
in jus‑tice he comes to the earth — O sing a new song!

4 Join with the hills and the sea
thunders of praise to prolong:
in judgement and justice he comes to the earth –
O sing to the Lord a new song!

from *Cantate Domino* (Psalm 98)
© Timothy Dudley-Smith (born 1926)

350

NORTHAMPTON   7 7 7 7

C. J. King (1859–1934)

1 *f* Songs of praise the angels sang,
      heaven with alleluias rang
      when creation was begun;
      when God spoke, and it was done.

2 *mf* Songs of praise announced the dawn
      when the Prince of peace was born;
      songs of praise arose when he
      captive led captivity.

3   Heaven and earth must pass away –
      songs of praise shall crown that day!
      God will make new heavens and earth –
      songs of praise shall greet their birth!

4 *mp* And must we alone be dumb
      till that glorious kingdom come?
  f No! the church delights to raise
      psalms and hymns and songs of praise.

5 *mf* Saints below, with heart and voice
      still in songs of praise rejoice;
      learning here by faith and love
      songs of praise to sing above.

6 *f* Hymns of glory, songs of praise,
      Father, these to you we raise;
      Saviour, Jesus, risen Lord,
      with the Spirit be adored.

J. Montgomery (1771–1854)

Alternative tune: CULBACH (258)

351

CARLISLE 6 6 8 6 (SM)

C. Lockhart (1745–1815)
descant S. H. Nicholson (1875–1947)
descant © Oxford University Press

Descant

5 Stand up and bless the Lord, the Lord your God a - dore;

stand up and praise his glo - rious name both now and ev - er - more.

1 Stand up and bless the Lord,
   you people of his choice;
   stand up and praise
             the Lord your God
   with heart and soul and voice.

2 Though high above all praise,
   above all blessing high,
   who would not fear
             his holy name,
   give thanks and glorify?

3 O for the living flame
   from his own altar brought,
   to touch our lips,
             our minds inspire,
   and wing to heaven
             our thought!

4 God is our strength and song,
   and his salvation ours;
   then be his love in Christ
             proclaimed
   with all our ransomed powers.

5 Stand up and bless the Lord,
   the Lord your God adore;
   stand up and praise
             his glorious name
   both now and evermore.

J. Montgomery (1771–1854)

352

ODE TO JOY   8 7 8 7 D   L. van Beethoven (1770–1827)

1 Sing to God new songs of worship –
all his deeds are marvellous;
he has brought salvation to us
with his hand and holy arm:
he has shown to all the nations
righteousness and saving power;
he recalled his truth and mercy
to his people Israel.

2 Sing to God new songs of worship –
earth has seen his victory;
let the lands of earth be joyful
praising him with thankfulness:
sound upon the harp his praises,
play to him with melody;
let the trumpets sound his triumph,
show your joy to God the king!

3 Sing to God new songs of worship –
let the sea now make a noise;
all on earth and in the waters
sound your praises to the Lord:
let the hills rejoice together,
let the rivers clap their hands,
for with righteousness and justice
he will come to judge the earth.

from *Cantate Domino* (Psalm 98)
© Michael Baughen (born 1930)†

353

DARWALL'S 148th   666688

J. Darwall (1731–1789)
descant S. H. Nicholson (1875–1947)
descant © Hymns Ancient & Modern Ltd

4 So take, my soul, your part; tri - umph in God a - bove, ___ and with a well - tuned heart sing out your songs of love: with joy pro- claim through all your days with cease - less praise his glo - rious name!

1   You holy angels bright
    who wait at God's right hand,
    or through the realms of light
    fly at your Lord's command:
        assist our song,
        or else the theme
        too high will seem
        for mortal tongue.

2   You faithful souls at rest,
    who ran this earthly race,
    and now from sin released
    behold the saviour's face:
        his praises sound
        and all unite
        in sweet delight
        to see him crowned.

3   You saints who serve below,
    adore your heavenly king,
    and as you onward go
    your joyful anthems sing:
        take what he gives
        and praise him still
        through good and ill,
        who ever lives.

4   So take, my soul, your part;
    triumph in God above,
    and with a well-tuned heart
    sing out your songs of love:
        with joy proclaim
        through all your days
        in ceaseless praise
        his glorious name!

R. Baxter (1615–1691)
© in this version Jubilate Hymns†

354

LAUDATE DOMINUM 10 10 11 11   C. H. H. Parry (1848–1918)

1 Sing praise to the Lord!
  praise him in the height;
  rejoice in his word
  you angels of light:
  you heavens, adore him
  by whom you were made,
  and worship before him
  in brightness arrayed.

2 Sing praise to the Lord!
  praise him upon earth
  in tuneful accord,
  you saints of new birth:
  praise him who has brought you
  his grace from above;
  praise him who has taught you
  to sing of his love.

3   Sing praise to the Lord!
     all things that give sound,
     each jubilant chord
     re-echo around:
     loud organs, his glory
     proclaim in deep tone,
     and sweet harp, the story
     of what he has done.

4   Sing praise to the Lord!
     thanksgiving and song
     to him be outpoured
     all ages along:
     for love in creation,
     for heaven restored,
     for grace of salvation,
     sing praise to the Lord!

     Amen, amen.

H. W. Baker (1821–1877)
© in this version Jubilate Hymns†

Unison

4 Sing praise to the Lord! thanks - giv - ing and

song to him be out - poured all a - ges a -

-long: for love in cre - a - tion, for_ hea - ven re -

- stored, for grace of sal - va - tion, sing praise to the Lord!

Harmony

A - men, _____ a - men.

For other hymns on this theme, see:
Sunday Themes index
  Section 33, The Ascension of Christ (p. xiii)

GOD'S CHURCH:
PENITENCE AND PRAYER

355

VIGILATE 7 7 7 3

W. H. Monk (1823–1889)

1 Christian, seek not yet repose,
cast your dreams of ease away:
you are in the midst of foes –
watch and pray.

2 Wicked forces, evil powers,
gathered in unseen array,
wait for your unguarded hours –
watch and pray.

3 Put your heavenly armour on,
wear it always night and day;
ambushed lies the evil one –
watch and pray.

4 Hear, above all, hear your Lord;
love him, serve him and obey,
treasure in your heart his word –
watch and pray.

5 Watch, as if on that alone
hung the issue of the day;
pray that victory shall be won –
watch and pray.

Charlotte Elliott (1789–1871)
© in this version Jubilate Hymns†

356

REPTON 8 6 8 8 6 extended   C. H. H. Parry (1848–1918)

An arrangement for choir of verse 3 is printed overleaf.

1 *mf* Dear Lord and Father of mankind,
forgive our foolish ways:
reclothe us in our rightful mind;
in purer lives your service find,
in deeper reverence praise,
in deeper reverence praise.

2 In simple trust like theirs who heard,
beside the Syrian sea,
the gracious calling of the Lord –
let us, like them, obey his word:
'Rise up and follow me,
rise up and follow me!'

3 *p* O sabbath rest by Galilee!
O calm of hills above,
when Jesus shared on bended knee
the silence of eternity
interpreted by love,
interpreted by love!

4 With that deep hush subduing all
our words and works that drown
the tender whisper of your call,
as noiseless let your blessing fall
as fell your manna down,
as fell your manna down.

5 Drop your still dews of quietness,
till all our strivings cease;
take from our souls the strain and stress,
and let our ordered lives confess
the beauty of your peace,
the beauty of your peace.

6 *mf* Breathe through the heats of our desire
your coolness and your balm;
let sense be dumb, let flesh retire,
speak through the earthquake, wind, and fire,
O still small voice of calm,
O still small voice of calm!

J. G. Whittier (1807–1892)
© in this version Jubilate Hymns†

Arrangement David Willcocks (born 1919)
© Oxford University Press

* Low notes should be sung if possible, particularly if this verse is unaccompanied.
If wished this arrangement may be accompanied by the version of Repton printed
on the previous page.

357

WOODLANDS 10 10 10 10

W. Greatorex (1877–1949)
© Oxford University Press

A descant may be found at 42.

1 Father and God, from whom our world derives
   all fatherhood in every family,
   we bow our knees for power to fill our lives –
   your mighty grace, your Spirit's energy:

2 For Christ to make his home in every heart,
   to plant and build us in his love's pure strength;
   to help his church to grasp in every part
   love's boundless height and depth, and breadth and length.

3 With all God's fulness let us now be filled,
   and know the splendour of his love unknown;
   expect the gifts a father gives his child
   and see the trophies that our king has won.

4 To God be praise! His power in us can do
   far more than we can ask or understand;
   through Jesus Christ who by his church makes new
   for every age the glories God has planned.

from Ephesians 3
© Christopher Idle (born 1938)†

Alternative tune: ELLERS (281)

358

KUM BA YAH   8 8 8 5

Traditional melody
© arranged David Peacock (born 1949)†

1 Father God in heaven,
    Lord most high:
hear your children's prayer,
    Lord most high:
hallowed be your name,
    Lord most high –
O Lord, hear our prayer.

2 May your kingdom come
    here on earth;
may your will be done
    here on earth,
as it is in heaven
    so on earth –
O Lord, hear our prayer.

3 Give us daily bread
    day by day,
and forgive our sins
    day by day,
as we too forgive
    day by day –
O Lord, hear our prayer.

4 Lead us in your way,
    make us strong;
when temptations come
    make us strong;
save us all from sin,
    keep us strong –
O Lord, hear our prayer.

5 All things come from you,
    all are yours –
kingdom, glory, power,
    all are yours;
take our lives and gifts,
    all are yours –
O Lord, hear our prayer.

from *The Lord's Prayer*
J. E. Seddon (1915–1983)
© Mrs. M. Seddon†

359

RIVAULX   8 8 8 8 (LM)   J. B. Dykes (1823–1876)

1   Father of heaven, whose love profound
     a ransom for our souls has found:
     before your throne we sinners bend –
     to us your pardoning love extend.

2   Almighty Son, incarnate Word,
     our prophet, priest, redeemer, Lord:
     before your throne we sinners bend –
     to us your saving grace extend.

3   Eternal Spirit, by whose breath
     the soul is raised from sin and death:
     before your throne we sinners bend –
     to us your living power extend.

4   Jehovah – Father, Spirit, Son –
     mysterious Godhead, Three-in-One:
     before your throne we sinners bend –
     grace, pardon, life to us extend.

E. Cooper (1770–1833)

360(i)

GOTT WILL'S MACHEN 8 7 8 7

J. L. Steiner (1668–1761)

(ii)

MARCHING 8 7 8 7

M. E. F. Shaw (1875–1958)

360(iii)

SUSSEX 8 7 8 7

English traditional melody
adapted R. Vaughan Williams (1872–1958)
arrangement © Oxford University Press

1 Father, hear the prayer we offer –
   not for ease our prayer shall be,
   but for strength that we may ever
   live our lives courageously.

2 Not for ever in green pastures
   do we ask our way to be;
   but the steep and rugged pathway
   may we tread rejoicingly.

3 Not for ever by still waters
   would we idly rest and stay;
   but would strike the living fountains
   from the rocks along our way.

4 Be our strength in hours of weakness,
   in our wanderings be our guide;
   through endeavour, failure, danger,
   Father, be there at our side.

Love M. Willis (1824–1908)

361

FARLEY CASTLE   10 10 10 10   H. Lawes (1596–1662)

1   God made me for himself, to serve him here
     with love's pure service and in filial fear;
     to show his praise, to labour for him now,
     then see his glory where the angels bow.

2   All needful grace was mine through his dear Son
     whose life and death my full salvation won;
     grace that would give me strength
               and hold me fast,
     grace that would seal and crown my work at last.

3   And I, poor sinner, threw it all away,
     lived for the work or pleasure of each day –
     as if no Christ had shed his precious blood,
     as if I owed no homage to my God.

4   O Holy Spirit, with your fire divine
     melt into tears this thankless heart of mine:
     teach me to love what once I seemed to hate
     and live to God before it is too late.

H. W. Baker (1821–1877)
© in this version Jubilate Hymns†

Alternative tune: ELLERS (281)

362

BILLING 8 6 8 6 (CM)

R. R. Terry (1865–1938)
© Search Press Ltd

1 How can we sing with joy to God,
   how can we pray to him,
   when we are far away from God
   in selfishness and sin?

2 How can we claim to do God's will
   when we have turned away
   from things of God to things of earth,
   and willed to disobey?

3 How can we praise the love of God
   which all his works make known,
   when all our works turn from his love
   to choices of our own?

4 God knows the sinful things we do,
   the Godless life we live,
   yet in his love he calls to us,
   so ready to forgive.

5 So we will turn again to God –
   his ways will be our ways,
   his will our will, his love our love,
   and he himself our praise!

Brian Foley (born 1919)
© Faber Music Ltd

Alternative tune: JACKSON (572)

363(i)

ABRIDGE 8 6 8 6 (CM)   I. Smith (1734–1805)

An arrangement of this tune (with the melody in the tenor) may be found at 374.

(ii)

OSWALD'S TREE 8 6 8 6 (CM)   H. Walford Davies (1869–1941)

363(iii)

IRISH   8 6 8 6 (CM)   Melody from *Hymns and Sacred Poems* Dublin 1749

1 Great Shepherd of your people, hear!
  your presence now display;
  as you have given a place for prayer,
  so give us hearts to pray.

2 Within these walls let holy peace
  and love and friendship dwell;
  here give the troubled conscience ease,
  the wounded spirit heal.

3 May we in faith receive your word,
  in faith present our prayers;
  and in the presence of our Lord
  unburden all our cares.

4 The hearing ear, the seeing eye,
  the contrite heart bestow;
  and shine upon us from on high,
  that we in grace may grow.

J. Newton (1725–1807)

364

CASWALL 6565   F. Filitz (1804–1876)

1 Jesus, stand among us
   in your risen power;
   let this time of worship
   be a hallowed hour.

2 Breathe the Holy Spirit
   into every heart;
   bid the fears and sorrows
   from each soul depart.

3 Thus with quickened footsteps
   we'll pursue our way,
   watching for the dawning
   of the eternal day.

W. Pennefather (1816–1873)

Alternative tune: NORTH COATES (384)

365

LISTENING 6 5 6 5

1 Listen to my prayer, Lord,
  hear my humble cry;
  when my heart is fainting,
  to your throne I fly.

2 In earth's farthest corner
  you will hear my voice:
  set me on your rock, Lord,
  then I shall rejoice.

3 You have been my shelter
  when the foe was near,
  as a tower of refuge
  shielding me from fear.

4 I will rest for ever
  in your care and love,
  guarded and protected
  as by wings above.

5 All that I have promised,
  help me to fulfil;
  and in all who love you
  work your perfect will.

6 May your truth and mercy
  keep me all my days;
  let my words and actions
  be my songs of praise!

from Psalm 61
J. E. Seddon (1915–1983)

366(i)

WOODLANDS   10 10 10 10

W. Greatorex (1877–1949)
© Oxford University Press

Unison

1   'Lift up your hearts!' We lift them to the Lord,
    and give to God our thanks with one accord;
    it is our joy and duty, all our days
    to lift our hearts in grateful thanks and praise.

2   Above the level of the former years,
    the mire of sin, the slough of guilty fears,
    the mist of doubt, the blight of love's decay –
    O Lord of light, lift all our hearts today!

366(ii)

YANWORTH   10 10 10 10

©John Barnard (born 1948)†

3   Above the swamps of subterfuge and shame,
    the deeds, the thoughts,
            that honour may not name,
    the halting tongue that dares not tell the whole –
    O Lord of truth, lift every Christian soul!

4   Above the storms that darken human life –
    pride, jealousy and envy, rage and strife;
    where cold mistrust
            holds friend and friend apart –
    O Lord of love, lift every Christian heart!

5   Then, with the trumpet call as Christ appears,
    'Lift up your hearts!' rings, pealing in our ears;
    still shall our hearts respond with full accord –
    'We lift them up, we lift them to the Lord!'

H. M. Butler (1833–1918)

367

ST. HUGH   8 6 8 6 (CM)   E. J. Hopkins (1818–1901)

1 Lord, teach us how to pray aright
   with reverence and with fear:
   though dust and ashes in your sight,
   we may, we must draw near.

2 We perish if we cease from prayer:
   O grant us power to pray;
   and when to meet you we prepare,
   Lord, meet us by the way.

3 O God of love, before your face
   we come with contrite heart
   to ask from you these gifts of grace –
   truth in the inward part:

4 Faith in the only Sacrifice
   that can for sin atone;
   to found our hopes, to fix our eyes
   on Christ, and Christ alone:

5 Patience to watch and weep and wait,
   whatever you may send;
   courage that will not hesitate
   to trust you to the end.

6 Give these, and then your will be done;
   thus, strengthened with all might,
   we through your Spirit and your Son
   shall pray, and pray aright.

J. Montgomery (1771–1854)

368

CAITHNESS   8 6 8 6 (CM)   *Scottish Psalter* Edinburgh 1615

1   O for a closer walk with God,
     the calm of sins forgiven,
     a light to shine upon the road
     that leads at last to heaven.

2   O gentle Messenger, return –
     return, O holy Dove;
     I hate the sins that made you mourn
     and grieved your heart of love.

3   Restore the happiness I knew
     when first I saw the Lord;
     refresh me with the radiant view
     of Jesus and his word!

4   From every idol I have known
     now set my spirit free;
     O make me worship you alone,
     and reign supreme in me.

5   So shall my walk be close with God,
     my wanderings be forgiven;
     so shall his light mark out the road
     that leads at last to heaven.

              W. Cowper (1731–1800)
              © in this version Jubilate Hymns†

Alternative tune: ST. HUGH (367)

369

WESTMINSTER 8 6 8 6 (CM)

J. Turle (1802–1882)
descant © Norman Warren (born 1934)†

6 Fa-ther of Je-sus, love's re-ward, great king up-on your throne,

what joy to see you as you are and know as I am known!

1 My God, how wonderful you are,
  your majesty how bright;
  how beautiful your mercy-seat
  in depths of burning light!

2 Creator from eternal years
  and everlasting Lord,
  by holy angels day and night
  unceasingly adored!

3 How wonderful, how beautiful
  the sight of you must be –
  your endless wisdom, boundless power,
  and awesome purity!

4 O how I fear you, living God,
  with deepest, tenderest fears,
  and worship you with trembling hope
  and penitential tears!

5 But I may love you too, O Lord,
  though you are all-divine,
  for you have stooped to ask of me
  this feeble love of mine.

6 Father of Jesus, love's reward,
  great king upon your throne,
  what joy to see you as you are
  and know as I am known!

F. W. Faber (1814–1863)
© in this version Jubilate Hymns†

370

HALTON HOLGATE   8 7 8 7

Later form of melody by
W. Boyce (1711–1779)
harmony from S. S. Wesley (1810–1876)

1 May the grace of Christ our saviour
  and the Father's boundless love,
  with the Holy Spirit's favour,
  rest upon us from above.

2 So may we remain in union
  with each other and the Lord,
  and possess, in sweet communion,
  joys which earth cannot afford.

J. Newton (1725–1807)

371

WAREHAM 8 8 8 8 (LM)

W. Knapp (1698–1768)
descant S. H. Nicholson (1875–1947)
descant © Hymns Ancient & Modern Ltd

5 Lord, we are few, but you are near; your arm can save, your ear can hear: break through the heavens, come quick-ly down, and make a thou-sand hearts your own!

1 *mf* Lord Jesus, when your people meet
   they come before your mercy-seat;
   where you are sought, you shall be found,
   and every place is holy ground.

2 Your presence, by no walls confined,
   is known within the humble mind;
   the meek will bring you where they come,
   and going take you to their home.

3 *f* Great Shepherd of your chosen few,
   your former mercies here renew;
   here to our waiting hearts proclaim
   the greatness of your saving name.

4 *mp* Here may we prove the power of prayer
   to strengthen faith and sweeten care;
   to teach our faint desires to rise
   and bring all heaven before our eyes.

5 *mf* Lord, we are few, but you are near;
   your arm can save, your ear can hear:
   f break through the heavens, come quickly down,
   and make a thousand hearts your own!

W. Cowper (1731–1800)

372

SONG 67   8 6 8 6 (CM)   Later form of melody in E. Prys' *Psalter* 1621
                                          Bass by Orlando Gibbons (1583–1625)

1 Prayer is the soul's
             supreme desire
   expressed in thought or word;
   the burning of a hidden fire,
   a longing for the Lord.

2 Prayer is the simplest sound
             we teach
   when children learn God's name;
   and yet it is the noblest speech
   that human lips can frame.

3 Prayer is the secret battleground
   where victories are won;
   by prayer the will of God is found
   and work for him begun.

4 Prayer is the Christian's
             vital breath,
   the Christian's native air,
   our watchword
             at the gates of death;
   we enter heaven with prayer.

5 Prayer is the church's
             glorious song,
   our task and joy supreme;
   we name our Lord
             in every tongue,
   and praise is all our theme.

6 Jesus, by whom we come
             to God,
   the true and living way,
   the humble path of prayer
             you trod,
   Lord, teach us how to pray.

J. Montgomery (1771–1854)
© in this version Jubilate Hymns✝

373(i)

BLAENWERN 8 7 8 7 D   W. P. Rowlands (1860–1937)

(ii)

CONVERSE 8 7 8 7 D   C. C. Converse (1832–1918)

1 What a friend we have in Jesus,
   all our sins and griefs to bear;
   what a privilege to carry
   everything to God in prayer!
   O what peace we often forfeit,
   O what needless pain we bear,
   all because we do not carry
   everything to God in prayer.

2 Have we trials and temptations,
   is there trouble anywhere?
   We should never be discouraged:
   take it to the Lord in prayer.
   Can we find a friend so faithful
   who will all our sorrows share?
   Jesus knows our every weakness –
   take it to the Lord in prayer.

3 Are we weak and heavy-laden,
   burdened with a load of care?
   Jesus is our mighty saviour:
   he will listen to our prayer.
   Do your friends despise, forsake you?
   take it to the Lord in prayer;
   in his arms he will enfold you
   and his love will shield you there.

J. M. Scriven (1819–1886)

374(i)

ABRIDGE 8 6 8 6 (CM)

I. Smith (1734–1805)

Arrangement by G. T. Shaw (1879–1943)
© Novello & Co Ltd

Melody in Tenor

374(ii)

BALLERMA   8 6 8 6 (CM)   F. H. Barthélémon (1741–1808)

1 O Lord our guardian and our guide,
   be near us when we call;
   uphold us when our footsteps slide,
   and raise us when we fall.

2 The world, the flesh and Satan dwell
   around the path we tread;
   O save us from the snares of hell,
   Deliverer from the dead!

3 And if we tempted are to sin,
   and evil powers are strong;
   be present, Lord, keep watch within
   and save our souls from wrong.

4 Still let us always watch and pray,
   and know that we are frail;
   that if the tempter cross our way,
   yet he shall not prevail.

from Psalm 17
I. Williams (1802–1865)
© in this version Jubilate Hymns†

For other hymns on this theme, see:

GOD'S CHURCH:
THE LORD'S DAY

375

MADRID 888888 W. Matthews (1759–1830)

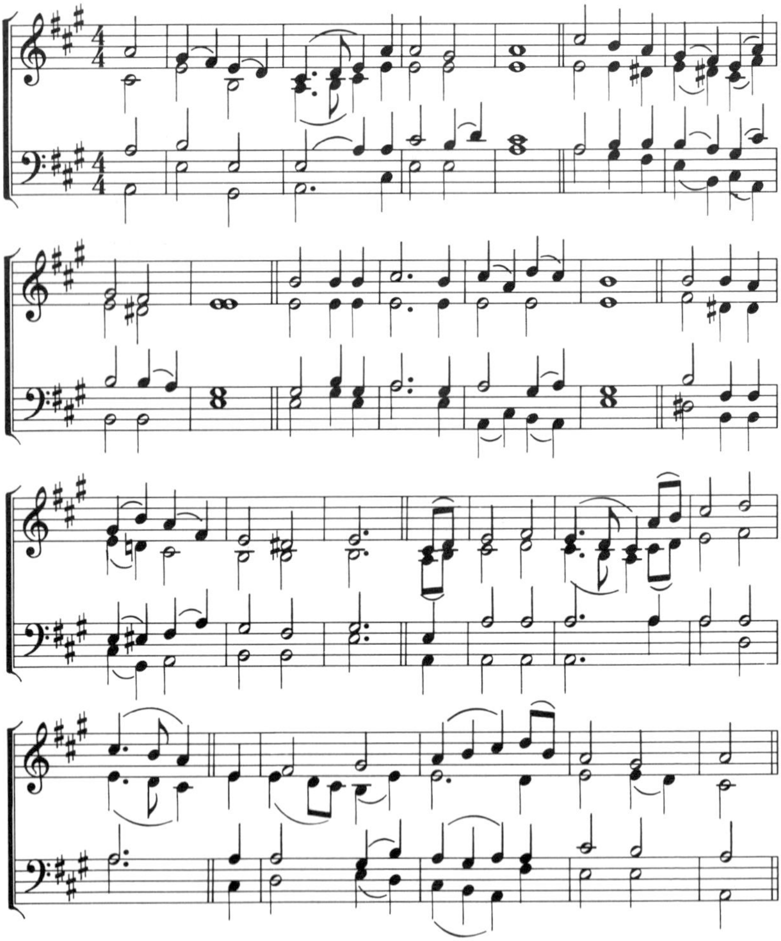

1   Come, let us with our Lord arise!
     our Lord who made both earth and skies,
     who died to save the world he made
     and rose triumphant from the dead:
     he rose, the prince of life and peace,
     and stamped the day for ever his.

2   This is the day the Lord has made
     that all may see his love displayed,
     may feel his resurrection's power
     and rise again to fall no more,
     in perfect righteousness renewed
     and filled with all the life of God.

3   Then let us render him his own,
     with solemn prayer approach the throne,
     with meekness hear the gospel word,
     with thanks his dying love record,
     our joyful hearts and voices raise
     and fill his courts with songs of praise.

C. Wesley (1707–1788)

376

GALILEE   8 8 8 8 (LM)   P. Armes (1836–1908)

1 First of the week and finest day,
   when God commanded light to shine:
   cast darkness and its works away
   to celebrate with bread and wine!

2 First of the week was Easter morn
   when Christ the Lord from death was raised;
   new life, fresh hope that day was born
   and God in heaven and earth was praised.

3 First of the week the Spirit came
   to fill the church with grace and power;
   the rushing wind and tongues of flame
   were heralds of that promised hour.

4 First of the week we set aside
   to meet, to learn, to give, to pray;
   to spread Christ's gospel far and wide –
   in truth, this is the Lord's own day!

© David Mowbray (born 1938)†

377

DEEP HARMONY   8 8 8 8 (LM)   H. Parker (1854–1928)

1   Sweet is the work, my God, my King,
    to praise your name, give thanks and sing;
    to show your love by morning light,
    and talk of all your truth at night.

2   Sweet is the day, the first and best,
    on which I share your sacred rest;
    so let my heart in tune be found,
    like David's harp of joyful sound.

3   My heart shall triumph in the Lord
    and bless his works, and bless his word:
    God's works of grace, how bright they shine –
    how deep his counsels, how divine!

4   Soon I shall see and hear and know
    all I desired on earth below,
    and all my powers for God employ
    in that eternal world of joy.

                                        I. Watts (1674–1748)

378

STEEPLE BELLS 9 8 9 8   © Norman Warren (born 1934)†

1 Ring from your steep-le, bells of glad - ness!
this is the day the world was born;
God's voice rang out a-cross the dark - ness,
light filled the sky that pri - mal

morn.

1 Ring from your steeple, bells of gladness!
   this is the day the world was born;
   God's voice rang out across the darkness,
   light filled the sky that primal morn.

2 Ring from your steeple, bells of victory!
   this is the day death's sting was drawn;
   God's voice rang out, the tomb was empty,
   hope sprang alive that Easter morn.

3 Ring from your steeple, bells of power!
   this is the day when, at the dawn,
   God's voice rang out through wind and fire,
   hearts became strong that Whitsun morn.

4 Ring from your steeple, bells of heaven!
   this is the day when none shall mourn;
   God's voice rings out this one-in-seven,
   joy fills his church this Sunday morn.

379

BISHOPTHORPE 8 6 8 6 (CM)

J. Clarke (c. 1674–1707)

1 This is the day the Lord has made,
  he calls the hours his own:
  let heaven rejoice, let earth be glad,
  and praise surround the throne.

2 Today he rose and left the dead,
  and Satan's empire fell;
  today the saints his triumphs spread,
  and all his wonders tell.

3 Hosanna to the anointed king,
  to David's holy Son!
  help us, O Lord; descend and bring
  salvation from your throne.

4 Blessed be the Lord, who freely came
  to save our sinful race;
  he comes, in God his Father's name,
  with words of truth and grace.

5 Hosanna in the highest strains
  the church on earth can raise!
  the highest heaven in which he reigns
  shall give him nobler praise.

I. Watts (1674–1748)

380

DOMINICA 6 6 8 6 (SM)   H. S. Oakeley (1830–1903)

1 *f* This is the day of light –
       let there be light today!
       Arise, O Christ, to end our night
       and chase its gloom away.

2 *mp* This is the day of rest –
        our inner strength renew;
        on lives by many cares oppressed
        send your refreshing dew.

3 *p* This is the day of peace –
       with peace our spirits fill;
       bid all the blasts of discord cease,
       the waves of strife be still.

4 *mp* This is the day of prayer –
        let earth to heaven draw near!
        Lift up our hearts to seek you there;
        come down to meet us here.

5 *f* This is the first of days:
       come, with your living breath
       and wake dead souls to love and praise,
       O Victor over death!

                              J. Ellerton (1826–1893)

For other hymns on this theme, see:
Sunday Themes index
    Section 28 (1), The Upper Room (p. xii)
Song Section
    This is the day, this is the day (S.28)

GOD'S CHURCH:
CHRISTIAN INITIATION

381

SILCHESTER 5 5 8 D

W. K. Stanton (1891–1978)
© Oxford University Press

1 Baptized in water,
sealed by the Spirit,
cleansed by the blood of Christ our king;
heirs of salvation,
trusting his promise –
faithfully now God's praise we sing.

2 Baptized in water,
sealed by the Spirit,
dead in the tomb with Christ our king;
one with his rising,
freed and forgiven
thankfully now God's praise we sing.

3 Baptized in water,
sealed by the Spirit,
marked with the sign of Christ our king;
born of one Father,
we are his children –
joyfully now God's praise we sing.

© Michael Saward (born 1932)†

Alternative tune: SCHÖNSTER HERR JESU (209)

382

PASSFIELD 557D

© Simon Beckley (born 1938)†
© arranged Noël Tredinnick (born 1949)†

1 Born of the water,
born of the Spirit –
    called by the wind and the fire;
sealed with his promise,
we shall inherit
    more than the most we desire.

2 One through redemption,
one with the Father –
    children of grace and of heaven;
joyfully sharing
faith with each other,
    sinners whose sins are forgiven.

3 Glory, all glory,
glory to Jesus –
    die we in him and we live!
friends for his service,
heirs to the treasures
    God, and God only, can give.

© Michael Perry (born 1942)†

383

SALVE FESTA DIES Irregular
R. Vaughan Williams (1872–1958)

(This refrain is repeated after verses 1 to 3) © Oxford University Press

Unison

Chris-tians, lift up your hearts, and make this a day of re - joi - cing;

God is our strength and song — glo - ry and praise to his name!

1 Here God's life - giv - ing word once more is proclaimed to his peo - ple,

up - lift-ing those who are down, chal-leng-ing all with its truth:

Repeat refrain

2 All those bap-tized in-to Christ share the glo-ry of his re-sur-rec-tion,
3 Summoned by Christ's command his people draw near to his ta-ble,

dy-ing with him un-to sin, walk-ing in new - ness of life:
glad-ly to greet their Lord known in the break - ing of bread:

Repeat refrain

© John Bowers (born 1923)

384

NORTH COATES 6 5 6 5

T. R. Matthews (1826–1910)

1 Father, now behold us
and this child, we pray;
in your love enfold us,
wash our sins away.

2 Christ's eternal blessing
for this life we claim:
faith, by ours, professing;
signed in Jesus' name.

3 By the Spirit tended,
childhood grow to youth;
from all ill defended,
full of grace and truth.

4 God of all creation,
stoop from heaven's throne,
and by Christ's salvation
make this child your own!

© Timothy Dudley-Smith (born 1926)

385

OBIIT 878787

W. Parratt (1841–1924)

1 God the Father, name we treasure,
   each new generation draws
   from the past that you have given
   for the future that is yours:
   may these children, in your keeping,
   love your ways, obey your laws.

2 Christ, the name that Christians carry;
   Christ, who from the Father came,
   calling us to share your sonship,
   for these children grace we claim:
   may they be your true disciples,
   yours in deed as well as name.

3 Holy Spirit, from the Father
   on the friends of Jesus poured:
   may our children share those graces
   promised to them in the word,
   and their gifts find rich fulfilment,
   dedicated to our Lord.

© Basil Bridge (born 1927)

386

BINCHESTER 8 6 8 6 (CM)

W. Croft (1678–1727)

1 Have you not heard? Do you not know
  that Christ has died for you?
  that through his death he conquered death
  to pay the ransom due.

2 What shall we say? How shall we live?
  since through his word revealed
  he calls on us to die with him,
  deep in his tomb concealed.

3 Is there no hope? Is there no joy?
  Yes! Bursting from the grave,
  baptized in him we rise to life
  freed by his power to save.

4 One in his death, one in his life,
  in baptism restored,
  we trust his promise, know his power
  and serve our mighty Lord.

387

ACH, GOTT UND HERR 8 7 8 7

Neu-Leipziger Gesangbuch 1682
arranged J. S. Bach (1685–1750)

1   My trust I place in God's good grace
     his promises believing,
     for now I see Christ died for me
     my pardon thus achieving.

2   By water's sign this gift is mine,
     my guilt has gone for ever;
     for Christ the Son and I are one –
     this bond no power can sever.

3   His word is true, my heart is new,
     my life is joy unbounded,
     for he will save me from the grave
     while Satan stands confounded.

4   So now I sing of Christ my king,
     his holy name confessing
     who by this deed gives all I need
     and fills me with his blessing.

© Michael Saward (born 1932)†

388

FOSSEBRIDGE 8 8 8 8 (LM)

© John Barnard (born 1948)†

1   This is the truth which we proclaim,
    God makes a promise firm and sure;
    marked by this sign made in his name,
    here, for our sickness, God's own cure.

2   This is the grave in which we lie:
    pierced to the heart by sin's sharp sword,
    risen with Christ, to self we die
    and live to praise our reigning Lord.

3   This is the sacrament of birth:
    sealed by a Saviour's death for sin,
    trust in his mercy all on earth,
    open your hearts and let him in!

4   This is the covenant of grace –
    God to the nations shows his love;
    people of every tribe and race,
    born by his Spirit from above.

5   This is the badge we proudly wear:
    washed by our God, the Three-in-One;
    welcomed in fellowship, we share
    hope of eternal life begun.

© Michael Saward (born 1932)†

Alternative tune: FULDA (16)

389

ENGELBERG   10 10 10 4   C. V. Stanford (1852–1924)

1   We know that Christ is raised and dies no more;
    embraced by futile death he broke its hold,
    and our despair he turned to blazing joy:
        Alleluia!

2   We share by water in his saving death;
    this union brings to being one new cell,
    a living and organic part of Christ:
        Alleluia!

3   The Father's splendour clothes the Son with life,
    the Spirit's fission shakes the church of God;
    baptized we live with God the Three-in-One:
        Alleluia!

4   A new creation comes to life and grows
    as Christ's new body takes on flesh and blood;
    the universe restored and whole will sing:
        Alleluia! (Amen.)

390

ST. BOTOLPH 8 6 8 6 (CM)

G. A. Slater (1896–1979)
© Oxford University Press

1 Now through the grace of God we claim
  this life to be his own,
  baptized with water in the name
  of Father, Spirit, Son.

2 For Jesus Christ the crucified,
  who broke the power of sin,
  now lives to plead for those baptized
  in unity with him.

3 So let us act upon his word,
  rejoicing in our faith,
  until we rise with Christ our Lord
  and triumph over death!

© Michael Perry (born 1942)†

For other hymns on this theme, see:
Sunday Themes index
  Section 37 (1), The Life of the Baptized (p. xv)

GOD'S CHURCH:
HOLY COMMUNION

391

ISTE CONFESSOR   11 11 11 5

Melody from *Poitiers Antiphoner* 1746
as in *The Australian Hymn Book* 1977

1 All-holy Father, king of endless glory,
   faithful creator, look on your creation:
   singing we praise you in this banquet given
        for our salvation.

2 Now we remember how your servant Jesus
   fed his companions, bread and wine supplying;
   gave them his presence in these holy tokens,
        pledge of his dying.

3 Father, we bless you in this celebration:
   praise for the body broken for our healing,
   praise for the sacred blood of our redemption,
        mercy revealing.

4 Hear our petitions which we bring before you:
   guard us in weakness – comfort the forsaken,
   strengthen the tempted; give to all the faithful
        victory unshaken.

© Angela Tilby (born 1950)

Alternative tune: CLOISTERS (529)

392(i)

UNDE ET MEMORES 10 10 10 10 10 10   W. H. Monk (1823–1889)

1 *mf* And now, O Father, mindful of the love
        which bought us once for all on Calvary's tree,
        and having with us Christ who reigns above,
        we celebrate with joy for all to see
        that only offering perfect in your eyes:
        the one true, pure, immortal sacrifice.

2 *mp* Look, Father, look on his anointed face,
        and only look on us as found in him;
        look not on our misusings of your grace,
        our prayer so feeble and our faith so dim;
        for, set between our sins and their reward,
        we see the cross of Christ, your Son, our Lord.

392(ii)

SONG 1   10 10 10 10 10 10 10

Orlando Gibbons (1583–1625)
arrangement attributed to R. Vaughan Williams (1872–1958)
arrangement © Oxford University Press

3   And so we come: O draw us to your feet,
     most patient Saviour, who can love us still;
     and by this food, so awesome and so sweet,
     deliver us from every touch of ill;
 mf for your glad service, Master, set us free,
     and make of us what you would have us be.

W. Bright (1824–1901)
© in this version Jubilate Hymns†

393

SOMMERLIED 5 6 6 4

C. Bonner (1859–1938)
© National Christian Education Council

Unison

1   As we break the bread
    and taste the life of wine,
    we bring to mind our Lord,
    man of all time.

2   Grain is sown to die;
    it rises from the dead,
    becomes through human toil
    our common bread.

3   Pass from hand to hand
    the living love of Christ!
    machine and man provide
    bread for this feast.

4   Jesus binds in one
    our daily life and work;
    he is of all mankind
    symbol and mark.

5   Having shared the bread
    that died to rise again,
    we rise to serve the world,
    scattered as grain.

Fred Kaan (born 1929)
© 1968 Galliard Ltd,
Stainer & Bell Ltd

394

LIEBSTER JESU 7 8 7 8 8 8

J. R. Ahle (1625–1673)
arranged J. S. Bach (1685–1750)

1 At the supper, Christ the Lord
gathered friends and said the blessing;
bread was broken, wine was poured,
faith in Israel's God expressing:
signs of the forthcoming passion,
tokens of a great salvation.

2 After supper, Jesus knelt,
taking towel and bowl of water;
washing the disciples' feet,
servant now as well as master:
'You,' said he, 'have my example –
let your way of life be humble!'

3 In the fellowship of faith
Christ himself with us is present;
supper of the Lord in truth,
host and master all-sufficient!
From this table, gladly sharing,
send us, Lord, to love and caring.

395

AUTHOR OF LIFE   6 6 6 6 8 8   J. Stainer (1840–1901)

1 Author of life divine,
    we see your table spread
    with drink – the mystic wine,
    and food – the eternal bread:
    preserve the life that you have given
    that we may eat with you in heaven.

2 Our hungry souls sustain
    with fresh supplies of love,
    till all your life we gain
    and all your strength we prove;
    till we receive your perfect grace
    and rise to see you face to face.

from J. and C. Wesley's
Hymns on the Lord's Supper 1745
© in this version Jubilate Hymns†

396

RENDEZ À DIEU 9 8 9 8 D

L. Bourgeois (c. 1510–c. 1561)
Genevan Psalter 1551

1 Bread of the world in mercy broken, wine of the
soul in mercy shed; by whom the words of life were spoken
and in whose death our sins are dead: 2 Look on the heart by sorrow
broken, look on the tears by sinners shed, and make your
feast to us the token that by your grace our souls are fed.

R. Heber (1783–1826)

397(i)

RUSHFORD   8 8 8 8 (LM)

H. G. Ley (1887–1962)

© Chappell Music Ltd/International Music Publications

1   Behold the eternal King and Priest
    here brings for me the bread and wine;
    himself the master of the feast,
    his flesh and blood the food divine.

2   Lord Christ, I come, I hear your call,
    I eat and drink at your command;
    low at your feet I humbly fall –
    O touch me with your nail-pierced hand!

3   Wash clean my heart and make it new,
    to beat with love for you alone;
    so let me find my life in you,
    and have no will except your own.

4   In strength or weakness, be my rest,
    in joy or sorrow, be my friend:
    so all my life I shall be blessed,
    and by your mercy, gain my end.

unknown (c.1887)
© in this version Jubilate Hymns†

397(ii)

MELCOMBE   8 8 8 8 (LM)

S. Webbe the elder (1740–1816)

1   Behold the eternal King and Priest
    here brings for me the bread and wine;
    himself the master of the feast,
    his flesh and blood the food divine.

2   Lord Christ, I come, I hear your call,
    I eat and drink at your command;
    low at your feet I humbly fall –
    O touch me with your nail-pierced hand!

3   Wash clean my heart and make it new,
    to beat with love for you alone;
    so let me find my life in you,
    and have no will except your own.

4   In strength or weakness, be my rest,
    in joy or sorrow, be my friend:
    so all my life I shall be blessed,
    and by your mercy, gain my end.

unknown (c.1887)
© in this version Jubilate Hymns†

398(i)

ARFON 777777

Traditional Welsh or Breton melody
arranged H. Davies (1844–1907)

1 Bread of heaven, on you we feed,
   for your flesh is food indeed;
   always may our souls be fed
   with this true and living bread;
   day by day our strength supplied
   through your life, O Christ, who died.

2 Vine of heaven, your precious blood
   seals today our peace with God;
   Lord, your wounds our healing give,
   to your cross we look and live:
   Jesus, with your power renew
   those who live by faith in you!

J. Conder (1789–1855)
© in this version Jubilate Hymns†

398(ii)

BREAD OF HEAVEN   7 7 7 7 7 7   W. D. Maclagan (1826–1910)

1 Bread of heaven, on you we feed,
   for your flesh is food indeed;
   always may our souls be fed
   with this true and living bread;
   day by day our strength supplied
   through your life, O Christ, who died.

2 Vine of heaven, your precious blood
   seals today our peace with God;
   Lord, your wounds our healing give,
   to your cross we look and live:
   Jesus, with your power renew
   those who live by faith in you!

J. Conder (1789–1855)
© in this version Jubilate Hymns†

Alternative tune: PETRA (444)

399(i)

LAVENDON 10 10 10 10   © Paul Edwards (born 1955)†

1 Come, risen Lord, as guest among your own!
  come and preside that we with you may dine;
  here at your table make your presence known
  in this our sacrament of bread and wine.

2 We meet as in that upper room they met,
  here with your word of blessing now you stand;
  this is your body: you are with us yet –
  faith still receives the cup as from your hand.

3 We are one body, for we all partake –
  one church united in communion blessed;
  one name we bear, one bread of life we break,
  with all your saints on earth and saints at rest.

4 One with each other, Lord, and one in you –
  Jesus, our saviour and our living head;
  we are your people: come, our faith renew,
  be known to us in breaking of the bread.

G. W. Briggs (1875–1959)
© Oxford University Press
and in this version Jubilate Hymns

399(ii)

SURSUM CORDA   10 10 10 10

A. M. Smith (1879–1971)
© Mrs. D. W. Smith

Unison

1   Come, risen Lord, as guest among your own!
    come and preside that we with you may dine;
    here at your table make your presence known
    in this our sacrament of bread and wine.

2   We meet as in that upper room they met,
    here with your word of blessing now you stand;
    this is your body: you are with us yet –
    faith still receives the cup as from your hand.

3   We are one body, for we all partake –
    one church united in communion blessed;
    one name we bear, one bread of life we break,
    with all your saints on earth and saints at rest.

4   One with each other, Lord, and one in you –
    Jesus, our saviour and our living head;
    we are your people: come, our faith renew,
    be known to us in breaking of the bread.

G. W. Briggs (1875–1959)
© Oxford University Press
and in this version Jubilate Hymns

400

SCHMÜCKE DICH 8 8 8 8 D

J. Crüger (1598–1662)

1 Deck yourself, my soul, with gladness;
  leave the gloomy haunts of sadness.
  Come into the daylight's splendour,
  there with joy your praises render
  to the Lord whose grace unbounded
  has this royal banquet founded:
  though all other powers excelling,
  with my soul he makes his dwelling.

2 Lord, I bow before you lowly,
  filled with joy most deep and holy,
  as with trembling awe and wonder
  all your mighty works I ponder –
  how, by mystery surrounded,
  depth no-one has ever sounded,
  none may dare to pierce unbidden
  secrets that in you are hidden.

3 Shining sun, my life you brighten,
  radiance, you my soul enlighten;
  joy, the best of all our knowing,
  fountain, swiftly in me flowing:
  at your feet I kneel, my Maker –
  let me be a fit partaker
  of this sacred food from heaven,
  for our good, your glory, given.

4 Jesus, Bread of life, I pray you,
  let me gladly here obey you;
  never to my hurt invited,
  always by your love delighted:
  from this banquet let me measure,
  Lord, how vast and deep its treasure;
  through the gifts your hands have given
  let me be your guest in heaven.

after J. Franck (1618–1677)
Catherine Winkworth (1827–1878)
© in this version Jubilate Hymns†

401

ELBERTON   10 10

B. Harwood (1859–1949)
© Executors of the late B. Harwood

1 Draw near and take the body of the Lord
  and drink by faith the blood for you outpoured:

2 Saved by that body and that holy blood,
  with souls refreshed give humble thanks to God.

3 Christ our redeemer, God's eternal Son,
  once by his cross and blood the victory won:

4 He gave his life for greatest as for least;
  himself the victim and himself the priest.

5 Victims were offered by the law of old –
  shadows themselves, of Jesus' death they told:

6 Lord of all life and saviour of our race,
  Christ has restored our hope
          and brought us grace.

7 Approach him now with trusting hearts sincere
  and take the pledges of salvation here:

8 Christ who in this life all his saints defends,
  gives to believers life that never ends.

9 He feeds the hungry with the bread of heaven
  to those who thirst his living streams are given:

10 Judge of the nations, all to him must bow,
   the king of ages, he is with us now.

from the Latin (seventh century)
after J. M. Neale (1818–1866)
© in this version Jubilate Hymns†

402

CHRISTE FONS JUGIS   11 11 11 5

Rouen church melody
arranged R. Vaughan Williams (1872–1958)
arrangement © Oxford University Press

1 Father almighty, we your humble servants,
   fed by the blood and body of our saviour,
   offer ourselves, our souls and bodies to you –
      thanking you always.

2 We, as a living sacrifice, now ask you:
   send us to work, empowered by your Spirit,
   that we may live to bring you praise and glory –
      so let it be, Lord.

after W. H. H. Jervois (1852–1905)
© Michael Saward (born 1932)†

403

J. Stainer (1840–1901)

1   For the bread which you have broken,
    for the wine which you have poured,
    for the words which you have spoken,
    now we give you thanks, O Lord.

2   By these pledges that you love us,
    by your gift of peace restored,
    by your call to heaven above us,
    consecrate our lives, O Lord:

3   In your service, Lord, defend us,
    help us to obey your word;
    in the world to which you send us
    let your kingdom come, O Lord!

                        L. F. Benson (1855–1930)

404

ST. COLUMBA   8 7 8 7

Irish traditional melody

1 Here, Lord, we take the broken bread
   and drink the wine, believing
   that by your life our souls are fed,
   your parting gifts receiving.

2 As you have given, so we would give
   ourselves for others' healing;
   as you have lived, so we would live
   the Father's love revealing.

C. V. Pilcher (1879–1961)
© F. E. V. Pilcher

405

SELFLESS LOVE   8 6 8 6 D (DCM)   © Andrew Maries (born 1949)

1 He gave his life in selfless love,
     for sinners once he came;
  he had no stain of sin himself
     but bore our guilt and shame:
  he took the cup of pain and death,
     his blood was freely shed;
  we see his body on the cross,
     we share the living bread.

2 He did not come to call the good
     but sinners to repent;
  it was the lame, the deaf, the blind
     for whom his life was spent:
  to heal the sick, to find the lost –
     it was for such he came,
  and round his table all may come
     to praise his holy name.

3 They heard him call his Father's name –
     then 'Finished!' was his cry;
  like them we have forsaken him
     and left him there to die:
  the sins that crucified him then
     are sins his blood has cured;
  the love that bound him to a cross
     our freedom has ensured.

4 His body broken once for us
     is glorious now above;
  the cup of blessing we receive,
     a sharing of his love:
  as in his presence we partake,
     his dying we proclaim
  until the hour of majesty
     when Jesus comes again.

406

ST. AGNES (LANGRAN) 10 10 10 10   J. Langran (1835–1909)

1 Here, O my Lord, I see you face to face,
  here faith can touch and handle things unseen;
  here I will grasp with firmer hand your grace
  and all my weariness upon you lean.

2 Here I will feed upon the bread of God,
  here drink with you the royal wine of heaven;
  here I will lay aside each earthly load,
  here taste afresh the calm of sin forgiven.

3 I have no help but yours, nor do I need
  another arm but yours to lean upon;
  it is enough, my Lord, enough indeed,
  my hope is in your strength, your strength alone.

4 Mine is the sin, but yours the righteousness;
  mine is the guilt, but yours the cleansing blood:
  here is my robe, my refuge, and my peace;
  your blood, your righteousness, O Lord my God.

5 Too soon we rise, the symbols disappear;
  the feast, though not the love, is past and done:
  gone are the bread and wine, but you are here,
  nearer than ever, still my shield and sun.

6 Feast after feast thus comes and passes by,
  yet, passing, points to that glad feast above;
  giving sweet foretaste of the festal joy,
  the Lamb's great bridal feast of bliss and love.

H. Bonar (1808–1889)

Alternative tune: FARLEY CASTLE (361)

407

BANGOR 8 6 8 6 (CM)

W. Tans'ur's *Harmony of Syon* 1734

1 I am not worthy, holy Lord,
   that you should come to me:
   but speak the word! – one gracious word
   can set the sinner free.

2 I am not worthy – cold and bare
   the lodging of my soul:
   how can you stoop to enter here?
   Lord, speak and make me whole.

3 I am not worthy; yet, my God,
   shall I turn you away
   when you have given your flesh and blood
   my ransom price to pay?

4 Come, feed me now with food divine
   in the appointed hour,
   and this unworthy heart of mine
   fill with your love and power!

H. W. Baker (1821–1877)
© in this version Jubilate Hymns†

408(i)

UNIVERSITY 8 6 8 6 (CM)

C. Collignon (1725–1785)

1 I come with joy to meet my Lord,
   forgiven, loved, and free;
   in awe and wonder to recall
   his life laid down for me.

2 I come with Christians far and near
   to find, as all are fed,
   the new community of love
   in Christ's communion bread.

3 As Christ breaks bread and bids us share,
   each proud division ends;
   the love that made us, makes us one,
   and strangers now are friends.

4 And thus with joy we meet our Lord;
   his presence, always near,
   is in such friendship better known:
   we see and praise him here.

5 Together met, together bound,
   we'll go our different ways;
   and as his people in the world
   we'll live and speak his praise.

Brian Wren (born 1936)
© Oxford University Press

408(ii)

BARCHESTER FAIR   8 6 8 6 (CM)   © Christian Strover (born 1932)†

409(i)

IBSTONE 6 6 6 6

Maria Tiddeman (1837–1915)

(ii)

ECCLES 6 6 6 6

B. Luard-Selby (1853–1918)

1 *mp* I hunger and I thirst,
Jesus, my manna be:
O living waters, burst
out of the rock for me!

2 O bruised and broken bread,
my life-long needs supply:
as living souls are fed,
so feed me, or I die.

3 O true lifegiving vine,
let me your goodness prove:
by your life sweeten mine,
refresh my soul with love.

4 Rough paths my feet have trod
since first their course began:
renew me, bread of God,
restore me, Son of man.

5 For still the desert lies
behind me and before:
mf O living waters, rise
within me evermore!

J. S. B. Monsell (1811–1875)

410

ROSELAND   8 6 8 6 (CM)   © Norman Warren (born 1934)†

1 O Lord, you gave in love divine
your body and your blood;
that living bread, that heavenly wine
is our immortal food:

2 You met with us in breaking bread;
so as we now depart,
O Saviour, stay with us and spread
your table in our heart.

after J. Montgomery (1771–1854)
© in this version Jubilate Hymns†

Alternative tune: ST. TIMOTHY (269)

411

STENKA RAZIN 8 7 8 7

Russian folk tune
© arranged Noël Tredinnick (born 1949)†

* The more familiar
ending may be used
instead of the original

1 In the quiet consecration
   of this glad communion hour,
   here we rest in you, Lord Jesus,
   taste your love and touch your power.

2 Here we learn through sacred symbol
   all your grace can be and do,
   by this wonderful indwelling –
   you in us, and we in you.

3 Christ the living bread from heaven,
   Christ whose blood is drink indeed,
   here by faith and with thanksgiving
   in our hearts on you we feed.

4 By your death for sin atoning,
   by your resurrection-life,
   hold us fast in joyful union,
   strengthen us to face the strife.

5 While afar in solemn radiance
shines the feast that is to come –
after conflict, heaven's glory,
your great feast of love and home.

Constance Coote (1844–1936)

Alternative tune: STUTTGART (8)

412

SALTFLEETBY ALL SAINTS   8 6 8 6 (CM)   © Paul Edwards (born 1955)†

1 In memory of the Saviour's love
we keep the sacred feast,
where every humble contrite heart
is made a welcome guest.

2 By faith we take the bread of life
by which our souls are fed,
and drink the token of his blood
that was for sinners shed.

3 Around his table here we sing
the wonders of his love,
and so anticipate by faith
the heavenly feast above.

T. Cotterill (1779–1823)

Alternative tune: ST. PETER (211)

413(i)

MARYTON   8 8 8 8 (LM)

H. P. Smith (1825–1898)

(ii)

GONFALON ROYAL   8 8 8 8 (LM)

P. C. Buck (1871–1947)
© Oxford University Press

413(iii)

WAREHAM   8 8 8 8 (LM)   W. Knapp (1698–1768)

1   Jesus, the joy of loving hearts,
    true source of life, our lives sustain:
    from the best bliss that earth imparts
    we turn unfilled to you again.

2   Your truth unchanged has ever stood,
    you rescue those who on you call:
    to those yet seeking, you are good –
    to those who find you, all-in-all.

3   We taste of you, the living bread,
    and long to feast upon you still;
    we drink from you, the fountain-head,
    our thirsty souls from you we fill.

4   Our restless spirits long for you,
    whichever way our lot is cast,
    glad when your gracious smile we view,
    blessed when our faith can hold you fast.

5   Jesus, for ever with us stay,
    make all our moments calm and bright;
    chase the dark night of sin away,
    spread through the world your holy light. (Amen.)

                                        from the Latin (twelfth century)
                                        R. Palmer (1808–1887)

Alternative tune: HAWKHURST (137)

414

CALYPSO PRAISE 8 8 8 8 10 8 © Jonah Brrand (born 1975)†

The refrain may be repeated after v. 3 — the melody will be found
to be compatible with the introduction.

1 Let us talents and tongues employ,
   reaching out with a shout of joy:
   bread is broken, the wine is poured,
   Christ is spoken and seen and heard.
       Jesus lives again, earth can breathe again,
       pass the Word around: loaves abound!

2 Christ is able to make us one,
   at the table he sets the tone,
   teaching people to live to bless,
   love in word and in deed express.
       Jesus lives again . . .

3 Jesus calls us in, sends us out
   bearing fruit in a world of doubt,
   gives us love to tell, bread to share:
   God Emmanuel everywhere!
      Jesus lives again . . .

415

ST. THOMAS   6 6 8 6 (SM)   A. Williams' *New Universal Psalmodist* 1770

1 The Son of God proclaim!
   the Lord of time and space,
   the God who bade the light
      break forth
   now shines in Jesus' face.

2 He, God's creative Word,
   the church's Lord and head,
   here bids us gather as his friends
   and share his wine and bread.

3 The Lord of life and death
   with wondering praise we sing;
   we break the bread
      at his command
   and name him God and king.

4 We take this cup in hope,
   for he who gladly bore
   the shameful cross, is risen again
   and reigns for evermore.

416

ST. HELEN   878787

G. C. Martin (1844–1916)

1 Lord, enthroned in heavenly splendour,
   glorious first-born from the dead,
   you alone our strong defender
   lifting up your people's head:
       Alleluia, alleluia,
   Jesus, true and living bread!

2 Prince of life, for us now living,
   by your body souls are healed;
   Prince of peace, your pardon giving,
   by your blood our peace is sealed:
       Alleluia, alleluia,
   Word of God in flesh revealed.

3 Paschal Lamb! your offering finished,
   once for all, when you were slain;
   in its fulness undiminished
   shall for evermore remain:
       Alleluia, alleluia,
   cleansing souls from every stain.

4 Great High Priest of our profession,
   through the veil you entered in,
   by your mighty intercession
   grace and mercy there to win:
       Alleluia, alleluia,
   only sacrifice for sin.

5 Life-imparting heavenly Manna,
   stricken rock, with streaming side;
   heaven and earth, with loud hosanna,
   worship you, the Lamb who died:
       Alleluia, alleluia,
   risen, ascended, glorified!

                    G. Bourne (1840–1925)

417

LIVING LORD 9 8 8 8 8 3

Patrick Appleford (born 1925)
© Josef Weinberger Ltd

1 Lord Jesus Christ, you have come to us,
   you are one with us, Mary's son;
   cleansing our souls from all their sin,
   pouring your love and goodness in:
   Jesus, our love for you we sing –
       living Lord!

At communion, this may be sung:

2 Lord Jesus Christ, now and every day
   teach us how to pray, Son of God;
   you have commanded us to do
   this in remembrance, Lord, of you:
   into our lives your power breaks through –
       living Lord!

3 Lord Jesus Christ, you have come to us,
   born as one of us, Mary's son;
   led out to die on Calvary,
   risen from death to set us free:
   living Lord Jesus, help us see
       you are Lord!

4 Lord Jesus Christ, I would come to you,
  live my life for you, Son of God;
  all your commands I know are true,
  your many gifts will make me new:
  into my life your power breaks through –
      living Lord!

Harmony

418

ROCKINGHAM 8 8 8 8 (LM)   Adapted E. Miller (1735–1807)

1   My God, now is your table spread,
     your cup with love still overflows:
     so may your children here be fed
     as Christ to us his goodness shows.

2   This holy feast, which Jesus makes
     a banquet of his flesh and blood –
     how glad each one who comes and takes
     this sacred drink, this royal food!

3   His gifts that richly satisfy
     are yet to some in vain displayed:
     did not for them the saviour die –
     may they not share the children's bread?

4   My God, here let your table be
     a place of joy for all your guests,
     and may each one salvation see
     who now its sacred pledges tastes.

P. Doddridge (1702–1751)
© in this version Jubilate Hymns†

419

KILLIBEGS   8 8 8 8 (LM)   © William Davies (born 1921)

1 *mf* Now let us from this table rise
    renewed in body, mind and soul;
    with Christ we die and live again,
    his selfless love has made us whole.

2   With minds alert, upheld by grace,
     to spread the word in speech and deed,
     we follow in the steps of Christ,
     at one with us in hope and need.

3   To fill each human house with love,
     it is the sacrament of care;
     the work that Christ began to do
     we humbly pledge ourselves to share.

4 *f* Then give us courage, Father God,
       to choose again the pilgrim way,
       and help us to accept with joy
       the challenge of tomorrow's day!

Fred Kaan (born 1929)
© 1968 Galliard Ltd
Stainer & Bell Ltd

420

SONG 1   10 10 10 10 10 10 10

Orlando Gibbons (1583–1625)
arrangement attributed to R. Vaughan Williams (1872–1958)
arrangement © Oxford University Press

1   O Christ, at your first eucharist you prayed
    that all your church might be for ever one;
    at every eucharist this prayer is made
    with longing heart and soul, 'Your will be done':
        O may we all one bread, one body be
        through this blessed sacrament of unity.

2   For all your church, O Lord, we intercede
    that you will make our sad divisions cease:
    O draw us nearer each to each, we plead,
    by drawing all to you, the prince of peace.
        Thus may we all one bread, one body be
        through this blessed sacrament of unity.

3 We pray for those who wander from your fold:
  O bring them back, great Shepherd of the sheep –
  back to the faith which saints believed of old,
  the faith for all your holy church to keep.
      Soon may we all one bread, one body be
      through this blessed sacrament of unity.

4 So, Lord, at length when sacraments shall cease,
  may we be one with all your church above;
  one with your saints in one unbroken peace,
  one with your saints in one unbounded love:
      Far happier then, in peace and love to be
      one with the Trinity-in-Unity!

W. H. Turton (1856–1938)
© Hymns Ancient & Modern Ltd
and in this version Jubilate Hymns

421

ST. FLAVIAN 8 6 8 6 (CM)   Day's *Psalter* 1562

1 O God, unseen yet ever near,
  your presence may we feel;
  and thus, inspired with holy fear,
  around your table kneel.

2 Here may your faithful people know
  the blessings of your love,
  the streams that through the desert
      flow,
  the manna from above.

3 We come, obedient to your word,
  to feast on heavenly food;
  to eat the body of the Lord,
  and drink his precious blood.

4 O living Bread, enduring Vine,
  your words we shall obey,
  and go, renewed with strength
      divine,
  rejoicing on our way.

E. Osler (1798–1863)
© in this version Jubilate Hymns†

422

HIGHWOOD   11 10 11 10

R. R. Terry (1865–1938)
© Oxford University Press

1   O joy of God, we seek you in the morning
    and long to see the glory of your face:
    rise on our darkness
                with your sun's new dawning –
    flood all our being in this feast of grace.

2   O life of God, for you our spirits hunger –
    unless we feed on you we surely die:
    with love and faith renewed
                and hope grown younger
    send us from here to serve you, Lord most high.

3   O peace of God, you pass our understanding –
    safe through each moment keep us every day:
    with joy divine and mercy never ending,
    direct our path and prosper all our way.

after C. H. Boutflower (1863–1942)
© in this version Word & Music†

Alternative tune: O PERFECT LOVE (297)

423

ACH, GOTT UND HERR   8 7 8 7

Neu-Leipziger Gesangbuch 1682
arranged J. S. Bach (1685–1750)

1   Strengthen for service, Lord, the hands
     that holy things have taken;
     let ears that now have heard your songs
     to clamour never waken.

2   Lord, may the tongues which 'Holy' sang
     keep free from all deceiving;
     the eyes which saw your love be bright,
     the glorious hope perceiving:

3   The feet that tread your holy courts
     from light be never banished;
     the bodies by your Body fed,
     be with new life replenished.

from a Syriac liturgy (fifth century)
J. M. Neale (1818–1866)
C. Humphreys (1840–1921) and
P. Dearmer (1867–1936)

424

FRAMLINGHAM 8 8 8 6 D   ©John Barnard (born 1948)†

* last verse

1   O Sacrifice of Calvary,
     O Lamb whose sacred blood was shed,
     O great High Priest on heaven's throne,
     O Victor from the dead!
     here I recall your agony,
     here see again your bloodstained brow;
     beyond the sign of bread and wine
     I know your presence now.

2   Your royal presence intercedes
     eternally for me above,
     and here my hungry spirit feeds
     upon these gifts of love;
     before your holy table laid
     I kneel once more in hope and peace,
     your blood and flesh my soul refresh
     with joy that shall not cease.

© Michael Saward (born 1932)†

For other hymns on this theme, see:

Sunday Themes index
  Section 28 (2), The Bread of Life (p. xii)
Hymn Section
  O God beyond all praising (36)
  Tell his praise in song and story (41)
  Thank you, O Lord (43)
  The king of love my shepherd is (44)
  The Lord my shepherd (45)
  You are coming, O my Saviour (202)
  Welcome to another day (272)

'Lift up your hearts' (366)
Christians, lift up your hearts (383)
Lord God, your love (480)
Love is his word (481)
Look, Lord, in mercy (498)
The church's one foundation (501)
Guide me, O my great Redeemer (528)
God is here! As we his people (560)
  We come as guests invited (602)
Song Section
  Alleluia, alleluia! As we walk (S.1)
  Broken for me (S.6)

GOD'S CHURCH:
FAITH AND TRUST

425

EVENTIDE   10 10 10 10   W. H. Monk (1823–1889)

1   Abide with me, fast falls the eventide;
    the darkness deepens: Lord, with me abide.
    When other helpers fail and comforts flee,
    help of the helpless, O abide with me.

2   Swift to its close ebbs out life's little day;
    earth's joys grow dim, its glories pass away.
    Change and decay in all around I see –
    you never change, O Lord: abide with me!

3   I need your presence every passing hour:
    what but your grace can foil the tempter's power?
    Who like yourself my guide and strength can be?
    Through cloud and sunshine,
                    Lord, abide with me!

4   I have no fear with you at hand to bless;
    ills have no weight and tears no bitterness.
    Where is death's sting?
                    Where, grave, your victory?
    I triumph still if you abide with me.

5   Hold now your cross before my closing eyes;
    shine through the gloom
                    and point me to the skies!
    Heaven's morning breaks
                    and earth's vain shadows flee:
    in life, in death, O Lord, abide with me!

H. F. Lyte (1793–1847)

426

CAITHNESS   8 6 8 6 (CM)   *Scottish Psalter* Edinburgh 1635

1 Can we by searching find out God
   or formulate his ways?
   Can numbers measure what he is
   or words contain his praise?

2 Although his being is too bright
   for human eyes to scan,
   his meaning lights our shadowed world
   through Christ, the Son of Man.

3 Our boastfulness is turned to shame,
   our profit counts as loss,
   when earthly values stand beside
   the manger and the cross.

4 We there may recognise his light,
   may kindle in its rays,
   find there the source of penitence,
   the starting-point for praise.

5 There God breaks in upon our search,
   makes birth and death his own:
   he speaks to us in human terms
   to make his glory known.

427

SHIPSTON 8 7 8 7

English traditional melody
arranged R. Vaughan Williams (1872–1958)
arrangement © Oxford University Press

1 God the Father of creation,
  master of the realms sublime,
  Lord of light and life's foundation:
      we believe and trust in him.

2 Christ who came from highest heaven,
  God from God before all time,
  Son for our redemption given:
      we believe and trust in him.

3 Spirit, God in us residing,
  power of life and love supreme,
  intercessor – pleading, guiding:
      we believe and trust in him.

4 Trinity of adoration!
  earth responds to heaven's theme;
  one the church's acclamation:
      we believe and trust in him!

© Michael Perry (born 1942)†

428

ALLELUIA   8 7 8 7 D

S. S. Wesley (1810–1876)

1 Christ, our king before creation,
   Life before all life began,
   crowned in deep humiliation
   by your partners in God's plan:
   make us humble in believing,
   and, believing, bold to pray
        'Lord, forgive our self-deceiving,
        come and reign in us today!'

2 Lord of time and Lord of history,
   giving, when the world despairs,
   faith to wrestle with the mystery
   of a God who loves and cares:
   make us humble in believing,
   and, believing, bold to pray
        'Lord, by grace beyond conceiving,
        come and reign in us today!'

3 Word that ends our long debating,
   Life of God which sets us free,
   through your body recreating
   Life as life is meant to be:
   make us humble in believing,
   and, believing, bold to pray
        'Lord, in us your aim achieving,
        come and reign in us today!'

© Ivor Jones (born 1934)

Alternative tune: ABBOT'S LEIGH (494)

429(i)

HALTON HOLGATE   8 7 8 7

Later form of melody by W. Boyce (1711–1779)
harmony from S. S. Wesley (1810–1876)

(ii)

OTTERY ST. MARY   8 7 8 7

H. G. Ley (1887–1962)
© Chappell Music Ltd/International Music Publications

429(iii)

SHIPSTON 8787

English traditional melody
arranged R. Vaughan Williams (1872–1958)
arrangement © Oxford University Press

1 Firmly I believe and truly
  God is Three and God is One;
  and I next acknowledge duly
  manhood taken by the Son.

2 And I trust and hope most fully
  in that manhood crucified;
  and each thought and deed unruly
  do to death, for he has died.

3 Simply to his grace and wholly
  light and life and strength belong;
  and I love supremely, solely,
  Christ the holy, Christ the strong.

4 And I make this affirmation
  for the love of Christ alone:
  holy Church is his creation
  and his teachings are her own.

5 Honour, glory, power, and merit
  to the God of earth and heaven,
  Father, Son, and Holy Spirit –
  praise for evermore be given!

J. H. Newman (1801–1890)
© in this version Jubilate Hymns†

430

MONTGOMERY   11 11 11 11   Melody probably by S. Jarvis (died c. 1785)

1   How firm a foundation, you people of God,
    is laid for your faith in his excellent word!
    What more can he say to you than he has said
    to everyone trusting in Jesus our head?

2   Since Jesus is with you, do not be afraid;
    since he is your Lord, you need not be dismayed:
    he strengthens you, guards you,
            and helps you to stand,
    upheld by his righteous, omnipotent hand.

3   When through the deep waters he calls you to go,
    the rivers of trouble shall not overflow;
    the Lord will be with you, to help and to bless,
    and work for your good
            through your deepest distress.

4   When through fiery trials
            your pathway shall lead,
    his grace shall sustain you with all that you need;
    the flames shall not hurt you – his only design
    your dross to consume and your gold to refine.

5 Whoever has come to believe in his name
   will not be deserted, and not put to shame;
   though hell may endeavour that Christian to shake
   his Lord will not leave him, nor ever forsake.

R. Keen (c.1787)
© in this version Jubilate Hymns†

Alternative tune: ST. DENIO (21)

431

ST. ETHELWALD 6 6 8 6 (SM)   W. H. Monk (1823–1889)

1 Have faith in God, my heart,
  trust and be unafraid;
  God will fulfil in every part
  each promise he has made.

2 Have faith in God, my mind,
  although your light burns low;
  God's mercy holds a wiser plan
  than you can fully know.

3 Have faith in God, my soul,
  his cross for ever stands;
  and neither life nor death can pluck
  his children from his hands.

4 Lord Jesus, make me whole;
  grant me no resting place
  until I rest, heart, mind, and soul,
  the captive of your grace.

B. Rees (1911–1983)
© Mrs. M. E. Rees

432

EWHURST 8 8 8 7

C. J. Allen (1886–1973)
copyright information sought

1 I am not skilled to understand
what God has willed, what God has planned;
I only know at his right hand
stands one who is my saviour.

2 I take him at his word and deed:
'Christ died to save me,' this I read;
and in my heart I find a need
of him to be my saviour.

3 That he should leave his place on high
and come for sinners here to die;
you find it strange? So once did I,
before I knew my saviour.

4 I hope that Christ my Lord may see
fulfilment of his work in me;
and with his child contented be,
as I with my dear saviour.

5 Yes, living, dying, let me bring
my strength, my comfort, from this spring:
that he who lives to be my king
once died to be my saviour.

Dorothy Greenwell (1821–1882)

433

BULLINGER 8 5 8 3   E. W. Bullinger (1837–1913)

1 I am trusting you, Lord Jesus,
  you have died for me;
  trusting you for full salvation
  great and free.

2 I am trusting you for pardon –
  at your feet I bow;
  for your grace and tender mercy,
  trusting now.

3 I am trusting you for cleansing,
  Jesus, Son of God;
  trusting you to make me holy
  by your blood.

4 I am trusting you to guide me –
  you alone shall lead;
  every day and hour supplying
  all my need.

5 I am trusting you for power –
  yours can never fail;
  words which you yourself shall give me
  must prevail.

6 I am trusting you, Lord Jesus –
  never let me fall;
  I am trusting you for ever,
  and for all.

Frances R. Havergal (1836–1879)

434

ALL FOR JESUS 8 7 8 7   J. Stainer (1840–1901)

1 I believe in God the Father
   who created heaven and earth;
   holding all things in his power,
   bringing light and life to birth.

2 I believe in God the Saviour,
   Son of Man and Lord most high,
   crucified to be redeemer,
   raised to life that death may die.

3 I believe in God the Spirit,
   wind of heaven and flame of fire,
   pledge of all that we inherit,
   sent to comfort and inspire.

4 Honour, glory, might and merit
   be to God, and God alone!
   Father, Son and Holy Spirit,
   One-in-Three and Three-in-One.

© Michael Perry (born 1942)†

Alternative tunes: SHIPSTON (282)
              STUTTGART (8)

435

ST. BRIDE   6 6 8 6 (SM)

S. Howard (1710–1782)

1 I bless the Christ of God,
   I rest on love divine,
   and with unfaltering voice
            and heart
   I call this Saviour mine.

2 For nothing I have done
   can save my guilty soul;
   no burden that my flesh has borne
   can make my spirit whole.

3 Not what I feel or do –
   no toil, nor pain nor blood,
   not all my prayers and sighs
            and tears
   can give me peace with God.

4 Your work alone, O Christ,
   can ease this weight of sin;
   your blood alone,
            O Lamb of God,
   can give me peace within.

5 Not love for you, O Lord,
   but your great love for me
   can rid me of this dark unrest
   and set my spirit free.

6 Your voice alone, O God,
   can speak the word of grace
   to calm the tempests
            in my heart
   and make its raging cease.

7 And so I bless your name,
   I trust your love divine;
   by grace, for all eternity,
   I dare to call you mine.

H. Bonar (1808–1889)

436

SOUTHWELL (DAMON)   6 6 8 6 (SM)   W. Damon's *Psalmes* 1579

1   I hear the words of love,
    I trust in Jesus' blood,
    I see the mighty sacrifice –
    and I have peace with God.

2   This everlasting peace,
    as certain as his name,
    is sure as God's eternal throne –
    unchangeably the same.

3   Though love is sometimes cold,
    and joy still ebbs and flows,
    yet peace with God remains secure –
    such faithfulness he shows.

4   I change, but he does not:
    his truth can never lie;
    his love, not mine, upholds my faith –
    for Jesus shall not die.

                    H. Bonar (1808–1889)
                    © in this version Jubilate Hymns†

Alternative tune: ST. PAUL'S (316)

437

BODMIN 8 8 8 8 (LM)   A. S. Scott-Gatty (1847–1918)

1 *mf* Lord, I was blind; I could not see
         in your marred visage any grace:
         but now the beauty of your face
         in radiant vision dawns on me.

2   Lord, I was deaf; I could not hear
        the thrilling music of your voice:
        but now I hear you and rejoice,
        and all your spoken words are dear.

3   Lord, I was dumb; I could not speak
        the grace and glory of your name:
        but now as touched with living flame
        my lips will speak for Jesus' sake.

4 *mp* Lord, I was dead; I could not move
         my lifeless soul from sin's dark grave:
   mf but now the power of life you gave
         has raised me up to know your love.

5 *f*   Lord, you have made the blind to see,
         the deaf to hear, the dumb to speak,
         the dead to live – and now I break
         the chains of my captivity!

                    W. T. Matson (1833–1899)
                    © in this version Jubilate Hymns†

Alternative tune: FULDA (519)

438(i)

HOLLINGSIDE 7 7 7 7 D

J. B. Dykes (1823–1876)

1 Jesus, lover of my soul,
  let me to your presence fly,
  while the gathering waters roll,
  while the tempest still is high.
  Hide me, O my Saviour, hide,
  till the storm of life is past;
  safe into the haven, guide
  and receive my soul at last.

2 Other refuge have I none,
  all my hope in you I see:
  leave, O leave me, not alone;
  still support and comfort me.
  All my trust on you is stayed,
  all my help from you I bring:
  cover my defenceless head
  with the shadow of your wing.

438(ii)

LITTLE HEATH   7 7 7 7 D   © David Wilson (born 1940)†

3   You, O Christ, are all I want,
    more than all in you I find:
    raise the fallen, cheer the faint,
    heal the sick and lead the blind.
    Just and holy is your name,
    I am all unworthiness;
    false and full of sin I am,
    you are full of truth and grace.

4   Plenteous grace with you is found,
    grace to wash away my sin:
    let the healing streams abound;
    make and keep me clean within.
    Living Fountain, now impart
    all your life and purity;
    spring for ever in my heart,
    rise to all eternity!

C. Wesley (1707–1788)

438(iii)

ABERYSTWYTH 7777D

J. Parry (1841–1903)

1 Jesus, lover of my soul,
   let me to your presence fly,
   while the gathering waters roll,
   while the tempest still is high.
   Hide me, O my Saviour, hide,
   till the storm of life is past;
   safe into the haven, guide
   and receive my soul at last.

2   Other refuge have I none,
    all my hope in you I see:
    leave, O leave me, not alone;
    still support and comfort me.
    All my trust on you is stayed,
    all my help from you I bring:
    cover my defenceless head
    with the shadow of your wing.

3   You, O Christ, are all I want,
    more than all in you I find:
    raise the fallen, cheer the faint,
    heal the sick and lead the blind.
    Just and holy is your name,
    I am all unworthiness;
    false and full of sin I am,
    you are full of truth and grace.

4   Plenteous grace with you is found,
    grace to wash away my sin:
    let the healing streams abound;
    make and keep me clean within.
    Living Fountain, now impart
    all your life and purity;
    spring for ever in my heart,
    rise to all eternity!

                C. Wesley (1707–1788)

Descant and arrangement G. T. Shaw (1879–1943)
                                    © Novello & Co Ltd

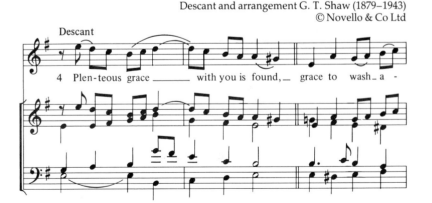

4 Plen-teous grace _____ with you is found, __ grace to wash _ a -

-way my sin: ___ let ___ the heal - ing streams a - bound; ___

make and ___ keep ___ me ___ clean with-in. Liv - ing Fount-ain,

now im - part all your life and pur - i - ty; ___

spring for ev - er in ___ my heart, rise ___ to ___ all ___ e - ter - ni - ty!

439

SONG 20   6 6 8 6 (SM)

Melody and bass
Orlando Gibbons (1583–1625)

1 What offering shall we give
   or what atonement bring
   to God by whom alone we live,
   high heaven's eternal king?

2 For all the blood of beasts
   on Jewish altars slain
   could never give the conscience peace
   or wash away its stain:

3 But Christ, the heavenly Lamb,
   takes all our sins away –
   a sacrifice of nobler name
   and richer blood than they.

4 In faith I lay my hand
   upon his head divine
   while as a penitent I stand
   and there confess my sin.

5 So I look back to see
   the weight he chose to bear
   when hanging on the cross for me –
   because my guilt was there.

6 Believing, we rejoice
   to know our sins forgiven;
   we bless the Lamb with heart and voice
   and join the praise of heaven.

I. Watts (1674–1748)
© in this version Jubilate Hymns†

440(i)

SAFFRON WALDEN   8 8 8 6   A. H. Brown (1830–1926)

(ii)

WOODWORTH   8 8 8 6 extended   W. B. Bradbury (1816–1868)

O Lamb of God, I come, I come.

1   Just as I am, without one plea
    but that you died to set me free,
    and at your bidding 'Come to me!'
    O Lamb of God, I come.

440(iii)

MISERICORDIA 8 8 8 6

H. T. Smart (1813–1879)

2 Just as I am, without delay
  your call of mercy I obey –
  your blood can wash my sins away:
      O Lamb of God, I come.

3 Just as I am, though tossed about
  with many a conflict, many a doubt,
  fightings within and fears without,
      O Lamb of God, I come.

4 Just as I am, poor, wretched, blind!
  Sight, riches, healing of the mind –
  all that I need, in you to find:
      O Lamb of God, I come.

5 Just as I am! You will receive,
  will welcome, pardon, cleanse, relieve:
  because your promise I believe,
      O Lamb of God, I come.

6 Just as I am! Your love unknown
  has broken every barrier down:
  now to be yours, yes, yours alone,
      O Lamb of God, I come.

7 Just as I am! Of that free love
  the breadth, length, depth and height to prove,
  here for a time and then above,
      O Lamb of God, I come.

Charlotte Elliott (1789–1871)
© in this version Jubilate Hymns†

441

LITTLE HINTON 8 6 8 6 (CM)   © Paul Edwards (born 1955)†

1 O come, our all-victorious Lord,
   your power to us make known;
   strike with the hammer of your word
   and break these hearts of stone.

2 If only we might all begin
   our foolishness to mourn,
   to turn at once from every sin
   and to our saviour turn!

3 Ourselves and God we need to know
   in this your gracious day;
   repentance, faith, and life bestow,
   and take our sins away.

4 Convict us first of unbelief,
   and freely then release;
   fill every soul with sacred grief
   and then with sacred peace.

5 Lord, make us poor; help us believe,
   and so make rich the poor;
   the knowledge of our sickness give,
   and knowledge of its cure.

6 The healthy sense of guilt impart
   and then remove the load;
   disturb, and then set free the heart
   by your atoning blood.

7 Our desperate state through sin declare,
then speak our sins forgiven;
for perfect holiness prepare
and take us into heaven.

C. Wesley (1707–1788)
© in this version Jubilate Hymns†

Alternative tune: ST. STEPHEN (483)

442

FESTUS   8 8 8 8 (LM)   Adapted from a melody in J. A. Freylinghausen's
Geistreiches Gesangbuch Halle 1704

1 O happy day that fixed my choice
on you, my Saviour and my God!
well may this grateful heart rejoice
and tell of Christ's redeeming blood.

2 It's done, the great transaction's done!
I am my Lord's, and he is mine;
he led me, and I followed on
responding to the voice divine.

3 Now rest, my long-divided heart,
in Jesus Christ who loves you, rest
and never from your Lord depart –
enriched in him, by him possessed!

4 So God, who heard my solemn vow,
in daily prayer shall hear my voice
till in my final breath I bow
and bless the day that fixed my choice.

P. Doddridge (1702–1751)
© in this version Jubilate Hymns†

443(i)

CROSS OF JESUS   8 7 8 7

J. Stainer (1840–1901)

(ii)

ANIMAE HOMINUM   8 7 8 7

A. Blanchet (1868–1926)
© arranged Christian Strover (born 1932)†

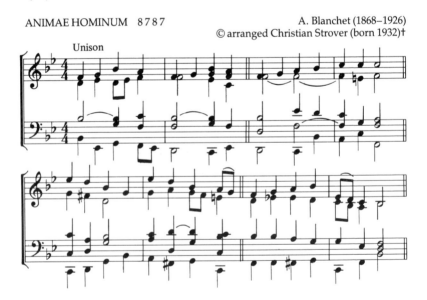

1 Restless souls, why do you scatter
   like a flock of frightened sheep?
   Doubting hearts, why do you wander
   from a love so true and deep?

2 There's a wideness in God's mercy
   like the wideness of the sea;
   there's a kindness in his justice
   which is more than liberty.

3 There is no place where earth's sorrows
   are more keenly felt than heaven;
   there is no place where earth's failings
   have such gracious judgement given.

4 There is plentiful redemption
   through the blood that Christ has shed;
   there is joy for all the members
   in the sorrows of the head.

5 For the love of God is broader
   than the measure of our mind,
   and the heart of the eternal
   is most wonderfully kind.

6 If our love were but more simple
   we should take him at his word,
   and our lives would find fulfilment
   in the goodness of the Lord.

F. W. Faber (1814–1863)
© in this version Jubilate Hymns†

444(i)

PETRA 7 7 7 7 7 7   R. Redhead (1820–1901)

1 *mf* Rock of ages, cleft for me,
hide me now, my refuge be;
let the water and the blood
from your wounded side which flowed,
be for sin the double cure,
cleanse me from its guilt and power.

2   Not the labours of my hands
can fulfil your law's demands;
could my zeal no respite know,
could my tears for ever flow,
all for sin could not atone:
you must save and you alone.

444(ii)

TOPLADY 777777

A. M. Toplady (1740–1778)

3 *mp* Nothing in my hand I bring,
simply to your cross I cling;
naked, come to you for dress,
helpless, look to you for grace;
stained by sin, to you I cry:
'Wash me, Saviour, or I die!'

4   While I draw this fleeting breath,
when my eyelids close in death,
   mf when I soar through realms unknown,
bow before the judgement throne:
hide me then, my refuge be,
Rock of ages, cleft for me.

A. M. Toplady (1740–1778)
© in this version Jubilate Hymns†

(see also traditional version, 593)

445(i)

CREATOR GOD   8 6 8 6 (CM)   © Norman Warren (born 1934)†

(ii)

STANTON   8 6 8 6 (CM)   © John Barnard (born 1948)†

1   Safe in the shadow of the Lord,
    beneath his hand and power,
        I trust in him,
        I trust in him,
    my fortress and my tower.

2   My hope is set on God alone
    though Satan spreads his snare;
        I trust in him,
        I trust in him
    to keep me in his care.

3   From fears and phantoms of the night,
    from foes about my way,
        I trust in him,
        I trust in him
    by darkness as by day.

4   His holy angels keep my feet
    secure from every stone;
        I trust in him,
        I trust in him,
    and unafraid go on.

5   Strong in the everlasting name,
    and in my Father's care,
        I trust in him,
        I trust in him
    who hears and answers prayer.

6   Safe in the shadow of the Lord,
    possessed by love divine,
        I trust in him,
        I trust in him,
    and meet his love with mine.

        from Psalm 91
        © Timothy Dudley-Smith (born 1926)

446

FINLANDIA 11 10 11 10 11 10

J. Sibelius (1865–1957)
from *Finlandia*
© Breitkopf & Härtel, Wiesbaden

1 We trust in you, our shield and our defender;
    we do not fight alone against the foe:
    strong in your strength,
           safe in your keeping tender,
    we trust in you, and in your name we go.
        Strong in your strength . . .

2 We trust in you, O Captain of salvation!
    in your dear name, all other names above:
    Jesus our righteousness, our sure foundation,
    our prince of glory and our king of love.
        Jesus, our righteousness . . .

3 We go in faith, our own great weakness feeling,
    and needing more each day your grace to know;
    yet from our hearts a song of triumph pealing,
    'We trust in you, and in your name we go.'
        Yet from our hearts . . .

4 We trust in you, our shield and our defender:
    yours is the battle – yours shall be the praise!
    when passing through
           the gates of dazzling splendour,
    victors, we rest in you through endless days.
        When passing through . . .

Edith G. Cherry (1872–1897)
© in this version Jubilate Hymns†

447

HARTS 7 7 7 7

B. Milgrove (1731–1810)

1 Out of darkness let light shine!
Formless void its Lord obeyed;
at his word, by his design,
sun and moon and stars were made.

2 Still his brightness shines abroad,
darkened lives his light have known;
all the glories of the Lord
in the face of Christ are shown.

3 New creation's second birth
bids eternal night depart;
as the dawn of dawn on earth
morning breaks within the heart.

4 Out of darkness let light shine,
as it shone when light began;
earth be filled with light divine,
Christ be light for everyman!

from 2 Corinthians 4
© Timothy Dudley-Smith (born 1926)

For other hymns on this theme, see:
Sunday Themes index

GOD'S CHURCH:
HOPE AND CONFIDENCE

448

KILMARNOCK   8 6 8 6 (CM)   N. Dougall (1776–1862)

1   I'm not ashamed to name my Lord,
    or to defend his cause,
    maintain the honour of his word,
    the glory of his cross.

2   Jesus, my God! – I know his name,
    his name is all my trust;
    he will not put my soul to shame
    nor let my hope be lost.

3   Firm as his throne his promise stands,
    and he can well secure
    what he entrusted to my hands
    until that final hour.

4   Then he'll make known my worthless name
    before his Father's face,
    and in the new Jerusalem
    appoint to me a place.

I. Watts (1674–1748)
© in this version Jubilate Hymns†

449

TREWEN 8888D

D. E. Evans (1843–1913)

1 A debtor to mercy alone,
  of covenant-mercy I sing;
  nor fear, with your righteousness on,
  my person and offering to bring:
  the terrors of law and of God
  with me can have nothing to do;
  my saviour's obedience and blood
  hide all my transgressions from view.

2 The work which his goodness began,
the arm of his strength will complete;
his promise is 'Yes' and 'Amen',
and never was forfeited yet:
things future, nor things that are now,
nor all things below or above,
can make him his purpose forgo,
or sever my soul from his love.

3 Eternity will not erase
my name from the palms of his hands;
in marks of indelible grace
impressed on his heart it remains:
yes, I to the end shall endure,
as sure as the promise is given;
more happy, but not more secure
the glorified spirits in heaven.

A. Toplady (1740–1778)

450

CELESTE   8 8 8 8   *Lancashire Sunday School Songs* 1857

1 How good is the God we adore!
our faithful, unchangeable friend:
his love is as great as his power
and knows neither measure nor end.

2 For Christ is the first and the last;
his Spirit will guide us safe home:
we'll praise him for all that is past
and trust him for all that's to come.

J. Hart (1712–1768)

451(i)

MEINE HOFFNUNG   8 7 8 7 3 3 7   J. Neander's *Alpha and Omega* 1680

1 All my hope on God is founded,
   all my trust he shall renew;
   he, my guide through changing order,
   only good and only true:
        God unknown,
        he alone,
   calls my heart to be his own.

2 Human pride and earthly glory,
   sword and crown betray his trust;
   what with care and toil we fashion,
   tower and temple, fall to dust;
        but God's power
        hour by hour
   is my temple and my tower.

451(ii)

MICHAEL 8 7 8 7 3 3 7
Unison

H. N. Howells (1892–1983)
© Novello & Co Ltd

3 Day by day our mighty giver
   grants to us his gifts of love;
   in his will our souls find pleasure,
   leading to our home above:
       Love shall stand
       at his hand,
   joy shall wait for his command.

4 Still from earth to God eternal
   sacrifice of praise be done;
   high above all praises praising
   for the gift of Christ his Son:
       Hear Christ's call
       one and all –
   we who follow shall not fall.

after J. Neander (1650–1680)
R. Bridges (1844–1930)

452

SAGINA 8 8 8 8 8 8 extended   T. Campbell's *Bouquet* 1825

1 And can it be that I should gain an in-terest in the Sa-viour's blood? Died he for me, who caused his pain; for me, who him to death pur-sued? A-ma-zing love! – how can it be that you, my God, should die for me?

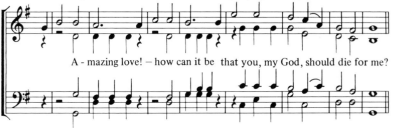

A-ma-zing love! – how can it be that you, my God, should die for me?

A - mazing love! – how can it be that you, my God, should die for me?

1   And can it be that I should gain
    an interest in the Saviour's blood?
    Died he for me, who caused his pain;
    for me, who him to death pursued?
    Amazing love! – how can it be
    that you, my God, should die for me?

2   What mystery here! – the Immortal dies;
    who can explore his strange design?
    In vain the first-born seraph tries
    to sound the depths of love divine.
    Such mercy this! – let earth adore;
    let angel minds enquire no more.

3   He left his Father's throne above –
    so free, so infinite his grace –
    emptied himself of all but love,
    and bled for Adam's helpless race.
    What mercy this, immense and free,
    for, O my God, it found out me!

4   Long my imprisoned spirit lay,
    fast bound in sin and nature's night:
    your sunrise turned that night to day;
    I woke – the dungeon flamed with light.
    My chains fell off, your voice I knew;
    I rose, went out and followed you!

5   No condemnation now I dread;
    Jesus, and all in him, is mine!
    Alive in him, my living head,
    and clothed in righteousness divine,
    bold I approach the eternal throne
    and claim the crown through Christ my own.

C. Wesley (1707–1788)
© in this version Jubilate Hymns†

(see also traditional version, 588)

453

BRESLAU   8 8 8 8 (LM)   Melody in *As Hymnodus Sacer* Leipzig 1625

1   Before the throne of God above
    I have a strong, a perfect plea:
    a great high priest, whose name is Love,
    who ever lives and pleads for me.

2   My name is written on his hands,
    my name is hidden in his heart;
    I know that while in heaven he stands
    no power can force me to depart.

3   When Satan tempts me to despair
    and tells me of the guilt within,
    upward I look, and see him there
    who made an end of all my sin.

4   Because the sinless Saviour died,
    my sinful soul is counted free;
    for God, the just, is satisfied
    to look on him and pardon me.

5   Behold him there! the risen Lamb,
    my perfect, sinless Righteousness,
    the great unchangeable I AM,
    the King of glory and of grace!

6   One with my Lord, I cannot die:
    my soul is purchased by his blood,
    my life is safe with Christ on high,
    with Christ, my saviour and my God.

Charitie L. de Chenez (1841–1923)

454

NEWCASTLE 86886

H. K. Morley (1830–1916)

1 Eternal light, eternal light!
  how pure the soul must be
  when, placed within your searching sight,
  it does not fear, but with delight
  can face such majesty.

2 The spirits who surround your throne
  may bear that burning bliss;
  but that is surely theirs alone,
  since they have never, never known
  a fallen world like this.

3 There is a way for us to rise
  to that sublime abode:
  an offering and a sacrifice,
  a Holy Spirit's energies,
  an advocate with God.

4 Such grace prepares us for the sight
  of holiness above;
  the child of ignorance and night
  may dwell in the eternal light
  through the eternal love.

T. Binney (1798–1874)

455

MORDEN   868686

© Norman Warren (born 1934)†

Unison

1 Father, although I cannot see
      the future you have planned,
   and though the path is sometimes dark
      and hard to understand:
   yet give me faith, through joy and pain,
      to trace your loving hand.

2 When I recall that in the past
      your promises have stood
   through each perplexing circumstance
      and every changing mood,
   I rest content that all things work
      together for my good.

3 Whatever, then, the future brings
      of good or seeming ill,
   I ask for strength to follow you
      and grace to trust you still;
   and I would look for no reward,
      except to do your will.

John Eddison (born 1916)
© Scripture Union

456

IT WAS A MAN   7 7 5 7 5 7 3

© David Wilson (born 1940)†

1 It was
    a man who was born
    when no one expected it,
    a king above all
    though no one suspected it.
    My God pledged his love,
    my joy has reflected it.
  So it was.

2 It was
    as though I'd been born
    when no one expected it,
    released from a past
    though no one suspected it;
    the future a gift,
    my joy has reflected it.
  So it is.

© Ernest Palfrey (born 1931)

457(i)

SOUTHWELL (IRONS) 8 6 8 6 (CM)   H. S. Irons (1834–1905)

1 *mf* He lives in us, the Christ of God,
        his Spirit joins with ours;
     he brings to us the Father's grace
        with powers beyond our powers.
  mp And if enticing sin grows strong,
        when human nature fails,
     God's Spirit in our inner self
        fights with us, and prevails.

2 Our pangs of guilt and fears of death
        are Satan's stratagems –
     by Jesus Christ who died for us
        God pardons; who condemns?
     And when we cannot feel our faith,
        nor bring ourselves to pray,
     the Spirit pleads with God for us
        in words we could not say.

3 *mf* God gave his Son to save us all –
        no other love like this!
     then shall he ever turn away
        from those he marks as his?
  f And God has raised him from the grave,
        in this we stand assured;
     so none can tear us from his love
        in Jesus Christ our Lord.

from Romans 8
© Michael Perry (born 1942)†

457(ii)

KINGSFOLD 8 6 8 6 D (DCM)

English traditional melody
arranged R. Vaughan Williams (1872–1958)
arrangement © Oxford University Press

458

PENLAN 7 6 7 6 D

D. Jenkins (1848–1915)

1 In heavenly love abiding,
   no change my heart shall fear:
   and safe is such confiding,
   for nothing changes here:
   the storm may roar around me,
   my heart may low be laid;
   my Father's arms surround me,
   how can I be afraid?

2 Wherever he may guide me
   no want shall turn me back;
   my shepherd is beside me
   and nothing can I lack:
   his wisdom is for ever,
   his sight is never dim;
   his love deserts me never
   and I will walk with him.

3 Green pastures are before me,
   which yet I have not seen;
   bright skies will shine with glory
   where threatening clouds have been:
   my hope I cannot measure,
   my path to life is free;
   my saviour has my treasure,
   and he will walk with me.

Anna L. Waring (1823–1910)
© in this version Jubilate Hymns†

459

YANWORTH 10 10 10 10　　　　　　　　　　　　© John Barnard (born 1948)†

1　In Christ shall all be made alive, we sing!
　　in him God's children into life shall spring;
　　though seed of Adam, creatures of the dust,
　　we rise again through Christ in whom we trust.

2　This Christ shall reign, and sin and death defeat,
　　beside the Father he will take his seat;
　　then shall God's children share that victory
　　and stand, new-clothed with immortality.

3　Yet here and now this faith is far from vain
　　for in God's Son a forward glimpse we gain;
　　in life's distress, with no fresh strength to draw,
　　we rise, through him,
　　　　　　　　to heights undreamed before.

4　In Christ shall all be made alive, we sing!
　　with him God's faithful servants he will bring;
　　gathered with joy before the Father's throne,
　　there we shall know, as we ourselves are known.

© David Mowbray (born 1938)†

460

GALILEE   8 8 8 8 (LM)   P. Armes (1836–1908)

1 Jesus, your blood and righteousness
   my beauty are, my glorious dress!
   mid flaming worlds, in these arrayed
   with joy shall I lift up my head.

2 Bold shall I stand in that great day,
   and none condemn me, try who may:
   fully absolved through Christ I am
   from sin and fear, from guilt and shame.

3 This stainless robe its beauty wears
   when all else fades with passing years;
   no age can change its glorious hue –
   the robe of Christ is ever new.

4 When from the dust of death I rise
   to claim my home beyond the skies,
   then this shall be my only plea –
   that Jesus died and lives for me!

5 O let the dead now hear your voice,
   let those once lost in sin rejoice!
   their beauty this, their glorious dress:
   Jesus, your blood and righteousness.

after N. L. von Zinzendorf (1700–1760)
J. Wesley (1703–1791)
© in this version Jubilate Hymns†

Alternative tune: FULDA (16)

461

JESU, MEINE FREUDE   6 6 5 6 6 5 7 8 6

J. Crüger (1598–1662)
arranged J. S. Bach (1685–1750)

1 Jesus, priceless treasure,
source of purest pleasure,
friend most sure and true:
long my heart was burning,
fainting much and yearning,
thirsting, Lord, for you:
yours I am, O spotless Lamb,
so will I let nothing hide you,
seek no joy beside you!

2 Let your arms surround me:
those who try to wound me
cannot reach me here;
though the world is shaking,
earth and nations quaking,
Jesus calms my fear:
Satan's force must run its course
and his bitter storms assail me;
Jesus will not fail me.

3 Banish thoughts of sadness
for the Lord of gladness,
Jesus, enters in;
though the clouds may gather,
those who love the saviour
still have peace within:
though I bear much sorrow here
still in you lies purest pleasure,
Jesus, priceless treasure!

after J. Franck (1618–1677)
Catherine Winkworth (1827–1878)
© in this version Jubilate Hymns†

462(i)

ST. CATHERINE 8 8 8 8 8 8

H. F. Hémy (1818–1888)
adapted J. G. Walton (1821–1905)

1 My hope is built on nothing less
   than Jesus' blood and righteousness;
   no merit of my own I claim,
   but wholly trust in Jesus' name.
         On Christ, the solid rock, I stand –
         all other ground is sinking sand.

2 When weary in this earthly race,
   I rest on his unchanging grace;
   in every wild and stormy gale
   my anchor holds and will not fail.
         On Christ, the solid rock . . .

3 His vow, his covenant and blood
   are my defence against the flood;
   when earthly hopes are swept away
   he will uphold me on that day.
         On Christ, the solid rock . . .

462(ii)

SURREY   888888

Later form of melody by
H. Carey (c. 1687–1743)

4   When the last trumpet's voice shall sound,
    O may I then in him be found!
    clothed in his righteousness alone,
    faultless to stand before his throne.
        On Christ the solid rock . . .

E. Mote (1797–1874)
© in this version Jubilate Hymns†

463

WYE VALLEY   6 5 6 5 Triple

J. Mountain (1844–1933)

1 Like a river glorious
   is God's perfect peace,
   over all victorious,
   in its bright increase:
   perfect, yet still flowing
   fuller every day;
   perfect, yet still growing
   deeper all the way.
        Trusting in the Father
        hearts are fully blessed,
        finding as he promised
        perfect peace and rest.

2 Hidden in the hollow
   of his mighty hand
   where no harm can follow,
   in his strength we stand:
   we may trust him fully
   all for us to do;
   those who trust him wholly
   find him wholly true.
        Trusting in the Father . . .

Frances R. Havergal (1836–1879)
© in this version Jubilate Hymns†

464

ST. MATTHIAS 888888

W. H. Monk (1823–1889)

1   Still near me, O my Saviour, stand
    and guard me in temptation's hour;
    within the hollow of your hand
    uphold me by your saving power:
    no force in earth or hell shall move
    or ever tear me from your love.

2   Still let your love point out my way –
    what gifts of grace your love has brought!
    still counsel me from day to day,
    direct my work, inspire my thought:
    and if I fall, soon let me hear
    your voice, and know that love is near.

3   In suffering, let your love be peace,
    in weakness let your love be power:
    and when the storms of life shall cease,
    Jesus, in that tremendous hour,
    through death to life still be my guide
    and save me then, for whom you died!

verse 1 C. Wesley (1707–1788)
verses 2 and 3 after P. Gerhardt (1607–1676)
J. Wesley (1703–1791)
© in this version Jubilate Hymns†

465

EBENEZER 8 7 8 7 D

T. J. Williams (1869–1944)
© representatives of the late Gwenlyn Evans

1 Oh the deep, deep love of Jesus,
  vast, unmeasured, boundless, free,
  rolling as a mighty ocean
  in its fulness over me!
  Underneath me, all around me,
  is the current of his love;
  leading onward, leading homeward
  to that glorious rest above.

2 Oh the deep, deep love of Jesus –
  spread his praise from shore to shore!
  he who loves us, ever loves us,
  changes never, nevermore:
  he who died to save his loved ones
  intercedes for them above;
  he who called them his own people
  watches over them in love.

3 Oh the deep, deep love of Jesus,
  love of every love the best;
  vast the ocean of his blessing,
  sweet the haven of his rest!
  Oh the deep, deep love of Jesus –
  for my Heaven of heavens is he;
  this my everlasting glory –
  Jesus' mighty love for me!

S. T. Francis (1834–1925)
© in this version Jubilate Hymns†

466

MARCHING 8 7 8 7

M. E. F. Shaw (1875–1958)
© J. Curwen & Sons Ltd/William Elkin Music Services

1 Through the night of doubt and sorrow
   onward goes the pilgrim band,
   singing songs of expectation,
   marching to the promised land.

2 One the hymn a thousand voices
   sing as from the heart of one;
   one the conflict, one the danger,
   one the march in God begun:

3 One the object of our journey,
   one the faith that never tires,
   one the urgent looking forward,
   one the hope our God inspires:

4 Courage, therefore, Christian pilgrims;
   with the cross before your eyes,
   bear its shame, and fight its battle –
   die with Christ, with Christ arise!

5 Soon shall come the great awakening,
   soon the bursting of the tomb;
   then the scattering of all shadows,
   and the end of tears and gloom.

after B. S. Ingemann (1789–1862)
S. Baring-Gould (1834–1924)
© in this version Jubilate Hymns†

467

PAX TECUM 10 10

G. T. Caldbeck (1852–1918)
and C. J. Vincent (1852–1934)

1 Peace, perfect peace, in this dark world of sin?
  the blood of Jesus gives us peace within.

2 Peace, perfect peace,
            by troubled thoughts oppressed?
  to do the will of Jesus, this is rest.

3 Peace, perfect peace,
            when loved ones are in need?
  in Jesus' keeping we are safe indeed.

4 Peace, perfect peace,
            the future all unknown?
  we know that Jesus reigns upon the throne.

5 Peace, perfect peace,
            death shadowing us and ours?
  Christ Jesus conquered death and all its powers.

6 Jesus is Lord! Earth's struggles soon shall cease,
  and we shall come to heaven's perfect peace.

E. H. Bickersteth (1825–1906)
© in this version Jubilate Hymns†

Alternative tune: SONG 46 (149)

For other hymns on this theme, see:
Sunday Themes index
    Section 37 (2), The Church's Confidence in Christ (p. xv)
    Section 55, The Christian Hope (p. xix)

GOD'S CHURCH:
LOVE AND DEVOTION

468

SONG 46   10 10   Orlando Gibbons (1583–1625)

1   Beloved, let us love: for love is of God;
    in God alone love has its true abode.

2   Beloved, let us love: for those who love,
    they only, are his children from above.

3   Beloved, let us love: for love is rest,
    and those who do not love cannot be blessed.

4   Beloved, let us love: for love is light,
    and those who do not love still live in night.

5   Beloved, let us love: for only thus
    shall we see God, the Lord, who first loved us.

H. Bonar (1808–1889)

469

J. Stainer (1840–1901)

1 All for Jesus, all for Jesus!
   this our song shall ever be:
   you our only hope, our saviour,
   yours the love that sets us free!

2 All for Jesus: you will give us
   strength to serve you hour by hour:
   none can move us from your presence
   while we trust your grace and power.

3 All for Jesus – you have loved us,
   all for Jesus – you have died,
   all for Jesus – you are with us;
   all for Jesus crucified.

4 All for Jesus, all for Jesus,
   all our talents and our powers,
   all our thoughts and words and actions,
   all our passing days and hours.

5 All for Jesus, all for Jesus!
   this the church's song shall be
   till at last her children gather,
   one in him eternally.

   W. J. Sparrow-Simpson (1859–1952)
   and Jubilate Hymns
   © amended text Novello and Company Ltd
   Printed by permission

470

OASIS 767666446

T. Brian Coleman (born 1920)
© Stainer & Bell Ltd

Unison

Instrumental or vocalized descant

1   As water to the thirsty,
    as beauty to the eyes,
    as strength that follows weakness,
    as truth instead of lies,
    as songtime and springtime
    and summertime to be,
        so is my Lord,
        my living Lord,
    so is my Lord to me.

2   Like calm in place of clamour,
    like peace that follows pain,
    like meeting after parting,
    like sunshine after rain,
    like moonlight and starlight
    and sunlight on the sea,
        so is my Lord,
        my living Lord,
    so is my Lord to me.

3   As sleep that follows fever,
    as gold instead of grey,
    as freedom after bondage,
    as sunrise to the day;
    as home to the traveller
    and all we long to see,
        so is my Lord,
        my living Lord,
    so is my Lord to me.

471(i)

BEYOND ALL KNOWLEDGE   10 10 10 10 4   © David Peacock (born 1949)†

1   Beyond all knowledge is your love divine,
    my Saviour, Jesus! Yet this soul of mine
    would of your love, in all its breadth and length,
    its height and depth, and everlasting strength,
        know more and more.

2   Beyond all telling is your love divine,
    my Saviour, Jesus! Yet this voice of mine
    would gladly share with sinners far and near
    your love which can remove all guilty fear
        and give love birth.

471(ii)

IT PASSETH KNOWLEDGE   10 10 10 10 4

I. D. Sankey (1840–1908)

3   Beyond all praising is your love divine,
    my Saviour, Jesus! Yet this heart of mine
    would sing your love, so full, so rich, so free,
    which brings a rebel sinner, such as me,
        back home to God.

4   O fill me, Saviour, Jesus, with your love!
    renew me with your Spirit from above;
    to you in simple faith let me draw near
    to know, to tell, to sing your love so dear,
        my Lord and king.

Mary Shekleton (1827–1883)
© in this version Jubilate Hymns†

472

ORIENTIS PARTIBUS (i)   7 7 7 7   P. de Corbeil (died 1222)

1 *mf* Christian, do you hear the Lord?
Jesus speaks his gracious word;
gently sounds the saviour's call,
'Do you love me best of all?'

2 'I delivered you when bound,
and when bleeding, healed your wound;
saw you wandering, set you right,
turned your darkness into light.'

3 'Can a mother's tenderness
for her own dear child grow less?
Though she may forgetful be,
you are always dear to me.'

4 'Mine is an unchanging love,
higher than the heights above,
deeper than the depths beneath,
free and faithful, strong as death.'

5 'You shall see my glory soon,
when the work of grace is done;
crowned with splendour you shall be:
Christian, come and follow me!'

6 *mp* Lord, it is my chief complaint
that my love is weak and faint;
mf yet I love you, and adore –
O for grace to love you more!

W. Cowper (1731–1800)
© in this version Jubilate Hymns†

473

BINCHESTER   8 6 8 6 (CM)

W. Croft (1678–1727)

1   Happy are they, they who love God,
    whose hearts have Christ confessed;
    who by his cross have found their life,
    beneath his yoke, their rest.

2   Glad is the praise, sweet are the songs,
    when they together sing;
    and strong the prayers that bow the ear
    of heaven's eternal king.

3   Christ gives their homes pleasure and peace
    and makes their loves his own;
    but O what weeds the evil one
    has in God's garden sown!

4   Sad were our life, evil this earth
    did not its sorrows prove
    the path by which the sheep may find
    the fold of Jesus' love.

5   Then they shall know, they who love him,
    how good shall come from pain;
    and death itself cannot unbind
    their happiness again.

after C. Coffin (1676–1749)
R. Bridges (1844–1930)

474(i)

CHARITY 7775

J. Stainer (1840–1901)

(ii)

GUILDFORD CATHEDRAL 7775

Grayston Ives (born 1948)
© Basil Ramsay Publishers of Music Ltd

Gently moving (𝅗𝅥 = c. 44)

For the above tune the composer suggests v. 1 full S.A.T.B., v. 2 soprano solo,
v. 3 full S.A.T.B. unacc., v. 4 tenor solo, v. 5 sopranos, v. 6 full unison or harmony.

1   Holy Spirit, gracious guest,
    hear and grant our heart's request
    for that gift supreme and best:
      holy heavenly love.

2   Faith that mountains could remove,
    tongues of earth or heaven above,
    knowledge, all things, empty prove
      if I have no love.

3   Though I as a martyr bleed,
    give my goods the poor to feed,
    all is vain if love I need:
      therefore give me love.

4   Love is kind and suffers long,
    love is pure and thinks no wrong,
    love than death itself more strong:
      therefore give us love.

5   Prophecy will fade away,
    melting in the light of day;
    love will ever with us stay:
      therefore give us love.

6   Faith and hope and love we see
    joining hand in hand agree –
    but the greatest of the three,
      and the best, is love.

from 1 Corinthians 13
C. Wordsworth (1807–1885)
© in this version Jubilate Hymns†

475

JANE 8 8 8 8 D (DLM)

© David Peacock (born 1949)†

1 *mf* I love you, O Lord, you alone,
my refuge on whom I depend;
my maker, my saviour, my own,
my hope and my trust without end:
the Lord is my strength and my song,
defender and guide of my ways;
my master to whom I belong,
my God who shall have all my praise.

2 *mp* The dangers of death gathered round,
the waves of destruction came near;
but in my despairing I found
the Lord who released me from fear:
I called for his help in my pain,
to God my salvation I cried;
mf he brought me his comfort again,
I live by the strength he supplied.

3 *f* My hope is the promise he gives,
my life is secure in his hand;
I shall not be lost, for he lives!
he comes to my aid – I shall stand!
Lord God, you are powerful to save,
your Spirit will spur me to pray;
your Son has defeated the grave:
I trust and I praise you today!

from Psalm 18
© Christopher Idle (born 1938)†

476(i)

ST. CHRYSOSTOM 8 8 8 8 8 8

J. Barnby (1838–1896)

Je-sus, my Lord, whom I ＿ a-dore, help me to love you more and more.

1   Jesus, my Lord, my God, my all –
      hear me, O Saviour, when I call;
      hear me, and from your dwelling-place
      pour down the riches of your grace:
         Jesus, my Lord, whom I adore,
         help me to love you more and more.

2   Jesus, too late I searched for you
      to pay the debt of love I owe:
      how can I sing your worthy fame,
      the glorious beauty of your name?
         Jesus, my Lord . . .

476(ii)

ST. MATTHIAS   888888   W. H. Monk (1823–1889)

3 Jesus, how strong your love must be
   that you should come to die for me;
   how great the joy that you have brought,
   so far exceeding hope or thought!
        Jesus, my Lord . . .

4 Jesus, your love shall be my song –
   to you my heart and soul belong:
   my life is yours, O Lord divine,
   and you, dear Saviour, you are mine:
        Jesus, my Lord . . .

H. Collins (1827–1919)
© in this version Jubilate Hymns†

477(i)

KING'S LYNN 7 6 7 6 D

English traditional melody
arranged R. Vaughan Williams (1872–1958)
arrangement © Oxford University Press

1 Light of the minds that know him,
    may Christ be light to mine!
my sun in risen splendour,
    my light of truth divine;
my guide in doubt and darkness,
    my true and living way,
my clear light ever shining,
    my dawn of heaven's day.

2 Life of the souls that love him,
    may Christ be ours indeed!
the living bread from heaven
    on whom our spirits feed;
who died for love of sinners
    to bear our guilty load,
and make of life's brief journey
    a new Emmaus road.

3 Strength of the wills that serve him,
    may Christ be strength to me,
who stilled the storm and tempest,
    who calmed the tossing sea;
his Spirit's power to move me,
    his will to master mine,
his cross to carry daily
    and conquer in his sign.

477(ii)

AURELIA 7 6 7 6 D

S. S. Wesley (1810–1876)

4 May it be ours to know him
  that we may truly love,
and loving, fully serve him
  as serve the saints above;
till in that home of glory
  with fadeless splendour bright,
we serve in perfect freedom
  our strength, our life, our light.

after Augustine (354–430)
© Timothy Dudley-Smith (born 1926)

Alternative tune: EWING (573)

478

ST. AGNES (DYKES)   8 6 8 6 (CM)

J. B. Dykes (1823–1876)

1 Jesus, the very thought of you
   makes every moment blessed,
   until we come where all is new
   and in your presence rest.

2 No ear can hear, no voice proclaim,
   nor can the heart recall
   a sweeter sound than Jesus' name,
   the saviour of us all.

3 Hope of each contrite, humble mind,
   joy of the poor and meek;
   to those who falter, you are kind,
   and good to those who seek!

4 But what to those who find? Ah, this
   no tongue nor pen can show!
   The love of Jesus – what it is
   none but his loved ones know.

5 Jesus, be all our glory here,
   our joy and prize alone;
   our all-in-all when we draw near
   to your eternal throne.

from the Latin (twelfth century)
E. Caswall (1814–1878)
© in this version Jubilate Hymns†

479

ST. FRANCIS XAVIER   8 6 8 6 (CM)   J. Stainer (1840–1901)

1 My God, I love you; not because
   I hope for heaven thereby,
   nor yet because if I do not
   I shall for ever die.

2 But you, Lord Jesus, on the cross
   once suffered in my place;
   for me you bore the nails and spear,
   the darkness and disgrace:

3 And griefs and torments numberless
   and sweat of agony,
   and even death itself, for one
   who was your enemy.

4 Then why, O Saviour Jesus Christ,
   should I not love you well?
   not for the sake of winning heaven
   nor of escaping hell:

5 Not with the thought of seeking gain
   nor working for reward,
   but as you gave yourself for me,
   O ever-loving Lord.

6 So now I love you, and will love,
   and in your praise will sing,
   solely because you are my God
   and my eternal king.

from the Latin (seventeenth century)
E. Caswall (1814–1878)
© in this version Jubilate Hymns†

Alternative tunes: BEULAH (108)
             STOCKTON (483)

480(i)

RYBURN 888888

N. Cocker (1889–1953)
© Oxford University Press

1 Lord God, your love has called us here
as we, by love, for love were made;
your living likeness still we bear,
though marred, dishonoured, disobeyed.
We come, with all our heart and mind
your call to hear, your love to find.

2 We come with self-inflicted pains
of broken trust and chosen wrong,
half-free, half-bound by inner chains,
by social forces swept along,
by powers and systems close confined
yet seeking hope for humankind.

3 Lord God, in Christ you call our name
and then receive us as your own
not through some merit, right or claim
but by your gracious love alone.
We strain to glimpse your mercy seat
and find you kneeling at our feet.

480 (ii)

MELITA 888888

J. B. Dykes (1823–1876)

4 Then take the towel, and break the bread,
  and humble us, and call us friends;
  suffer and serve till all are fed
  and show how grandly love intends
      to work till all creation sings,
      to fill all worlds, to crown all things.

5 Lord God, in Christ you set us free
  your life to live, your joy to share:
  give us your Spirit's liberty
  to turn from guilt and dull despair,
      and offer all that faith can do
      while love is making all things new.

Brian Wren (born 1936)
© Oxford University Press

481

CRESSWELL 8 8 9 7 10 7

Anthony Milner (born 1925)
© McCrimmon Publishing Co Ltd

Rich-er than gold is the love of my Lord, bet-ter than splen-dour and wealth.

1 Love is his word, love is his way,
feasting with all, fasting alone,
living and dying, rising again,
love, only love, is his way:
   Richer than gold is the love of my Lord,
   better than splendour and wealth.

2 Love is his way, love is his mark,
sharing his last Passover feast,
Christ at his table, host to the twelve,
love, only love, is his mark:
   Richer than gold . . .

3 Love is his mark, love is his sign,
bread for our strength, wine for our joy,
'This is my body, this is my blood' –
love, only love, is his sign:
   Richer than gold . . .

4 Love is his sign, love is his news,
'Do this,' he said, 'lest you forget
all my deep sorrow, all my dear blood' –
love, only love, is his news:
   Richer than gold . . .

5 Love is his news, love is his name,
we are his own, chosen and called,
family, brethren, cousins and kin,
love, only love, is his name:
   Richer than gold . . .

6 Love is his name, love is his law,
hear his command, all who are his:
'Love one another, I have loved you' –
love, only love, is his law.
   Richer than gold . . .

7 Love is his law, love is his word:
love of the Lord, Father and Word,
love of the Spirit, God ever one,
love, only love, is his word:
   Richer than gold . . .

L. Connaughton (1917–1979)
© McCrimmon Publishing Co Ltd

482(i)

EVERLASTING LOVE   7 7 7 7 D extended   J. Mountain (1844–1933)

1 Loved with everlasting love,
    led by grace that love to know;
    Spirit, breathing from above,
    you have taught me it is so:
    O what full and perfect peace,
    joy and wonder all divine!
    In a love which cannot cease,
    I am his and he is mine.
        In a love . . .

2 Heaven above is softer blue,
    earth around is richer green;
    something lives in every hue,
    Christless eyes have never seen:
    songs of birds in sweetness grow,
    flowers with deeper beauties shine,
    since I know, as now I know,
    I am his and he is mine.
        Since I know . . .

482(ii)

CALON LÂN 7777D

J. Hughes (1873–1932)
© arranged John Barnard (born 1948)†

When the tune CALON LÂN is used the last two lines of each verse are not repeated.

3 His for ever, his alone!
   who the Lord from me shall part?
   With what joy and peace unknown
   Christ can fill the loving heart!
   Heaven and earth may pass away,
   sun and stars in gloom decline,
   but of Christ I still shall say:
   I am his and he is mine.
      But of Christ . . .

G. W. Robinson (1838–1877)

483(i)

STOCKTON 8 6 8 6 (CM)

T. Wright (1763–1829)

1 O for a heart to praise my God –
 a heart from sin set free,
 a heart that's sprinkled with the blood
 so freely shed for me.

2 A heart resigned, submissive, meek,
 my great redeemer's throne;
 where only Christ is heard to speak,
 where Jesus reigns alone.

3 A humble, lowly, contrite heart,
 believing, true, and clean,
 which neither life nor death can part
 from him who dwells within.

4 A heart in every thought renewed,
 and full of love divine;
 perfect and right and pure and good –
 your life revealed in mine.

5 Your nature, gracious Lord, impart –
 come quickly from above,
 write your new name upon my heart,
 your new best name of love!

C. Wesley (1707–1788)

483(ii)

ST. STEPHEN   8 6 8 6 (CM)   W. Jones (1726–1800)

1   O for a heart to praise my God –
    a heart from sin set free,
    a heart that's sprinkled with the blood
    so freely shed for me.

2   A heart resigned, submissive, meek,
    my great redeemer's throne;
    where only Christ is heard to speak,
    where Jesus reigns alone.

3   A humble, lowly, contrite heart,
    believing, true, and clean,
    which neither life nor death can part
    from him who dwells within.

4   A heart in every thought renewed,
    and full of love divine;
    perfect and right and pure and good –
    your life revealed in mine.

5   Your nature, gracious Lord, impart –
    come quickly from above,
    write your new name upon my heart,
    your new best name of love!

                    C. Wesley (1707–1788)

484(i)

ST. BOTOLPH 8 6 8 6 (CM)

G. A. Slater (1896–1979)

(ii)

ST. BERNARD 8 6 8 6 (CM)

Tochter Zion Cologne 1741

484(iii)

METZLER   8 6 8 6 (CM)   R. Redhead (1820–1901)

1   O Jesus, king most wonderful
    and conqueror renowned;
    O sweetness inexpressible
    in whom all joys are found!

2   When you draw near and touch the heart
    then truth begins to shine;
    then this world's vanities depart,
    then kindles love divine.

3   O Jesus, light of all below,
    the fount of living fire,
    surpassing all the joys we know
    and all we can desire.

4   Jesus, may all confess your name,
    your tender love adore,
    and seeking you, themselves inflame
    to seek you more and more.

5   O Jesus whom our voices bless,
    whom we would love alone;
    for ever let our lives express
    the image of your own.

from the Latin (twelfth century)
E. Caswall (1814–1878)
© in this version Jubilate Hymns†

485(i)

PATER OMNIUM 888888

H. J. E. Holmes (1852–1938)
© Executors of the late Miss C. J. Holmes

1   O Lord my love, my strength, my tower,
     O Lord my hope, my joy, my crown:
     O let me love with all my power
     your works, yourself and you alone;
     and love until your sacred fire
     shall fill my soul with pure desire.

2   I thank you, uncreated Sun,
     that in my heart your radiance shined,
     that Satan's power was overthrown,
     that you restored my wounded mind;
     I welcome your life-giving voice,
     and in your freedom I rejoice.

485(ii)

ST. MATTHIAS   888888   W. H. Monk (1823–1889)

3 Support me in the strenuous race
   and do not let my footsteps stray;
   still strengthen me with heavenly grace
   to persevere upon your way;
   to serve you, Lord, with all my might
   and make your glory my delight.

4 O Lord my love, my strength, my tower,
   O Lord my hope, my joy, my crown:
   O let me love you in the hour
   of joy or pain – your smile or frown;
   and when my flesh and heart decay,
   that love shall flower in endless day.

after J. Scheffler (1624–1677)
J. Wesley (1703–1791)
© in this version Jubilate Hymns†

486

ST. MARGARET   8 8 8 8 6   A. L. Peace (1844–1912)

1 O love that will not let me go,
   revive your loveliness in me:
   I give you back the life I owe
   that in your ocean depths its flow
      may richer, fuller be.

2 O light that follows all my way,
   renew your radiance in me:
   I welcome your life-giving ray
   that in your sunshine's blaze each day
      may brighter, fairer be.

3 O joy that seeks for me through pain,
   restore your hopefulness to me;
   I trace the rainbow through the rain
   and trust your promise once again:
      that dawn shall tearless be.

4 O cross that raises up my head,
   remove the sinfulness from me:
   I lay in dust life's glory dead,
   and from the ground there blossoms red,
      life that shall endless be.

G. Matheson (1842–1906)
© in this version Word & Music†

487(i)

BOURNE   8 7 8 8 7 extended

F. B. Westbrook (1903–1975)

1   Oh the bitter shame and sorrow
    that a time could ever be
    when I let the Saviour's pity
    plead in vain, and proudly answered,
    'None of you and all of me!'

2   Yet you found me; there I saw you
    dying and in agony,
    heard you pray, 'Forgive them, Father',
    and my wistful heart said faintly,
    'Some of you and some of me.'

487(ii)

ST. JUDE 8 7 8 8 7

C. J. Vincent (1852–1934)

3 Day by day your tender mercy,
    healing, helping, full and free,
    firm and strong, with endless patience
    brought me lower, while I whispered,
    'More of you and less of me.'

4 Higher than the highest heaven,
    deeper than the deepest sea,
    Lord, your love at last has conquered:
    grant me now my spirit's longing,
    'All of you and none of me!'

T. Monod (1836–1921)
© in this version Jubilate Hymns†

488

LITTLE CORNARD 666688

M. E. F. Shaw (1875–1958)

1   Praise for the mighty love
    which God through Christ made known;
    love which for others lived,
    died on the cross alone;
    the love which heightens all our powers,
    the love which makes the future ours.

2   Courage to face the worst
    that others do or say,
    eloquence, faith or skill,
    fortunes to give away;
    the means to feed the human race
    or power to fathom farthest space:

3   Left unrefined by love
    all these are empty noise,
    like instruments untuned
    or useless, broken toys:
    but he who died for love outlives
    ambition's greatest victories.

4   Love makes the future bright,
    transcending greed and pride;
    life's possibilities
    by love are opened wide;
    and heights which seemed impossible
    by love are made accessible.

5   Love is the life of God
    lived in our lives again;
    this is the life for us,
    worth all its hurt and pain;
    and in the power of love we'll live
    to greet the future God will give!

© Alan Gaunt (born 1935)

For other hymns on this theme, see:
Sunday Themes index
   Section 41, The More Excellent Way (p. xvii)
Additional Hymns
   King of glory (603)
Song Section
   The new commandment (S.26)

GOD'S CHURCH:
UNITY AND GROWTH

489

MEAD HOUSE   8 7 8 7 D

1   All-creating heavenly Giver,
    bringing light and life to birth;
    all-sustaining heavenly Father
    of the families of earth:
        We, your children, lift our voices
        singing gladly of your love:
        never-ending are the praises
        rising to your throne above.

2   Ever-living Lord and Saviour,
    breaking chains of sin and shame;
    ever-loving Intercessor,
    all shall triumph in your name:
        We, your servants liberated
        at a fearful ransom-price,
        in your kingdom are united
        by that mighty sacrifice.

3   Life-conceiving Wind of heaven,
    breathing gifts upon us all;
    life-enhancing Spirit, given
    to enrich us, great and small:
        We, whose talents widely differ,
        now restore to you your own,
        and in true thanksgiving offer
        all we are before the throne.

4   Father, Son and Holy Spirit,
    blessing all within your hand:
    full the cup that we inherit,
    firm the ground on which we stand:
        We, your people, undeserving
        of the grace you freely give,
        now and ever, in thanksgiving
        to your praise and glory live.

490

LAUDATE DOMINUM   10 10 11 11   C. H. H. Parry (1848–1918)

1   As sons of the day and daughters of light,
    no longer we sleep like creatures of night:
    for Jesus has died that with him we may live;
    by all that he gave us, we learn how to give.

2   One body in Christ, let all play their part:
    the lazy be warned, the timid take heart;
    let those who are hurt never pay back with wrong,
    but serve one another: together be strong!

3   Be constant in prayer, at all times rejoice,
    in all things give thanks – let God hear your voice!
    alive to his Spirit, alert to his word,
    test all things, and hold to what pleases the Lord.

4   May God who first called, gave peace and made whole,
    preserve us from fault in body and soul:
    our Lord Jesus Christ keep us firm in his grace
    until at his coming we meet face to face.

from 1 Thessalonians 5
© Christopher Idle (born 1938)†

491

CULBACH 7 7 7 7

Adapted from a chorale in J. Scheffler's
Heilige Seelenlust Breslau 1657

1 Christ, from whom all blessings flow,
  by whose grace your people grow;
  Christ whose nature now we share,
  work in us, your body here.

2 Send your Spirit from above
  and unite us in your love;
  still for more to you we call –
  with your fulness fill us all.

3 Move and motivate and guide,
  varying gifts for each provide;
  placed according to your will,
  let us all our work fulfil.

4 Gladly may we all agree,
  bound in one community;
  kindly for each other care –
  all our joys and sorrows share.

5 Love has all our strife destroyed,
  rendered all divisions void;
  sects and names and parties fall:
  you, O Christ, are all in all.

C. Wesley (1707–1788)
© in this version Jubilate Hymns✝

492

VULPIUS 8 8 8 4

Melody M. Vulpius (c. 1560–1616)

Al - le - lu - ia, al - le - lu - ia, al - le - lu - ia!

1 Christ is the king! O friends rejoice;
brothers and sisters, with one voice
let the world know he is your choice.
    Alleluia, alleluia, alleluia!

2 O magnify the Lord, and raise
anthems of joy and holy praise
for Christ's brave saints of ancient days.
    Alleluia . . .

3 They with a faith for ever new
followed the king, and round him drew
thousands of servants brave and true.
    Alleluia . . .

4 O Christian women, Christian men,
all the world over, seek again
the way disciples followed then.
    Alleluia . . .

5 Christ through all ages is the same:
place the same hope in his great name;
with the same faith his word proclaim.
    Alleluia . . .

6 Let Love's unconquerable might
 your scattered companies unite
 in service to the Lord of light.
  Alleluia . . .

7 So shall God's will on earth be done,
 new lamps be lit, new tasks begun,
 and the whole church at last be one.
  Alleluia . . .

G. K. A. Bell (1883–1958)
© Oxford University Press

493

SANDYS 6 6 8 6 (SM)

English traditional melody
from W. Sandys' *Christmas Carols* 1833

1 Help us, O Lord, to learn
 the truths your word imparts,
 to study that your laws may be
 inscribed upon our hearts.

2 Help us, O Lord, to live
 the faith which we proclaim,
 that all our thoughts and words and deeds
 may glorify your name.

3 Help us, O Lord, to teach
 the beauty of your ways,
 that yearning souls may find the Christ
 and sing aloud his praise.

William Reid, junior (born 1923)
© 1959 by The Hymn Society of America/
Hope Publishing Company

494(i)

AUSTRIA 8787D

Croatian folk tune
adapted F. J. Haydn (1732–1809)
descant T. H. Ingham (1878–1948)
descant © Oxford University Press

Descant

4 Sa - viour, since of Zi -on's ci - ty I __ through grace a mem-ber am,

let the_world de - ride or pi - ty, I __ will glo - ry in your name:

fa-ding are the world's best plea-sures, all its_boast-ed__ pomp and show;

so-lid joys and last-ing trea-sures none but Zi - on's child-ren know.

1 Glorious things of you are spoken,
   Zion, city of our God;
   he whose word cannot be broken
   formed you for his own abode:
   on the rock of ages founded,
   what can shake your sure repose?
   with salvation's walls surrounded
   you may smile at all your foes.

2 See, the streams of living waters
   springing from eternal love!
   well supply your sons and daughters
   and all fear of want remove:
   who can faint while such a river
   ever flows their thirst to assuage?
   grace, which like the Lord the giver
   never fails from age to age.

3 Round each habitation hovering
   see the cloud and fire appear
   for a glory and a covering,
   showing that the Lord is near:
   thus they march, the pillar leading,
   light by night and shade by day;
   daily on the manna feeding
   which he gives them when they pray.

4 Saviour, since of Zion's city
   I through grace a member am,
   let the world deride or pity,
   I will glory in your name:
   fading are the world's best pleasures,
   all its boasted pomp and show;
   solid joys and lasting treasures
   none but Zion's children know.

                    J. Newton (1725–1807)

494(ii)

ABBOT'S LEIGH 8 7 8 7 D

Cyril Taylor (born 1907)
© Oxford University Press

A descant and arrangement for verse 4 is printed overleaf.

1 Glorious things of you are spoken,
   Zion, city of our God;
   he whose word cannot be broken
   formed you for his own abode:
   on the rock of ages founded,
   what can shake your sure repose?
   with salvation's walls surrounded
   you may smile at all your foes.

2 See, the streams of living waters
   springing from eternal love!
   well supply your sons and daughters
   and all fear of want remove:
   who can faint while such a river
   ever flows their thirst to assuage?
   grace, which like the Lord the giver
   never fails from age to age.

3 Round each habitation hovering
   see the cloud and fire appear
   for a glory and a covering,
   showing that the Lord is near:
   thus they march, the pillar leading,
   light by night and shade by day;
   daily on the manna feeding
   which he gives them when they pray.

4 Saviour, since of Zion's city
   I through grace a member am,
   let the world deride or pity,
   I will glory in your name:
   fading are the world's best pleasures,
   all its boasted pomp and show;
   solid joys and lasting treasures
   none but Zion's children know.

J. Newton (1725–1807)

494 – Glorious things of you are spoken

Descant and arrangement John Wilson (born 1905)
© Oxford University Press

4 Saviour, since of Zion's city I through grace a member am, let the world deride or pity, I will glory in your name:

fa – ding are the world's best pleasures, all its boast – ed pomp and show; so – lid joys and last – ing trea – sures none but Zi – on's child – ren know.

495

EPIPHANY HYMN   11 10 11 10   J. F. Thrupp (1827–1867)

1 God of eternity, Lord of the ages,
   Father and Saviour and Spirit you reign;
   yours is the glory of time's numbered pages,
   yours is the power to revive us again.

2 Thankful, we come to you, Lord of the nations,
   praising your faithfulness, mercy, and grace
   shown through the story of past generations,
   pledge of your love to each people and race.

3 Wherever home may be, parted by oceans,
   there is Jerusalem, there God adored;
   we lift our hearts in united devotions –
   ends of the earth, join in praise to the Lord!

4 Yours is the heritage, generous Giver!
   brightly the heavens your glory declare;
   bright streams the sunlight
                  on mountain and river,
   bright shines the cross over fields rich and fair.

5 Pardon our sinfulness, God of all pity,
   call to remembrance your mercies of old;
   strengthen your church to stand firm as a city
   set on a hill as a light for the world.

6 Head of the church on earth, risen, ascended,
   yours is the honour that lives in this place;
   as you have blessed us in years that have ended,
   still lift upon us the light of your face!

E. Merrington (1876–1953)
in © Christian Conference of Asia Hymnal
and in this version Jubilate Hymns
revised and reprinted by permission

496(i)

UNION 8 5 8 5

© David Iliff (born 1939)†

1 God our Father, bless your people
that we may be one;
one in heart and one in worship,
love's communion.

2 Christ our Saviour, keep your people
that we may be one;
one in prayer and one in service,
joyful union.

3 Holy Spirit, guide your people
that we may be one;
one in faith and one in purpose,
truth's dominion.

4 Praise together God the Father,
serving Christ alone;
in the Spirit be united:
God is Three in One!

© Michael Perry (born 1942)†

496(ii)

SHARNBROOK   8 5 8 5   © Paul Edwards (born 1955)†

God — is — Three in One!

1   God our Father, bless your people
    that we may be one;
    one in heart and one in worship,
    love's communion.

2   Christ our Saviour, keep your people
    that we may be one;
    one in prayer and one in service,
    joyful union.

3   Holy Spirit, guide your people
    that we may be one;
    one in faith and one in purpose,
    truth's dominion.

4   Praise together God the Father,
    serving Christ alone;
    in the Spirit be united:
    God is Three in One!

© Michael Perry (born 1942)†

497(i)

STEEPLE ASHTON   6 6 8 6 (SM)   © John Barnard (born 1948)†

(ii)

UNITED MAN   6 6 8 6 (SM)   © Norman Warren (born 1934)†

497(iii)

HOLYROOD 6 6 8 6 (SM)   J. Watson (1816–1880)

1 How good a thing it is,
  how pleasant to behold,
  when all God's people live at one,
  the law of love uphold!

2 As perfume, by its scent,
  breathes fragrance all around,
  so life itself will sweeter be
  where unity is found.

3 And like refreshing dew
  that falls upon the hills,
  true union sheds its gentle grace,
  and deeper love instils.

4 God grants his choicest gifts
  to those who live in peace;
  to them his blessings shall abound
  and evermore increase.

from Psalm 133
J. E. Seddon (1915–1983)
© Mrs. M. Seddon†

498

CHRISTMAS CAROL   8 6 8 6 D (DCM)

H. Walford Davies (1869–1941)
© Oxford University Press

1 Look, Lord, in mercy as we pray,
   on tasks as yet undone;
   fire us anew to seek the day
   that makes our churches one:
   heirs to one work of grace divine –
   one Spirit freely given,
   one pledge in sacrament and sign,
   one cross the hope of heaven.

2 One living faith be ours to learn
   with saints in every age,
   one timeless word of truth discern
   in scripture's sacred page:
   make us, with new resolve, begin
   one common call to own;
   to be one church one world to win,
   and make one saviour known.

3 Hear us who join in praise and prayer
   one act of faith to bring,
   children who own one Father's care,
   soldiers who serve one king:
   your kingdom come, O Lord, we pray,
   your will on earth be done;
   our sins and errors purge away
   and make our churches one.

499

LONDONDERRY AIR   11 10 11 10 D

Irish traditional melody
© arranged John Barnard (born 1948)†

1 *mf* Lord of the church, we pray for our renewing:
    Christ over all, our undivided aim.
    Fire of the Spirit, burn for our enduing,
    wind of the Spirit, fan the living flame!
  mp We turn to Christ amid our fear and failing,
    the will that lacks the courage to be free,
    the weary labours, all but unavailing,
    to bring us nearer what a church should be.

2   Lord of the church, we seek a Father's blessing,
    a true repentance and a faith restored,
    a swift obedience and a new possessing,
    filled with the Holy Spirit of the Lord!
    We turn to Christ from all our restless striving,
    unnumbered voices with a single prayer –
    the living water for our souls' reviving,
    in Christ to live, and love and serve and care.

3 *mf* Lord of the church, we long for our uniting,
    true to one calling, by one vision stirred;
    one cross proclaiming and one creed reciting,
    one in the truth of Jesus and his word!
   f So lead us on; till toil and trouble ended,
    one church triumphant one new song shall sing,
    to praise his glory, risen and ascended,
    Christ over all, the everlasting king!

© Timothy Dudley-Smith (born 1926)

500

NEW MALDEN   8 7 8 7 8 7

David McCarthy (born 1931)

1 *mf* Risen Lord, whose name we cherish,
  all the stars are in your hand!
  Walk today among your people,
  light each candle on its stand;
  look in mercy, not in judgement,
  on your church in every land.

2 *mp* For, divided in your service,
  we have chosen selfish ways,
  lived in bitterness of spirit,
  quickly let our anger blaze;
  often blindly followed leaders,
  sought our glory, not your praise.

3 *mf* Yet your church has also triumphed,
  told of love's great offering,
  in its life shown forth your goodness,
  drawn from death its cruel sting;
  wakened to the needs of many,
  soothed the sorrows life can bring.

4 *mp* So, we pray, that by your Spirit
  all your scattered flock may find
  that deep unity you prayed for
  and would share with all mankind;
  by this gift our fears and envies
  shall in truth be left behind.

5 *mf* Risen Lord, your hand is knocking
  at each church's bolted door!
  Enter now, and dwell within us,
  trust and fellowship restore;
 f that your Father's joys together
  all may taste for evermore.

© David Mowbray (born 1938)†

501

AURELIA 7 6 7 6 D

S. S. Wesley (1810–1876)

An arrangement with descant may be found at 502.

1 The church's one foundation
   is Jesus Christ her Lord;
   she is his new creation
   by water and the word:
   from heaven he came and sought her
   to be his holy bride;
   with his own blood he bought her
   and for her life he died.

2 Called out from every nation,
   yet one through all the earth;
   her charter of salvation –
   one Lord, one faith, one birth:
   one holy name she blesses,
   and shares one holy food;
   as to one hope she presses
   with every grace endued.

3 We see her long divided
   by heresy and sect;
   yet she by God is guided –
   one people, one elect:
   her vigil she is keeping,
   her cry goes up, 'How long?'
   and soon the night of weeping
   shall be the dawn of song.

4 In toil and tribulation,
   and tumult of her war,
   she waits the consummation
   of peace for evermore:
   till with the vision glorious
   her longing eyes are blessed;
   at last the church victorious
   shall be the church at rest!

5 Yet she on earth has union
   with God the Three-in-One;
   and mystic, sweet communion
   with those whose rest is won:
   O happy ones and holy!
   Lord, grant to us your grace,
   with them the meek and lowly,
   in heaven to see your face.

S. J. Stone (1839–1900)

502

AURELIA   7 6 7 6 D   S. S. Wesley (1810–1876)

1   O Christ the great foundation
        on which your people stand
    to preach your true salvation
        in every age and land:
    pour out your Holy Spirit
        to make us strong and pure,
    to keep the faith unbroken
        as long as worlds endure.

2 Baptized in one confession,
    one church in all the earth,
we bear our Lord's impression,
    the sign of second birth:
one fellowship united
    in love beyond our own –
by grace we were invited,
    by grace we make you known.

3 Where tyrants' hold is tightened,
    where strong devour the weak,
where innocents are frightened
    and righteous fear to speak,
there let your church awaking
    attack the powers of sin
and, all their ramparts breaking,
    with you the victory win.

4 The gates of hell are yielding,
    the hordes of Satan fly,
for Christ the Lord is wielding
    the sword of victory:
this is the moment glorious
    when he who once was dead
shall lead his church victorious,
    their champion and their head.

5 He comes with acclamation
    to claim his holy bride;
she stands in exultation,
    the Bridegroom at her side:
the Lord of all creation
    his Father's kingdom brings –
the final consummation,
    the glory of all things.

after T. T'ing Fang Lew (c.1936)
in © Christian Conference of Asia Hymnal
and in this version Jubilate Hymns
revised and reprinted by permission

Descant and arrangement © Noël Tredinnick (born 1949)†

5 He comes with ac-cla - ma - tion to_claim his ho-ly   bride; _   she

503

PARKSTONE   6 6 6 6   © David Peacock (born 1949)†

1   Now let us learn of Christ:
     he speaks, and we shall find
     he lightens our dark mind;
     so let us learn of Christ.

2   Now let us love in Christ
     as he has first loved us;
     as he endured the cross,
     so let us love in Christ.

3   Now let us grow in Christ
     and look to things above,
     and speak the truth in love;
     so let us grow in Christ.

4   Now let us stand in Christ
     in every trial we meet,
     in all his strength complete;
     so let us stand in Christ.

© Christopher Idle (born 1938)†

Alternative tunes: QUAM DILECTA (558)
               BEWELEY (250)

For other hymns on this theme, see:
Sunday Themes index
   Section 36 (2), The Church's Unity and Fellowship (p. xv)
Song Section
   Bind us together, Lord (S.4)

GOD'S CHURCH:
MISSION AND MINISTRY

504

LUX EOI   8 7 8 7 D

A. Sullivan (1842–1900)

1 Church of God, elect and glorious,
   holy nation, chosen race;
   called as God's own special people,
   royal priests and heirs of grace:
   know the purpose of your calling,
   show to all his mighty deeds;
   tell of love which knows no limits,
   grace which meets all human needs.

2 God has called you out of darkness
   into his most marvellous light;
   brought his truth to life within you,
   turned your blindness into sight.
   Let your light so shine around you
   that God's name is glorified;
   and all find fresh hope and purpose
   in Christ Jesus crucified.

3 Once you were an alien people,
   strangers to God's heart of love;
   but he brought you home in mercy,
   citizens of heaven above.
   Let his love flow out to others,
   let them feel a Father's care;
   that they too may know his welcome
   and his countless blessings share.

4 Church of God, elect and holy,
   be the people he intends;
   strong in faith and swift to answer
   each command your master sends:
   royal priests, fulfil your calling
   through your sacrifice and prayer;
   give your lives in joyful service –
   sing his praise, his love declare.

from 1 Peter 2
J. E. Seddon (1915–1983)
© Mrs. M. Seddon†

505(i)

YANWORTH   10 10 10 10   © John Barnard (born 1948)†

1   Go forth and tell! O church of God, awake!
    God's saving news to all the nations take;
    proclaim Christ Jesus, saviour, Lord, and king,
    that all the world his worthy praise may sing.

2   Go forth and tell! God's love embraces all;
    he will in grace respond to all who call:
    how shall they call if they have never heard
    the gracious invitation of his word?

3   Go forth and tell where still the darkness lies;
    in wealth or want, the sinner surely dies:
    give us, O Lord, concern of heart and mind,
    a love like yours which cares for all mankind.

505(ii)

GO FORTH   10 10 10 10

4   Go forth and tell! The doors are open wide:
    share God's good gifts – let no one be denied;
    live out your life as Christ your Lord shall choose,
    your ransomed powers for his sole glory use.

5   Go forth and tell! O church of God, arise!
    go in the strength
            which Christ your Lord supplies;
    go till all nations his great name adore
    and serve him, Lord and king for evermore.

506

MOSCOW   6 6 4 6 6 6 4   F. de Giardini (1716–1796)

1 *f* God, whose almighty word
   chaos and darkness heard,
   and took their flight:
 mf hear us, we humbly pray,
   and where the gospel-day
   sheds not its glorious ray,
 f   let there be light!

2 *mf* Saviour, who came to bring
   on your redeeming wing
   healing and sight,
   health to the sick in mind,
   sight to the inly blind:
   O now to all mankind
 f   let there be light!

3 *mf* Spirit of truth and love,
   life-giving, holy dove,
   speed on your flight!
   move on the water's face
   bearing the lamp of grace
   and, in earth's darkest place,
 f   let there be light!

4   Gracious and holy Three,
   glorious Trinity,
   wisdom, love, might:
   boundless as ocean's tide
   rolling in fullest pride
   through the world far and wide,
   let there be light!

J. Marriott (1780–1825)

Descant

4 Gra-cious and ho-ly__ Three, glo-ri-ous Tri — ni-ty,

wis-dom,_love, might: bound-less as o-cean's tide roll-ing in

full — est pride far _____ and wide, let_there be_ light!

507(i)

PEMBROKE 868688

P. A. S. Hadley (1899–1973)
© Oxford University Press

1 How shall they hear the word of God
unless his truth is told;
how shall the sinful be set free,
the sorrowful consoled?
To all who speak the truth today
impart your Spirit, Lord, we pray.

507(ii)

O JESU 8 6 8 6 8 8

Evangelisches Gesangbuch Hirschberg 1741

2 How shall they call to God for help
   unless they have believed;
   how shall the poor be given hope,
   the prisoner reprieved?
        To those who help the blind to see
        give light and love and clarity.

3 How shall the gospel be proclaimed
   that sinners may repent;
   how shall the world find peace at last
   if heralds are not sent?
        So send us, Lord, for we rejoice
        to speak of Christ with life and voice.

from Romans 10
© Michael Perry (born 1942)†

508

CRUCIFER   10 10 and refrain

S. H. Nicholson (1875–1947)
© Hymns Ancient & Modern Ltd

Lift high the cross, the love of Christ proclaim

till all the world ___ a - dores ___ his sac-red name! *Fine*

Lift high the cross, the love of Christ proclaim
till all the world adores his sacred name!

1 Come, Christians, follow where the captain trod,
the king victorious, Christ the Son of God:
    Lift high the cross . . .

2 Each new-born soldier of the crucified
is signed with the cross, the seal of him who died:
    Lift high the cross . . .

3 This is the sign that Satan's armies fear
and angels veil their faces to revere:
    Lift high the cross . . .

4 Saved by the cross on which their Lord was slain,
see Adam's children their lost home regain:
    Lift high the cross . . .

5 From north and south,
        from east and west they raise
in growing unison their songs of praise:
    Lift high the cross . . .

6 Let every race and every language tell
of him who saves our souls from death and hell!
    Lift high the cross . . .

7 O Lord, once lifted on the tree of pain,
draw all the world to seek you once again:
    Lift high the cross . . .

8 Set up your throne, that earth's despair may cease
beneath the shadow of its healing peace:
    Lift high the cross . . .

G. W. Kitchin (1827–1912)
and M. R. Newbolt (1874–1956)
© Hymns Ancient & Modern Ltd
and in this version Jubilate Hymns

509

Scottish Psalter Edinburgh 1635

1 Lift up your heads, you gates of brass! –
you bars of iron, yield,
and let the King of glory pass:
the cross is in the field.

2 The armies of the living God,
the warriors of his host,
where Christians yet have never trod
take their appointed post.

3 His servants wage a holy war,
a fierce and awesome strife,
as heaven and hell contend for more
than either death or life.

4 Obedient to their Lord's command,
and strong within his strength,
they fight for him in every land –
all must be his at length.

5 Rejoice then, Christians, fear not now,
in Jesus' name, be strong!
to him shall all the nations bow
and sing the triumph song.

6 Uplifted are the gates of brass,
the bars of iron yield
to let the King of glory pass:
the cross has won the field!

J. Montgomery (1771–1854)
© in this version Jubilate Hymns†

510

EISENACH   8 8 8 8 (LM)   J. H. Schein (1586–1630)

1 Lord, speak to me that I may speak
   in living echoes of your tone;
   as you have sought, so let me seek
   your wandering children, lost, alone.

2 O lead me, Lord, that I may lead
   the stumbling and the straying feet;
   and feed me, Lord, that I may feed
   your hungry ones with manna sweet.

3 O teach me, Lord, that I may teach
   the precious truths which you impart;
   and wing my words that they may reach
   the hidden depths of many a heart.

4 O fill me with your fulness, Lord,
   until my heart shall overflow
   in kindling thought and glowing word,
   your love to tell, your praise to show.

5 O use me Lord, use even me,
   just as you will, and when, and where;
   until at last your face I see,
   your rest, your joy, your glory share.

                        Frances R. Havergal (1836–1879)

Alternative tunes: OMBERSLEY (146)
                 MELCOMBE (270)

511

EVERTON 8 7 8 7 D

H. T. Smart (1813–1879)

1 Lord, your church on earth is seeking
  power and wisdom from above:
  teach us all the art of speaking
  with the accents of your love.
  We will heed your great commission
  sending us to every place –
  'Go, baptize, fulfil my mission;
  serve with love and share my grace!'

2 You release us from our bondage,
  lift the burdens caused by sin;
  give new hope, new strength and courage,
  grant release from fears within.
  Light for darkness, joy for sorrow,
  love for hatred, peace for strife –
  these and countless blessings follow
  as the Spirit gives new life.

3 In the streets of every city
  where the bruised and lonely live,
  we will show the saviour's pity
  and his longing to forgive.
  In all lands and with all races
  we will serve, and seek to bring
  all the world to render praises
  Christ, to you, redeemer king.

512

ST. LAURENCE   8 8 8 8 (LM)   L. G. Hayne (1836–1883)

1   Lord, you can make our spirits shine
    with light from brighter worlds above,
    and cause the dew of grace divine
    to fall on those who seek your love.

2   Now to the church your blessing give
    on all who teach and all who learn;
    that both in you may holier live
    and every light more brightly burn.

3   Give those who learn a listening ear,
    a godly heart and humble mind:
    such gifts can help the poorest here
    the riches of your truth to find.

4   Let those who teach, themselves be taught
    faith, hope and love, with zeal to pray;
    make pure their hearts and wise their thought
    as true disciples of your way.

5   O bless the shepherd, bless the sheep,
    that guide and guided may be one;
    one in the faithful watch they keep
    until this earthly life is done.

6   O Lord, let grace to us be given
    in you to live, in you to die;
    and so, before we rise to heaven,
    we taste our immortality.

J. Armstrong (1813–1856)
© in this version Jubilate Hymns†

Alternative tune: MELCOMBE (270)

513

GONFALON ROYAL   8 8 8 8 (LM)

P. C. Buck (1871–1947)
© Oxford University Press

1 O Spirit of the living God,
     in all the fulness of your grace,
     wherever human feet have trod,
     descend upon our fallen race:

2 Give tongues of fire
        and hearts of love
     to preach the reconciling word;
     anoint with power
        from heaven above
     whenever gospel truth is heard:

3 Let darkness turn to radiant light,
     confusion vanish from your path;
     those who are weak inspire with might:
     let mercy triumph over wrath!

4 O Spirit of our God, prepare
     the whole wide world the Lord to meet;
     breathe out new life, like morning air,
     till hearts of stone begin to beat:

5 Baptize the nations; far and near
     the triumphs of the cross record;
     till Christ in glory shall appear
     and every race declare him Lord! (Amen.)

J. Montgomery (1771–1854)

514

LADYWELL 8 6 8 6 D (DCM)

W. H. Ferguson (1874–1950)
© Royal School of Church Music

1   One holy apostolic church,
    the body of the Lord:
    our task, to witness to his name
    in full and glad accord –
    one Lord confessed, one faith believed,
    one baptism its sign;
    one God and Father over all,
    one fellowship divine.

2   By Christ redeemed, in Christ renewed,
    from every tongue and race,
    we live to share with all the world
    the wonder of his grace:
    as God is holy, we must be
    above reproach and blame;
    for royal service set apart,
    his gospel to proclaim.

3   With apostolic faith and zeal,
    the church in every land
    must bring God's love to every life
    as Jesus gave command:
    his partners in a common task
    uniting east and west,
    we serve as one to make Christ known
    in him shall all be blessed!

J. E. Seddon (1915–1983)
© Mrs. M. Seddon†

515(i)

CARLISLE 6 6 8 6 (SM)

C. Lockhart (1745–1815)
descant S. H. Nicholson (1875–1947)
descant © Oxford University Press

(ii)

VENICE 6 6 8 6 (SM)

W. Amps (1824–1910)

1 Revive your church, O Lord,
  in grace and power draw near;
  speak with the voice that wakes the dead,
  and make your people hear!

2 Revive your church, O Lord,
  disturb the sleep of death;
  give life to smouldering embers now
  by your almighty breath.

3 Revive your church, O Lord,
  exalt your precious name;
  and by your Holy Spirit come
  and set our love aflame.

4 Revive your church, O Lord,
  give us a thirst for you,
  a hunger for the bread of life
  our spirits to renew.

5 Revive your church, O Lord,
  and let your power be shown;
  the gifts and graces shall be ours,
  the glory yours alone!

A. Midlane (1825–1909)
© in this version Jubilate Hymns✝

516

TRURO   8 8 8 8 (LM)   T. Williams' *Psalmodia Evangelica* 1789

1 Jesus shall reign where'er the sun
   does his successive journeys run;
   his kingdom stretch from shore to shore
   till moons shall rise and set no more.

2 People and realms of every tongue
   declare his love in sweetest song,
   and children's voices shall proclaim
   their early blessings on his name.

3 Blessings abound where Jesus reigns –
   the prisoner leaps to lose his chains,
   the weary find eternal rest,
   the hungry and the poor are blessed.

4 To him shall endless prayer be made,
   and princes throng to crown his head;
   his name like incense shall arise
   with every morning sacrifice.

5 Let all creation rise and bring
   the highest honours to our king;
   angels descend with songs again
   and earth repeat the loud 'Amen!'

I. Watts (1674–1748)
© in this version Jubilate Hymns†

Alternative tune: GALILEE (376)

517

OLD CLARENDONIAN   8 8 8 8 (LM)   © Olwen Wonnacott (born 1930)

1 *mf* Send out the gospel! Let it sound
       northward and southward, east and west;
       tell all the world Christ died and lives –
       he gives us pardon, life and rest.

2   Send out the gospel, mighty Lord!
       Out of this chaos bring to birth
       your own creation's promised hope:
       the coming days of heaven on earth.

3 *mp* Send out your gospel, gracious Lord!
       Yours was the blood for sinners shed;
       your voice still pleads in human hearts –
       let all the world to you be led.

4 *mf* Send out your gospel, holy Lord!
       Kindle in us love's sacred flame;
       love giving all with heart and mind,
       for Jesus' sake, in Jesus' name.

5 *f*   Send out the gospel! Make it known!
       Christians, obey your master's call;
       sing out his praise! he comes to reign,
       the King of kings and Lord of all.

H. E. Fox (1841–1926)
© in this version Jubilate Hymns†

Alternative tunes: DUKE STREET (526)
               FULDA (519)

518

LIVING LORD   9 8 8 8 8 3

Patrick Appleford (born 1925)
© Josef Weinberger Ltd

1 To him we come –
   Jesus Christ our Lord,
   God's own living Word,
   his dear Son:
   in him there is no east and west,
   in him all nations shall be blessed;
   to all he offers peace and rest –
       loving Lord!

2 In him we live –
   Christ our strength and stay,
   life and truth and way,
   friend divine:
   his power can break the chains of sin,
   still all life's storms without, within,
   help us the daily fight to win –
       living Lord!

3 For him we go –
   soldiers of the cross,
   counting all things loss
   him to know;
   going to every land and race,
   preaching to all redeeming grace,
   building his church in every place –
       conquering Lord!

Harmony

This version is harmonically compatible with the Unison setting.

4 With him we serve –
his the work we share
with saints everywhere,
near and far;
one in the task which faith requires,
one in the zeal which never tires,
one in the hope his love inspires –
coming Lord!

5 Onward we go –
faithful, bold, and true,
called his will to do
day by day
till, at the last, with joy we'll see
Jesus, in glorious majesty;
live with him through eternity –
reigning Lord!

J. E. Seddon (1915–1983)
© Mrs. M. Seddon†

519

FULDA   8 8 8 8 (LM)   W. Gardiner's *Sacred Melodies* 1815

1 *mf* We have a gospel to proclaim,
       good news for all throughout the earth;
       the gospel of a saviour's name:
       we sing his glory, tell his worth.

2 *mp* Tell of his birth at Bethlehem,
       not in a royal house or hall
       but in a stable dark and dim:
       the Word made flesh, a light for all.

3 *p* Tell of his death at Calvary,
      hated by those he came to save;
      in lonely suffering on the cross
      for all he loved, his life he gave.

4 *f* Tell of that glorious Easter morn:
      empty the tomb, for he was free;
      he broke the power of death and hell
      that we might share his victory.

5 *mf* Tell of his reign at God's right hand,
       by all creation glorified;
       he sends his Spirit on his church
       to live for him, the lamb who died.

6 *f* Now we rejoice to name him king:
      Jesus is Lord of all the earth;
      this gospel-message we proclaim:
      we sing his glory, tell his worth.

© Edward Burns (born 1938)

520

PADERBORN   10 10 11 11   *Paderborn Gesangbuch* 1765

1   You servants of God, your master proclaim,
    and publish abroad his wonderful name;
    the name all-victorious of Jesus extol,
    his kingdom is glorious, and rules over all.

2   God rules in the height, almighty to save –
    though hid from our sight, his presence we have;
    the great congregation his triumph shall sing,
    ascribing salvation to Jesus our king.

3   'Salvation to God who sits on the throne!'
    let all cry aloud, and honour the Son;
    the praises of Jesus the angels proclaim,
    fall down on their faces and worship the Lamb.

4   Then let us adore and give him his right:
    all glory and power, all wisdom and might,
    all honour and blessing – with angels above –
    and thanks never ceasing, and infinite love.

                                    C. Wesley (1707–1788)

521

THORNBURY 7 6 7 6 D

B. Harwood (1859–1949)
© Executors of the late B. Harwood

A version of this tune in 4-part harmony is printed at 536.

1 Tell all the world of Jesus,
   our saviour, Lord and king;
   and let the whole creation
   of his salvation sing:
   proclaim his glorious greatness
   in nature and in grace;
   creator and redeemer,
   the Lord of time and space.

2 Tell all the world of Jesus,
   that everyone may find
   the joy of his forgiveness –
   true peace of heart and mind:
   proclaim his perfect goodness,
   his deep, unfailing care;
   his love so rich in mercy,
   a love beyond compare.

3 Tell all the world of Jesus,
   that everyone may know
   of his almighty triumph
   defeating every foe:
   proclaim his coming glory,
   when sin is overthrown,
   and he shall reign in splendour –
   the King upon his throne!

J. E. Seddon (1915–1983)
© Mrs. M. Seddon†

For other hymns on this theme, see:
Sunday Themes index
   Section 39 (2), The Church's Mission to All (p. xvi)
   Section 46, The Witnessing Community (p. xvii)
Song Section
   God forgave my sin (S.12)
   God has spoken to his people (S.13)
   Make us worthy, Lord (S.20)

GOD'S CHURCH:
CONFLICT AND ENDURANCE

522

EIN' FESTE BURG 8 7 8 7 6 6 6 6 7

M. Luther (1483–1546)
arranged J. S. Bach (1685–1750)

A less elaborate version of this tune may be found at 523.

1   Christ's church shall glory in his power
     and grow to his perfection;
     he is our rock, our mighty tower,
     our life, our resurrection:
          so by his skilful hand
          the church of Christ shall stand;
          the master-builder's plan
          he works, as he began,
          and soon will crown with splendour.

2   Christ's people serve his wayward world
     to whom he seems a stranger;
     he knows its welcome from of old,
     he shares our joy, our danger:
          so strong, and yet so weak,
          the church of Christ shall speak;
          his cross our greatest need,
          his word the vital seed
          that brings a fruitful harvest.

3   Christ's living lamp shall brightly burn,
     and to our earthly city
     forgotten beauty shall return,
     and purity and pity:
          to give the oppressed their right
          the church of Christ shall fight;
          and though the years seem long
          he is our strength and song,
          and he is our salvation.

4   Christ's body triumphs in his name;
     one Father, sovereign giver,
     one Spirit, with his love aflame,
     one Lord, the same for ever:
          to you, O God our prize,
          the church of Christ shall rise
          beyond all measured height,
          to that eternal light,
          where Christ shall reign all-holy.

© Christopher Idle (born 1938)†

523

EIN' FESTE BURG   878766667

M. Luther (1483–1546)

A more elaborate arrangement of this tune may be found at 522.

1   God is our fortress and our rock,
our mighty help in danger;
he shields us from the battle's shock
and thwarts the devil's anger:
      for still the prince of night
      prolongs his evil fight;
      he uses every skill
      to work his wicked will –
      no earthly force is like him.

2   Our hope is fixed on Christ alone,
the Man, of God's own choosing;
without him nothing can be won
and fighting must be losing:
      so let the powers accursed
      come on and do their worst,
      the Son of God shall ride
      to battle at our side,
      and he shall have the victory.

3   The word of God will not be slow
while demon hordes surround us,
though evil strike its cruellest blow
and death and hell confound us:
      for even if distress
      should take all we possess,
      and those who mean us ill
      should ravage, wreck, or kill,
      God's kingdom is immortal!

after M. Luther (1483–1546)
© Michael Perry (born 1942)†

524

UNIVERSITY COLLEGE 7 7 7 7

H. J. Gauntlett (1805–1876)

1 Christian soldiers, onward go!
  Jesus' triumph you shall know;
  fight the fight, maintain the strife,
  strengthened with the bread of life.

2 Join the war and face the foe!
  Christian soldiers, onward go;
  boldly stand in danger's hour,
  trust your captain, prove his power.

3 Let your drooping hearts be glad,
  march in heavenly armour clad;
  fight, nor think the battle long –
  soon shall victory be your song.

4 Sorrow must not dim your eye,
  soon shall every tear be dry;
  banish fear, you shall succeed –
  great your strength if great your need.

5 Onward, then, in battle move!
  more than conquerors you shall prove;
  though opposed by many a foe
  Christian soldiers, onward go!

H. K. White (1785–1806)
© in this version Jubilate Hymns†

525

MANNHEIM 878787   F. Filitz (1804–1876)

1 *mf* Lead us, heavenly Father, lead us
through this world's tempestuous sea;
guard us, guide us, keep us, feed us,
now and to eternity:
here possessing every blessing
if our God our Father be.

2 *mp* Saviour, by your grace restore us –
all our weaknesses are plain;
you have lived on earth before us,
you have felt our grief and pain:
tempted, taunted, yet undaunted,
from the depths you rose again.

3 *mf* Spirit of our God, descending,
fill our hearts with holy peace;
love with every passion blending,
pleasure that can never cease:
 f thus provided, pardoned, guided,
ever shall our joys increase.

J. Edmeston (1791–1867)
© in this version Jubilate Hymns†

(see also traditional version, 595)

526(i)

DUKE STREET 8 8 8 8 (LM)

J. Hatton (died 1793)

1 Fight the good fight with all your might,
  Christ is your strength, and Christ your right;
  lay hold on life, and it shall be
  your joy and crown eternally.

2 Run the straight race through God's good grace,
  lift up your eyes, and seek his face:
  life with its way before you lies,
  Christ is the path and Christ the prize.

3 Cast care aside, lean on your guide,
  his boundless mercy will provide;
  trust, and your trusting soul shall prove
  Christ is its life, and Christ its love.

4 Faint not, nor fear, his arms are near;
  he does not change, and you are dear;
  only believe and Christ shall be
  your all-in-all eternally.

J. S. B. Monsell (1811–1875)

526(ii)

OLD CLARENDONIAN   8 8 8 8 (LM)   © Olwen Wonnacott (born 1930)

1 Fight the good fight with all your might,
   Christ is your strength, and Christ your right;
   lay hold on life, and it shall be
   your joy and crown eternally.

2 Run the straight race through God's good grace,
   lift up your eyes, and seek his face:
   life with its way before you lies,
   Christ is the path and Christ the prize.

3 Cast care aside, lean on your guide,
   his boundless mercy will provide;
   trust, and your trusting soul shall prove
   Christ is its life, and Christ its love.

4 Faint not, nor fear, his arms are near;
   he does not change, and you are dear;
   only believe and Christ shall be
   your all-in-all eternally.

                    J. S. B. Monsell (1811–1875)

527

DAM BUSTERS MARCH 7 7 7 5 7 7 11

E. Coates (1886–1958)
arranged John Barnard (born 1948)†
© Chappell Music Ltd/International Music Publications

This version is harmonically compatible with the Unison setting.

1 God is our strength and refuge,
   our present help in trouble;
   and we therefore will not fear,
   though the earth should change!
   Though mountains shake and tremble,
   though swirling floods are raging,
   God the Lord of hosts is with us evermore!

2 There is a flowing river,
   within God's holy city;
   God is in the midst of her –
   she shall not be moved!
   God's help is swiftly given,
   thrones vanish at his presence –
   God the Lord of hosts is with us evermore!

3 Come, see the works of our maker,
   learn of his deeds all-powerful:
   wars will cease across the world
   when he shatters the spear!
   Be still and know your creator,
   uplift him in the nations –
   God the Lord of hosts is with us evermore!

from Psalm 46
© Richard Bewes (born 1934)†

528(i)

CWM RHONDDA   8 7 8 7 4 7 extended   J. Hughes (1873–1932)

1 *mf* Guide me, O my great Redeemer,
    pilgrim through this barren land;
    I am weak, but you are mighty,
    hold me with your powerful hand:
        Bread of heaven, bread of heaven,
        feed me now and evermore!

2   Open now the crystal fountain
    where the healing waters flow;
    let the fiery, cloudy pillar
    lead me all my journey through:
  f   Strong Deliverer, strong Deliverer,
        ever be my strength and shield.

528(ii)

BRYN CALFARIA 8 7 8 7 4 7 extended

W. Owen (1813–1898)
arranged R. Vaughan Williams (1872–1958)
arrangement © Oxford University Press

3 *mp* When I tread the verge of Jordan
    bid my anxious fears subside;
  f Death of death, and hell's Destruction,
    land me safe on Canaan's side:
      songs of praises, songs of praises,
    I will ever sing to you.

after W. Williams (1717–1791)
P. Williams (1721–1796) and others

529

CLOISTERS   11 11 11 5

J. Barnby (1838–1896)

1 Lord of our life, and God of our salvation,
   star of our night, and hope of every nation:
   hear and receive your church's supplication,
       Lord God almighty!

2 See round your church
             the angry tides are swirling,
   see how your foes their banners are unfurling;
   Lord, while their darts envenomed
             they are hurling,
       you can preserve us.

3 Lord, you can help when earthly armour fails us,
   Lord, you can save when deadly sin assails us:
   Lord, when at last that solemn trumpet hails us,
       keep and protect us!

4 Grant us your help till foes are backward driven,
   grant them your truth, that they may be forgiven;
   grant peace on earth and, after we have striven,
       peace in your heaven.

                          after M. A. von Löwenstern (1594–1648)
                          P. Pusey (1799–1855)

Alternative tune: ISTE CONFESSOR (391)

530

KOCHER 7 6 7 6

J. H. Knecht (1752–1817)
arranged W. H. Monk (1823–1889)

1 *mf* O happy band of pilgrims,
    if onward you will tread
    with Jesus as your brother
    and Jesus as your head!

2   O happy if you labour
    as Jesus did for all;
    O happy if you hunger
    and follow at his call!

3 *mp* The cross that Jesus carried,
    he carried as your due;
  f the crown that he is wearing
    he wears it now for you.

4 *mf* The faith by which you see him,
    the hope which bravely burns,
    the love that through all troubles
    to Jesus always turns:

5   What are they but his jewels
    of true celestial worth;
    what are they but a ladder
    set up to heaven on earth?

6   The trials that afflict you,
    the sorrows you endure:
    what are they but the testing
    that makes your calling sure?

7 *f* O happy band of pilgrims,
    look upward to the skies –
    beyond your earthly journey
    stands Jesus as your prize!

J. M. Neale (1818–1866)
© in this version Jubilate Hymns†

531

WOLVERCOTE   7 6 7 6 D

W. H. Ferguson (1874–1950)
© Oxford University Press

1 O Jesus, I have promised
   to serve you to the end –
   be now and ever near me,
   my Master and my Friend:
   I shall not fear the battle
   if you are by my side,
   nor wander from the pathway
   if you will be my guide.

2 O let me feel you near me,
   the world is ever near;
   I see the sights that dazzle,
   the tempting sounds I hear;
   my foes are ever near me,
   around me and within;
   but Jesus, draw still nearer
   and shield my soul from sin!

3 O let me hear you speaking
   in accents clear and still;
   above the storms of passion,
   the murmurs of self-will:
   O speak to reassure me,
   to hasten or control;
   and speak to make me listen,
   O Guardian of my soul.

4 O let me see your footmarks
   and in them place my own;
   my hope to follow truly
   is in your strength alone:
   O guide me, call me, draw me,
   uphold me to the end;
   and then in heaven receive me,
   my Saviour and my Friend.

J. E. Bode (1816–1874)

Alternative tune: THORNBURY (536)

532

ST. GERTRUDE   6 5 6 5 Triple   A. Sullivan (1842–1900)

On-ward, Christ-ian sold - iers, march-ing as to_ war
with_the

with the cross of Je - sus
cross   of   Je - sus   go - ing   on   be - fore.

with the cross of Je - sus

1 Onward, Christian soldiers! marching as to war,
   with the cross of Jesus going on before.
   Christ, the royal master, leads his armies on:
   forward into battle till the fight is won!
       Onward, Christian soldiers,
           marching as to war
       with the cross of Jesus going on before.

2 At the name of Jesus, Satan's armies flee:
   on then, Christian soldiers, on to victory!
   Hell's foundations tremble at the shout of praise –
   sing the song of triumph! loud your voices raise!
       Onward, Christian soldiers . . .

3 Like a mighty army moves the church of God:
   we are humbly treading
           where the saints have trod;
   Christ is not divided – all one body we,
   one in hope and calling, one in charity.
       Onward, Christian soldiers . . .

4 Crowns and thrones may perish,
           kingdoms rise and wane,
   but the church of Jesus ever shall remain;
   death and hell and Satan never shall prevail –
   we have Christ's own promise
           and that cannot fail.
       Onward, Christian soldiers . . .

5 Onward then, you people!
           march in faith, be strong!
   blend with ours your voices in the triumph song:
   Glory, praise and honour be to Christ the king!
   this through countless ages we with angels sing.
       Onward, Christian soldiers . . .

                    S. Baring-Gould (1834–1924)
                    © in this version Jubilate Hymns†

533(i)

ST. ETHELWALD 6 6 8 6 (SM)   W. H. Monk (1823–1889)

1   Soldiers of Christ, arise
    and put your armour on;
    strong in the strength which God supplies
    through his eternal Son.

2   Strong in the Lord of hosts,
    and in his mighty power;
    who in the strength of Jesus trusts
    is more than conqueror.

3   Stand then in his great might,
    with all his strength endued;
    and take, to arm you for the fight,
    the weapons of our God.

4   To keep your armour bright
    attend with constant care,
    still walking in your captain's sight
    and keeping watch with prayer.

5   From strength to strength go on:
    wrestle and fight and pray;
    tread all the powers of darkness down
    and win the well-fought day:

6   Till, having all things done
    and all your conflicts past,
    you overcome through Christ alone
    and stand complete at last.

C. Wesley (1707–1788)

533(ii)

FROM STRENGTH TO STRENGTH   6 6 8 6 (DSM)   E. W. Naylor (1867–1934)

534(i)

CRUCIS MILITES 7 7 7 7

M. B. Foster (1851–1922)

1 Soldiers of the cross, arise
  clothed in shining armour bright:
  mighty are your enemies,
  hard the battle you must fight.

2 In a faithless fallen world
  raise your banner to the sky;
  let it float there, wide unfurled,
  bear it onward, lift it high.

3 Where the shadows darkest fall,
  there display the saving sign;
  where our shameful crimes appal,
  let the light of Jesus shine.

4 Guard the helpless, seek the strayed,
  comfort troubles, banish grief;
  in the strength of God arrayed
  scatter sin and unbelief.

5 Keep the banner still unfurled,
  still unsheathed the Spirit's sword,
  till the kingdoms of the world
  are the kingdom of the Lord.

W. W. How (1823–1897)
© in this version Jubilate Hymns†

534(ii)

ORIENTIS PARTIBUS (i)   7 7 7 7   P. de Corbeil (died 1222)

(iii)

ORIENTIS PARTIBUS (ii)   7 7 7 7   P. de Corbeil (died 1222)
arranged R. Vaughan Williams (1872–1958)
arrangement © Oxford University Press

535

MORNING LIGHT 7 6 7 6 D

G. J. Webb (1803–1887)

1 Stand up, stand up for Jesus,
you soldiers of the cross!
lift high his royal banner,
it must not suffer loss:
from victory on to victory
his army he shall lead
till evil is defeated
and Christ is Lord indeed.

2 Stand up, stand up for Jesus!
the trumpet-call obey;
then join the mighty conflict
in this his glorious day:
be strong in faith and serve him
against unnumbered foes;
let courage rise with danger,
and strength to strength oppose.

3 Stand up, stand up for Jesus!
stand in his power alone,
for human might will fail you –
you dare not trust your own:
put on the gospel armour,
keep watch with constant prayer;
where duty calls or danger
be never failing there.

4 Stand up, stand up for Jesus!
the fight will not be long;
this day the noise of battle,
the next the victor's song:
to everyone who conquers,
a crown of life shall be;
we, with the king of glory,
shall reign eternally.

G. Duffield (1818–1888)
© in this version Jubilate Hymns†

Alternative tune: STAND UP (538)

536

THORNBURY 7 6 7 6 D

B. Harwood (1859–1949)
© Executors of the late B. Harwood

Unison

A version of this tune in four-part harmony is printed overleaf.

1 Your hand, O God, has guided
your flock, from age to age;
your faithfulness is written
on history's every page.
They knew your perfect goodness,
whose deeds we now record;
and both to this bear witness:
     one church, one faith, one Lord.

2 Your heralds brought the gospel
to greatest as to least;
they summoned us to hasten
and share the great king's feast.
And this was all their teaching
in every deed and word;
to all alike proclaiming:
     one church, one faith, one Lord.

3 Through many days of darkness,
through many scenes of strife,
the faithful few fought bravely
to guard the nation's life.
Their gospel of redemption –
sin pardoned, hope restored –
was all in this enfolded:
     one church, one faith, one Lord.

4 And we, shall we be faithless?
shall hearts fail, hands hang down?
shall we evade the conflict
and throw away the crown?
Not so! In God's deep counsels
some better thing is stored;
we will maintain, unflinching,
     one church, one faith, one Lord.

5 Your mercy will not fail us
nor leave your work undone;
with your right hand to help us,
the victory shall be won.
And then by earth and heaven
your name shall be adored;
and this shall be their anthem:
     one church, one faith, one Lord.

                    E. H. Plumptre (1821–1891)

Harmony

one Lord.

one church,   one   faith, one Lord, one faith, one Lord.

1   Your hand, O God, has guided
     your flock, from age to age;
     your faithfulness is written
     on history's every page.
     They knew your perfect goodness,
     whose deeds we now record;
     and both to this bear witness:
          one church, one faith, one Lord.

2   Your heralds brought the gospel
     to greatest as to least;
     they summoned us to hasten
     and share the great king's feast.
     And this was all their teaching
     in every deed and word;
     to all alike proclaiming:
          one church, one faith, one Lord.

3   Through many days of darkness,
     through many scenes of strife,
     the faithful few fought bravely
     to guard the nation's life.
     Their gospel of redemption –
     sin pardoned, hope restored –
     was all in this enfolded:
          one church, one faith, one Lord.

4   And we, shall we be faithless?
     shall hearts fail, hands hang down?
     shall we evade the conflict
     and throw away the crown?
     Not so! In God's deep counsels
     some better thing is stored;
     we will maintain, unflinching,
          one church, one faith, one Lord.

5   Your mercy will not fail us
     nor leave your work undone;
     with your right hand to help us,
     the victory shall be won.
     And then by earth and heaven
     your name shall be adored;
     and this shall be their anthem:
          one church, one faith, one Lord.

E. H. Plumptre (1821–1891)

537

MONKS GATE 6 5 6 5 6 6 6 5

English traditional melody
arranged R. Vaughan Williams (1872–1958)
arrangement © Oxford University Press

1   Who honours courage here,
        who fights the devil?
    who boldly faces fear,
        who conquers evil?
    We're not afraid to fight!
        we'll scorn the devil's spite:
    Christ gives to us the right
        to be his pilgrims.

2   Some may be terrified
        by Satan's testing,
    but faith is verified
        when we're resisting.
    There's no discouragement
        shall cause us to relent
    our firm declared intent
        to be his pilgrims.

3   Though evil powers intend
        to break our spirit,
    we know we at the end
        shall life inherit.
    So, fantasies, away!
        why fear what others say?
    We'll labour night and day
        to be his pilgrims.

            after J. Bunyan (1628–1688)
            © Michael Saward (born 1932)†

    (see also traditional version, 590)

For other hymns on this theme, see:
Sunday Themes index

GOD'S CHURCH:
COMMITMENT AND CHARACTER

538

STAND UP 7 6 7 6 D

G. Thalben-Ball (1896–1987)
© J. M. Thalben-Ball

1   Come, praise the name of Jesus
    for all his gracious powers,
    our only God and Saviour
    who makes his goodness ours;
    he calls us to his kingdom,
    the Lord of life and death,
    to see his face in glory
    and know him now by faith.

2   His virtue and his wisdom,
    endurance, self-control,
    his godliness and kindness,
    his love which crowns them all –
    this is his royal nature
    that we are called to share,
    his robe of perfect beauty
    that we are given to wear.

3   We see his shining splendour
    in every sunless place
    where Christ, the light of nations,
    appears in truth and grace.
    Transfigured by his likeness
    we make the vision known,
    reflecting in our faces
    the radiance of his own.

4   The king of grace inspires us
    to love him more and more,
    to grasp our hope more firmly
    and make our calling sure.
    Christ Jesus, Lord and Saviour,
    to this dark world you came;
    and for the dawn of heaven,
    we praise your holy name.

from 2 Peter 1
© Christopher Idle (born 1938)†

Alternative tunes: MORNING LIGHT (535)
ELLACOMBE (244)

539

RYBURN 888888

N. Cocker (1889–1953)
© Oxford University Press

Give us Christ's love, its depth— and length, its heart and soul and mind— and strength.

1 Father of all, whose laws have stood
   as signposts for our earthly good;
   whose Son has come with truth and grace,
   your likeness shining in his face:
        Give us Christ's love, its depth and length,
        its heart and soul and mind and strength.

2 The first and finest day is yours
   to consecrate all other hours;
   all other lords may we disown
   and worship bring to you alone:
        Give us Christ's love . . .

3 Surround our homes with joy and peace,
   with loyalty and cheerfulness;
   let partners live without pretence
   and children grow in confidence:
        Give us Christ's love . . .

4 May bitter hearts fresh mercy feel
and thieving hands no longer steal;
none damn their neighbour with a lie,
nor stoke the fires of jealousy:
    Give us Christ's love . . .

5 Father of all, whose laws have stood
as signposts for our earthly good;
whose Son has come with truth and grace,
your likeness shining in his face:
    Give us Christ's love . . .

© David Mowbray (born 1938)†

Alternative tune: ST. MATTHIAS (296)

540

DUNFERMLINE   8 6 8 6 (CM)   *Scottish Psalter* Edinburgh 1615

1 Help us to help each other, Lord,
   each other's load to bear;
   that all may live in true accord,
   our joys and pains to share.

2 Help us to build each other up,
   your strength within us prove;
   increase our faith,
            confirm our hope,
   and fill us with your love.

3 Together make us free indeed –
   your life within us show;
   and into you, our living head,
   let us in all things grow.

4 Drawn by the magnet of your love
   we find our hearts made new:
   nearer each other let us move,
   and nearer still to you.

after C. Wesley (1707–1788)
© in this version Jubilate Hymns†

541

RICHMOND   8 6 8 6 (CM)

Adapted from T. Haweis (1734–1820)
by S. Webbe the younger (c. 1770–1843)
descant C. S. Lang (1891–1971)
descant © Novello & Co Ltd

6 So shall no part of day — or — night
from — sa - cred - ness — be free; but all ——— my
life, — with you my God, in fel - low-ship — shall be.

An alternative arrangement of this tune may be found at 140.

1 Fill now my life, O Lord my God,
  in every part with praise;
  that my whole being may proclaim
  your being and your ways.

2 Not for the lip of praise alone,
  nor yet the praising heart,
  I ask, but for a life made up
  of praise in every part.

3 Praise in the common things of life,
  its goings out and in;
  praise in each duty and each deed,
  exalted or unseen.

4 Fill every part of me with praise;
  let all my being speak
  of you and of your love, O Lord,
  poor though I be and weak.

5 Then, Lord, from me you shall receive
  the praise and glory due;
  and so shall I begin on earth
  the song for ever new.

6 So shall no part of day or night
  from sacredness be free;
  but all my life, with you my God,
  in fellowship shall be.

H. Bonar (1808–1889)

542

DUKE STREET   8 8 8 8 (LM)   J. Hatton (died 1793)

1 Forth in the peace of Christ we go;
   Christ to the world with joy we bring:
   Christ in our minds, Christ on our lips,
   Christ in our hearts, the world's true king.

2 King of our hearts, Christ makes us kings;
   kingship with him his servants gain:
   with Christ, the Servant-Lord of all,
   Christ's world we serve to share Christ's reign.

3 Priests of the world, Christ sends us forth
   the world of time to consecrate,
   our world of sin by grace to heal,
   Christ's world in Christ to re-create.

4 Prophets of Christ, we hear his word:
   he claims our minds, to search his ways,
   he claims our lips, to speak his truth,
   he claims our hearts, to sing his praise.

5 We are his church; he makes us one:
   here is one hearth for all to find,
   here is one flock, one Shepherd-King,
   here is one faith, one heart, one mind.

© James Quinn S.J. (born 1919),
reprinted by permission of Cassell Publishers Ltd

Alternative tunes: BRESLAU (114)
                     ANGELS' SONG (306)

543

GOD BE IN MY HEAD   Irregular

H. Walford Davies (1869–1941)

Organ

God be in my head and in my un-der-stand-ing.
God be in my eyes and in my look-ing. God be in my
mouth and in my speak - ing. God be in my heart and in my
think - ing. God be at my end and at my de-part - ing.

after R. Pynson (c.1514)

544

FROM STRENGTH TO STRENGTH   6 6 8 6 D (DSM)   E. W. Naylor (1867–1934)

1   Freedom and life are ours
        for Christ has set us free!
    never again submit to powers
        that lead to slavery:
    Christ is the Lord who breaks
        our chains, our bondage ends,
    Christ is the rescuer who makes
        the helpless slaves his friends.

2   Called by the Lord to use
        our freedom and be strong,
    not letting liberty excuse
        a life of blatant wrong:
    freed from the law's stern hand
        God's gift of grace to prove,
    know that the law's entire demand
        is gladly met by love.

3   Spirit of God, come, fill,
        emancipate us all!
    speak to us, Word of truth, until
        before his throne we fall:
    glory and liberty
        our Father has decreed,
    and if the Son shall make us free
        we shall be free indeed!

© Christopher Idle (born 1938)†

545

SLANE   10 10 10 10

Irish traditional melody
arranged M. E. F. Shaw (1875–1958)
arrangement © Oxford University Press

1 Lord, be my vision, supreme in my heart,
   bid every rival give way and depart:
   you my best thought in the day or the night,
   waking or sleeping, your presence my light.

2 Lord, be my wisdom and be my true word,
   I ever with you and you with me, Lord:
   you my great father and I your true child,
   once far away, but by love reconciled.

3 Lord, be my breastplate, my sword for the fight:
   be my strong armour, for you are my might;
   you are my shelter and you my high tower –
   raise me to heaven, O Power of my power.

4 I need no riches, nor earth's empty praise:
   you my inheritance through all my days;
   all of your treasure to me you impart,
   high King of heaven, the first in my heart.

5   High King of heaven, when battle is done,
    grant heaven's joy to me, bright heaven's sun;
    Christ of my own heart, whatever befall,
    still be my vision, O Ruler of all.

546

TENHEAD   5 6 6 4   © John Barnard (born 1948)†

1   Lord, you need no house,
    no manger now, nor tomb;
    yet come, I pray, to make
    my heart your home.

2   Lord, you need no gift,
    for all things come from you;
    receive what you have given –
    my heart renew.

3   Lord, you need no skill
    to make your likeness known;
    create your image here –
    my heart your throne.

547

CHEDWORTH   10 11 11 11   © John Barnard (born 1948)†

1 Lord of all power, I give you my will,
   in joyful obedience your tasks to fulfil;
   your bondage is freedom, your service is song,
   and, held in your keeping,
               my weakness is strong.

2 Lord of all wisdom, I give you my mind;
   rich truth that surpasses our knowledge to find,
   what eye has not seen and what ear has not heard
   is taught by your Spirit
               and shines from your word.

3 Lord of all bounty, I give you my heart;
   I praise and adore you for all you impart –
   your love to inspire me, your counsel to guide,
   your presence to cheer me, whatever betide.

4 Lord of all being, I give you my all;
   for if I disown you I stumble and fall,
   but, sworn in glad service your word to obey,
   I walk in your freedom to the end of the way.

                              J. C. Winslow (1882–1974)
                              © Mrs. J. Tyrrell

548

CROSS OF SHAME   6 6 11 D

© Michael Baughen (born 1930)†
© arranged Noël Tredinnick (born 1949)†

1 Lord of the cross of shame,
   set my cold heart aflame
   with love for you, my saviour and my master;
       who on that lonely day
       bore all my sins away,
   and saved me from the judgement and disaster.

2 Lord of the empty tomb,
   born of a virgin's womb,
   triumphant over death, its power defeated;
       how gladly now I sing
       your praise, my risen king,
   and worship you, in heaven's splendour seated.

3 Lord of my life today,
   teach me to live and pray
   as one who knows the joy of sins forgiven;
       so may I ever be,
       now and eternally,
   one with my fellow-citizens in heaven.

© Michael Saward (born 1932)†

Alternative tune: DOWN AMPNEY (231)

549

HERONGATE   8 8 8 8 (LM)

English traditional melody
arranged R. Vaughan Williams (1872–1958)
arrangement © Oxford University Press

1 Lord Jesus, let these eyes of mine
  reflect your beauty and your grace;
  so joyful and so tender shine
  that other eyes shall seek your face.

2 Lord, use my ears, for I rejoice
  to hear the word of life – with awe
  I listen for the whispering voice
  that calls beyond the thunder's roar.

3 And holy Jesus, set my mind
  to search for truth and know your way;
  to think upon the good I find,
  to spurn the night and love the day:

4 And may my hands, which learned their skill
  at your direction, by your love,
  now deftly moving at your will
  console, encourage and improve.

5 So to your throne, O Christ, again
  my sense of sight and sound I bring;
  and in my mind I let you reign,
  and with my hands serve you, my king:

6 Speak through this voice that you have given,
  your love and mercy to proclaim,
  until we join the choirs of heaven
  and sing the glory of your name!

© Michael Perry (born 1942)†

Alternative tune: ANGELUS (315)

550

ST. LEONARD'S   8 7 8 5

A. C. Barham Gould (1891–1953)
© D. R. Gould

1 May the mind of Christ my saviour
 live in me from day to day,
 by his love and power controlling
 all I do and say.

2 May the word of God enrich me
 with his truth, from hour to hour,
 so that all may see I triumph
 only through his power.

3 May the peace of God my Father
 in my life for ever reign,
 that I may be calm to comfort
 those in grief and pain.

4 May the love of Jesus fill me
 as the waters fill the sea,
 him exalting, self abasing –
 this is victory!

5 May his beauty rest upon me
 as I seek to make him known;
 so that all may look to Jesus,
 seeing him alone.

Katie B. Wilkinson (1859–1928)
© in this version Jubilate Hymns†

551

ST. PETER   8 6 8 6 (CM)   A. R. Reinagle (1799–1877)

1 My God, accept my heart this day
   and make it yours alone;
   no longer let my footsteps stray
   from your belovèd Son.

2 Before the cross of him who died
   in awe and shame I fall:
   let every sin be crucified
   and Christ be all in all.

3 Anoint me with your heavenly grace
   and seal me as your own,
   that I may see your glorious face
   and worship at your throne.

4 Let every thought and work and word
   to you be ever given;
   then life shall be your service, Lord,
   and death the gate of heaven.

5 All glory to the Father be,
   the Spirit and the Son;
   all love and praise eternally
   to God the Three-in-One.

M. Bridges (1800–1894)
© in this version Jubilate Hymns†

552

HEREFORD   8 8 8 8 (LM)   S. S. Wesley (1810–1876)

1 O Lord, who came from realms above
   the pure celestial fire to impart,
   kindle a flame of sacred love
   upon the altar of my heart.

2 There let it for your glory burn
   with inextinguishable blaze,
   and trembling to its source return
   in humble prayer and fervent praise.

3 Jesus, confirm my heart's desire
   to work and speak and think for you;
   still let me guard the holy fire,
   and still in me your gift renew.

4 Here let me prove your perfect will,
   my acts of faith and love repeat,
   till death your endless mercies seal
   and make the sacrifice complete!

C. Wesley (1707–1788)
© in this version Jubilate Hymns†

(see also traditional version, 596)

553(i)

BINNEY'S 86886

E. H. Thiman (1900–1975)
© The United Reformed Church

1 O Master Christ, draw near to take
   your undisputed place;
   my gifts and faculties remake,
   form and re-fashion for your sake
   an instrument of peace.

2 O Master Christ, I choose to sow
   in place of hatred, love;
   where wounds and injuries are now
   may healing and forgiveness grow
   as gifts from God above.

553(ii)

REPTON   8 6 8 8 6 extended

C. H. H. Parry (1848–1918)

3   O Master Christ, I choose to plant
    hope where there is despair;
    a warmth of joy, a shaft of light
    where darkness has diminished sight,
    where sorrow leaves its scar.

4   O Master Christ, make this my goal –
    less to receive than give;
    to sympathise – and to make whole,
    to understand and to console
    and so, through death, to live.

from the traditional prayer
© David Mowbray (born 1938)†

554(i)

NOTTINGHAM 7 7 7 7

W. A. Mozart (1756–1791)

(ii)

LÜBECK 7 7 7 7

J. Freylinghausen's *Geistreiches Gesangbuch* 1704

1   Take my life and let it be
    all you purpose, Lord, for me;
    consecrate my passing days,
    let them flow in ceaseless praise.

2   Take my hands, and let them move
    at the impulse of your love;
    take my feet, and let them run
    with the news of victory won.

3   Take my voice, and let me sing
    always, only, for my King;
    take my lips, let them proclaim
    all the beauty of your name.

4   Take my wealth – all I possess,
    make me rich in faithfulness;
    take my mind that I may use
    every power as you shall choose.

5   Take my motives and my will,
    all your purpose to fulfil;
    take my heart – it is your own,
    it shall be your royal throne.

6   Take my love – my Lord, I pour
    at your feet its treasure-store;
    take myself, and I will be
    yours for all eternity.

Frances R. Havergal (1836–1879)
© in this version Jubilate Hymns†

Alternative tune: ABERYSTWYTH (438)

555

IBSTONE 6 6 6 6   Maria Tiddeman (1837–1915)

1 Your way, not mine, O Lord,
  whatever it may be:
  lead me by your own hand,
  choose out the path for me.

2 Smooth let it be or rough,
  it will be still the best;
  by winding paths or straight
  it leads me to your rest.

3 I dare not choose my life,
  I would not if I might:
  O choose for me, my God;
  your choice is sure and right.

4 Then fill my cup, O Lord,
  according to your will,
  with sorrow or with joy:
  you choose my good or ill.

5 Not mine but yours the choice
  in things both great and small!
  for you shall be my guide,
  my wisdom and my all.

H. Bonar (1808–1889)
© in this version Jubilate Hymns†

556

NEWINGTON   7777   W. D. Maclagan (1826–1910)

1 Yours for ever! God of love,
   hear us from your throne above;
   yours for ever let us be,
   here and in eternity.

2 Yours for ever! Lord of life,
   shield us through our earthly strife;
   Christ the life, the truth, the way:
   guide us to the realms of day.

3 Yours for ever! O, how blessed
   those who find in you their rest!
   Saviour, Guardian, heavenly Friend:
   O defend us to the end.

4 Yours for ever! You our guide;
   all our needs by you supplied,
   all our sins by you forgiven:
   lead us, Lord, from earth to heaven.

Mary F. Maude (1819–1913)
© in this version Jubilate Hymns†

557

ST. ALPHEGE 7 6 7 6   H. J. Gauntlett (1805–1876)

1 In full and glad surrender
   I give myself to you;
   to love and serve you only
   and all your will to do.

2 O Son of God, you love me;
   I will be yours alone,
   and all I have and am, Lord,
   from now shall be your own.

3 Reign over me, Lord Jesus,
   O make my heart your throne;
   it shall be yours, my Saviour,
   it shall be yours alone.

4 O come and reign, Lord Jesus,
   rule over everything;
   and keep me always loyal
   and true to you, my king.

Frances R. Havergal (1836–1879)

For other hymns on this theme, see:
Sunday Themes index
   Section 37 (1), The Life of the Baptized (p. xv)
   Section 52, The Offering of Life (p. xviii)
Song Section
   I want to walk with Jesus Christ (S.16)
   Make me a channel of your peace (S.19)

558

QUAM DILECTA 6 6 6 6   H. L. Jenner (1820–1898)

1 We love the place, O God,
   in which your honour dwells:
   the joy of your abode,
   all earthly joy excels.

2 We love the house of prayer:
   for where Christ's people meet,
   our risen Lord is there
   to make our joy complete.

3 We love the word of life,
   the word that tells of peace,
   of comfort in the strife
   and joys that never cease.

4 We love the cleansing sign
   of life through Christ our Lord,
   where with the name divine
   we seal the child of God.

5 We love the holy feast
   where, nourished with this food,
   by faith we feed on Christ,
   his body and his blood.

6 We love to sing below
   of mercies freely given,
   but O, we long to know
   the triumph-song of heaven.

7 Lord Jesus, give us grace
   on earth to love you more,
   in heaven to see your face
   and with your saints adore.

W. Bullock (1798–1874) and
H. W. Baker (1821–1877)
© in this version Jubilate Hymns†

559

WESTMINSTER ABBEY   8 7 8 7 8 7

H. Purcell (1659–1695)
descant James Gillespie (born 1929)
descant © Church Society

Descant

5 Praise and hon-our to __ the Fa-ther, praise and hon - our

to the __ Son, praise and hon - our to the Spi - rit,

1 *f* Christ is made the sure foundation,
       Christ the head and corner-stone
       chosen of the Lord and precious,
       binding all the Church in one;
       holy Zion's help for ever,
       and her confidence alone.

2   All within that holy city
       dearly loved of God on high,
       in exultant jubilation
       sing, in perfect harmony;
       God the One-in-Three adoring
       in glad hymns eternally.

3 *mf* We as living stones implore you:
        Come among us, Lord, today!
        with your gracious loving-kindness
        hear your children as we pray;
        and the fulness of your blessing
        in our fellowship display.

ev-er Three_ and ev-er_____ One: one in power_ and

one in glo-ry while e-ter-nal a-ges_____ run.

4 *mp* Here entrust to all your servants
what we long from you to gain –
that on earth and in the heavens
we one people shall remain,
   mf till united in your glory
evermore with you we reign.

5 *f* Praise and honour to the Father,
praise and honour to the Son,
praise and honour to the Spirit,
ever Three and ever One:
one in power and one in glory
while eternal ages run.

from the Latin (c. seventh century)
J. M. Neale (1818–1866)
© in this version Jubilate Hymns†

560

IVINGHOE   8 7 8 7 D

Greville Cooke (born 1894)
© Stainer & Bell Ltd

1 God is here! As we his people
   meet to offer praise and prayer,
   may we find in fuller measure
   what it is in Christ we share:
   here, as in the world around us,
   all our varied skills and arts
   wait the coming of his Spirit
   into open minds and hearts.

2 Here are symbols to remind us
   of our lifelong need of grace;
   here are table, font and pulpit,
   here the cross has central place:
   here in honesty of preaching,
   here in silence as in speech,
   here in newness and renewal
   God the Spirit comes to each.

3 Here our children find a welcome
   in the Shepherd's flock and fold;
   here, as bread and wine are taken,
   Christ sustains us as of old:
   here the servants of the Servant
   seek in worship to explore
   what it means in daily living
   to believe and to adore.

4 Lord of all, of church and kingdom,
   in an age of change and doubt,
   keep us faithful to the gospel,
   help us work your purpose out:
   here, in this day's dedication,
   all we have to give, receive;
   we who cannot live without you,
   we adore you! we believe!

F. Pratt Green (born 1903)
© Stainer & Bell Ltd

Alternative tune: LUX EOI (151)

561(i)

BUSHEY HALL 878777   © David Iliff (born 1939)†

1 God of light and life's creation,
   reigning over all supreme,
   daunting our imagination,
   prospect glorious yet unseen:
        Lord, whom earth and heaven obey,
        turn towards this house today!

2 God of alien, God of stranger,
   named by nations of the earth;
   poor and exile in a manger,
   God of harsh and humble birth:
        let us all with love sincere
        learn to welcome strangers here.

561(ii)

ALL SAINTS 878777

Later form of melody from
Geistreiches Gesangbuch Darmstadt 1698

3 God of justice in our nation,
   fearing neither rich nor strong,
   granting truth its vindication,
   passing sentence on all wrong:
        Lord, by whom we die or live,
        hear, and as you hear, forgive.

4 God the Father, Son, and Spirit,
   Trinity of love and grace,
   through your mercy we inherit
   word and worship in this place:
        let our children all their days
        to this house return with praise!

from 1 Kings 8
© Michael Perry (born 1942)†

562

ST. LEONARD   8 7 8 7 7 7   J. C. Bach (1642–1703)

1 *f* God our Father and creator,
    over all the earth you reign;
    God of cities, nations, planets,
    whom the heavens cannot contain:
  mf Come among your children here,
      come to bless this house of prayer.

2 *mp* Christ, whose undefended body
    human hands destroyed and killed;
    three days buried, till the moment
    God had chosen to rebuild:
  mf Raise your people from the dead,
      we your body, you our head.

3   Holy Spirit, wind of heaven,
    breaking earthly barriers down,
    pouring out your gifts and graces –
    life the seed, and love the crown:
      Fill us all, till all become
      your pure temple, your true home.

4   Living Lord of past and future,
    now through us your word fulfil;
    changing scenes and times of crisis
    prove that you are with us still.
  f   From one church, all praises be,
      praise to you, one Trinity!

© Christopher Idle (born 1938)†

Alternative tune: ALL SAINTS (561)

563(i)

ASHBURTON 777777

R. Jackson (1840–1914)

1 Here within this house of prayer
   all our Father's love declare;
   love that gave us birth, and planned
   days and years beneath his hand:
   praise to God whose love and power
   bring us to this present hour!

2 Here, till earthly praises end,
   tell of Christ the sinner's friend;
   Christ whose blood for us was shed,
   Lamb of God and living bread,
   life divine and truth and way,
   light of everlasting day.

563(ii)

DIX   7 7 7 7 7 7

C. Kocher (1786–1872)
arranged W. H. Monk (1823–1889)

The harmony of bars 1 to 4 may be repeated for bars 5 to 8, if preferred.

3   Here may all our faint desire
    feel the Spirit's wind and fire,
    souls that sleep the sleep of death
    stir to life beneath his breath:
    may his power upon us poured
    send us out to serve the Lord!

4   Here may faith and love increase,
    flowing forth in joy and peace
    from the Father, Spirit, Son,
    undivided, Three-in-One:
    his the glory all our days
    in this house of prayer and praise!

© Timothy Dudley-Smith (born 1926)

Alternative tunes: ARFON (398)
                    ENGLAND'S LANE (298)

564

HAREWOOD 666688   S. S. Wesley (1810–1876)

1 *f* Christ is our corner-stone,
        on him alone we build;
        with his true saints alone
        the courts of heaven are filled;
            on his great love
            our hopes we place
            of present grace
            and joys above.

2   With psalms and hymns
            of praise
        this holy place shall ring;
        our voices we will raise,
        the Three-in-One to sing;
            and thus proclaim
            in joyful song
            both loud and long,
            that glorious name.

3 *mp* Here, gracious God, draw near
        as in your name we bow;
        each true petition hear,
        accept each faithful vow;
            and more and more
            on all who pray
            each holy day
            your blessings pour.

4   Here may we gain from heaven
        the grace which we implore;
        and may that grace, once given,
        be with us evermore,
   mf   until that day
            when all the blessed
            to endless rest
            are called away.

from the Latin (c. seventh century)
J. Chandler (1806–1876)

Alternative tune: DARWALL'S 148th (171)

For other hymns on this theme, see:
Song Section
   We have come into this house (S.29)

GOD'S CHURCH:
THE CHURCH TRIUMPHANT: HEAVEN

565

CHRISTCHURCH 666688   C. Steggall (1826–1905)

1 Jerusalem on high
  my song and city is;
  my home when I shall die,
  the centre of my bliss:
      O happy place!
      when shall I be
      with God, to see
      him face to face?

2 There reigns my Lord, my king,
  judged here unfit to live;
  there angels to him sing,
  and lowly homage give:
      O happy place . . .

3 The patriarchs of old
  there from their travels cease;
  the prophets there behold
  the longed-for prince of peace:
      O happy place . . .

4 Sweet place, sweet place alone,
  the home of God most high;
  the Heaven of heavens, the throne
  of holiest majesty:
      O happy place . . .

S. Crossman (1624–1683)
ⓒ in this version Jubilate Hymns†

566(i)

MELLING 7777

J. Fawcett (1789–1867)
arranged G. T. Shaw (1879–1943)
arrangement © Oxford University Press

(ii)

INNOCENTS 7777

The Parish Choir 1850

1 Children of the heavenly king,
as you journey, sweetly sing;
sing your saviour's worthy praise,
glorious in his works and ways.

2 We are travelling home to God
in the way our fathers trod;
they are happy now, and we
soon their happiness shall see.

3 Lift your eyes and walk in light –
God's own city is in sight;
there our endless home shall be,
there our Lord we soon shall see.

4 Never fear, but boldly stand
on the borders of your land;
Christ, the everlasting Son,
gives you strength to journey on.

5 Lord, obediently we go,
gladly leaving all below:
Master, be our guide indeed –
we shall follow where you lead.

J. Cennick (1718–1755)

567

SINE NOMINE   10 10 10 4

R. Vaughan Williams (1872–1958)

Unison (vv. 1, 2, 3, 7, 8)

Al - le-lu - ia,   Al - le-lu - ia!

Harmony (vv. 4, 5, 6)

Al - le - lu - ia, ___ Al - le - lu - ia!

1 *f* For all the saints, who from their labours rest;
who to the world by faith their Lord confessed,
your name, O Jesus, be for ever blessed:
Alleluia, alleluia!

2 You were their rock, their fortress,
and their might;
you, Lord, their captain in the well-fought fight,
and in the darkness their unfailing light.
Alleluia, alleluia!

3 So may your soldiers, faithful, true and bold,
fight as the saints who nobly fought of old
and win with them the victor's crown of gold.
Alleluia, alleluia!

4 *mf* One holy people, fellowship divine!
we feebly struggle, they in glory shine –
in earth and heaven the saints in praise combine:
Alleluia, alleluia!

5 *mp* And when the fight is fierce, the warfare long,
far off we hear the distant triumph-song;
and hearts are brave again, and arms are strong.
Alleluia, alleluia!

6 The golden evening brightens in the west:
soon, soon to faithful warriors comes their rest,
the peaceful calm of paradise the blessed.
Alleluia, alleluia!

7 *mf* But look! – there breaks a yet more glorious day;
saints all-triumphant rise in bright array –
the king of glory passes on his way!
Alleluia, alleluia!

8 *f* From earth's wide bounds,
from dawn to setting sun,
through heaven's gates to God the Three-in-One
they come, to sing the song on earth begun:
Alleluia, alleluia!

W. W. How (1823–1897)
© in this version Jubilate Hymns†

568

NARENZA 6 6 8 6 (SM)

Adapted from J. Leisentritt
Catholicum Hymnologium 1584
arranged W. H. Havergal (1793–1870)

1 Give praise for famous men
from history's open page,
by whom our God unfolds his plan
for each succeeding age.

2 Some wore a kingdom's crown
and made themselves a name;
some by God's word brought kingdoms down
and with his judgement came.

3 Some fashioned wisest laws
to guard our liberty;
some champions of a lonely cause
set slaves and prisoners free.

4 Some gave their land its songs
of love and hope and faith;
some fought against malignant wrongs
unceasingly till death.

5 Some preached to courts and kings
a Saviour's sovereign claim;
some paid the price his service brings
through torture, blood, and flame.

6 Let us pursue the prize
and praise their deeds and words;
the life is theirs that never dies,
the glory is their Lord's.

from Ecclesiasticus 44
© Christopher Idle (born 1938)†

Alternative tune: HOLYROOD (497)

569

SOUTHWELL (IRONS) 8 6 8 6 (CM)   H. S. Irons (1834–1905)

1 Jerusalem, my happy home,
   name ever dear to me!
   when shall my sorrows have an end,
   your joys when shall I see?

2 When shall I leave this dying world
   and to that city rise;
   when shall those mighty walls and gates
   delight my wondering eyes?

3 That glorious hope, Jerusalem!
   in faith I make my prayer:
   O God, that all my grief might end,
   O God, that I were there!

4 Apostles, martyrs, prophets, saints
   around my saviour stand,
   and all I love in Christ below
   await his clear command.

5 Jerusalem, my happy home,
   when shall that glory be
   when all my labours have an end
   and all your joys I see?

6 Lord Jesus Christ, prepare me now
   for that dear home above;
   to see, and know, and worship you
   in your eternal love.

F. B. P. (sixteenth–seventeenth century)
© in this version Jubilate Hymns†

570

BLAENWERN   8 7 8 7 D

W. P. Rowlands (1860–1937)

1　Heavenly hosts in ceaseless worship
　　'Holy, holy, holy!' cry;
　　'He who is, who was and will be,
　　God almighty, Lord most high.'
　　Praise and honour, power and glory,
　　be to him who reigns alone!
　　we, with all his hands have fashioned,
　　fall before the Father's throne.

2　All creation, all redemption,
　　join to sing the saviour's worth;
　　Lamb of God whose blood has bought us,
　　kings and priests, to reign on earth.
　　Wealth and wisdom, power and glory,
　　honour, might, dominion, praise,
　　now be his from all his creatures
　　and to everlasting days!

from *Glory and Honour* (Revelation 4–5)
© Timothy Dudley-Smith (born 1926)

Alternative tune: ABBOT'S LEIGH (494)

571

O QUANTA QUALIA   11 10 11 10

Paris Antiphoner 1681

1 *f* Here from all nations, all tongues, and all peoples,
countless the crowd but their voices are one;
vast is the sight and majestic their singing –
'God has the victory: he reigns from the throne!'

2 *mf* These have come out of the hardest oppression,
now they may stand in the presence of God,
serving their Lord day and night in his temple,
ransomed and cleansed
        by the Lamb's precious blood.

3   Gone is their thirst
        and no more shall they hunger,
God is their shelter, his power at their side;
sun shall not pain them, no burning will torture,
Jesus the Lamb is their shepherd and guide.

4   He will go with them to clear living water
flowing from springs which his mercy supplies;
gone is their grief and their trials are over –
God wipes away every tear from their eyes.

5 *f* Blessing and glory and wisdom and power
be to the Saviour again and again;
might and thanksgiving and honour for ever
be to our God: Alleluia! Amen.

from Revelation 7
© Christopher Idle (born 1938)†

572(i)

ARDEN 8 6 8 6 (CM)

G. Thalben-Ball (1896–1987)
© J. M. Thalben-Ball

1   How bright these glorious spirits shine;
    whence all their white array?
    how have they come to this fair place
    of everlasting day?

2   These have endured through sufferings great
    and come to realms of light,
    and through the blood of Christ the Lamb
    their robes are pure and white.

3   Humble they stand before the throne,
    palm-branches in their hands;
    here they are serving him they love,
    fulfilling his commands.

572(ii)

JACKSON 8 6 8 6 (CM)

T. Jackson (1715–1781)
arranged D. Evans (1874–1948)
arrangement © Oxford University Press

4 No more can hunger hurt them now,
   nor shall they thirst again;
   no scorching heat can do them harm
   nor sun shall cause them pain.

5 For at the centre of the throne,
   Jesus the Lamb who died
   feeds them with nourishment divine,
   their shepherd and their guide.

6 In pastures green he'll lead his flock
   where living streams appear,
   and God the Lord from every eye
   shall wipe away each tear.

from Revelation 7
after I. Watts (1674–1748)
and W. Cameron (1751–1811)
© in this version Jubilate Hymns†

Alternative tune: BEATITUDO (240)

573

EWING 7676D

A. Ewing (1830–1895)

1 Jerusalem the golden
   in glory high above;
   O city of God's presence,
   O vision of God's love:
   how wonderful the pleasures
   and joys awaiting there;
   what radiancy of glory,
   what peace beyond compare!

2 They stand, those halls of Zion,
   all jubilant with song;
   and bright with many an angel,
   and all the martyr throng:
   the Prince is ever in them,
   the daylight is serene;
   the tree of life and healing
   has leaves of richest green.

3 There is the throne of David;
   and there from pain released,
   the shout of those who triumph,
   the song of those who feast:
   and all who with their leader
   have conquered in the fight,
   are garlanded with glory
   and robed in purest white.

4 How lovely is that city!
   the home of God's elect;
   how beautiful the country
   that eager hearts expect!
   Jesus, in mercy bring us
   to that eternal shore
   where Father, Son and Spirit
   are worshipped evermore.

after Bernard of Cluny (c.1140)
J. M. Neale (1818–1866)
© in this version Jubilate Hymns†

574

DUNDEE   8 6 8 6 (CM)   *Scottish Psalter* Edinburgh 1615

1 Let saints on earth together sing
   with those whose work is done;
   for all the servants of our king
   in earth and heaven, are one.

2 One family, we live in him,
   one church above, beneath,
   though now divided by the stream,
   the narrow stream of death.

3 One army of the living God,
   to his command we bow;
   part of his host have crossed the flood
   and part are crossing now.

4 But all unite in Christ their head,
   and love to sing his praise:
   Lord of the living and the dead,
   direct our earthly ways!

5 So we shall join our friends above
   who have obtained the prize;
   and on the eagle wings of love
   to joys celestial rise.

575

MENDIP 8 6 8 6 (CM)

English traditional melody
collected and adapted by
C. J. Sharp (1859–1924)

1 There is a land of pure delight
   where saints immortal reign,
   eternal day excludes the night
   and pleasures banish pain.

2 There everlasting spring abides,
   and never-withering flowers;
   death, like a narrow stream, divides
   this heavenly land from ours.

3 Sweet fields beyond the rolling flood
   stand dressed in living green,
   as once to Israel Canaan stood
   while Jordan flowed between.

4 But trembling mortals fear, and shrink
   to cross the narrow sea;
   they linger shivering on the brink,
   afraid to launch away.

5 If only we could all remove
   those gloomy doubts that rise,
   and see the Canaan that we love
   with clear unclouded eyes!

6 If we could climb where Moses stood
   and fear that view no more,
   not Jordan's stream, nor death's cold flood,
   would keep us from the shore.

I. Watts (1674–1748)
© in this version Jubilate Hymns†

Alternative tune: ST. BERNARD (484)

576

ALFORD 7 6 8 6 D

J. B. Dykes (1823–1876)

1   Ten thousand times ten thousand
    give glory to the Lamb;
    the angel hosts around the throne
    praise God, the great I AM.
    Triumphant alleluias
    fill earth and sea and sky,
    as countless voices join the song
    and worship God on high.

2   O day, for which creation
    and all its tribes were made!
    O joy, for all its former grief
    a thousandfold repaid!
    The armies of the ransomed
    have fought with death and sin:
    fling open wide the mighty gates
    to let the victors in!

3   Bring near your great salvation,
    O Lord, return again
    to gather all your chosen flock –
    then take your power and reign!
    Appear, Desire of Nations,
    your exiles long for home:
    show in the heavens your promised sign,
    then, Prince and Saviour, come!

H. Alford (1810–1871)
© in this version Jubilate Hymns†

577

LADYWELL   8 6 8 6 D (DCM)

W. H. Ferguson (1874–1950)

1 The Son of God rides out to war
  the ancient foe to slay;
  his blood-red banner streams afar –
  who follows him today?
  Who bears his cross? who shares his grief?
  who walks his narrow way?
  who faces rampant unbelief?
  who follows him today?

2 The martyr Stephen's eagle eye
  could pierce beyond the grave;
  he saw his master in the sky
  and called on him to save.
  By zealots he was stoned to death
  and, as he knelt to pray,
  he blessed them with his final breath –
  who follows him today?

3 The valiant twelve, the chosen few,
  on them the Spirit fell;
  and faithful to the Lord they knew
  they faced the hosts of hell.
  They died beneath the brandished steel,
  became the tyrant's prey,
  yet did not flinch at their ordeal –
  who follows them today?

4 A noble army – young and old –
  from every nation came;
  some weak and frail, some strong and bold,
  to win the martyr's fame.
  Eternal joy to all is given
  who trust you and obey:
  O give us strength, great God of heaven,
  to follow them today!

R. Heber (1783–1826)
© in this version Michael Saward (born 1932)†

For other hymns on this theme, see:
Sunday Themes index
    Section 57, Citizens of Heaven (p. xix)

DOXOLOGY: GLORY TO GOD

578

LAUS DEO 8 7 8 7

R. Redhead (1820–1901)

1 *mf* Bright the vision that delighted
    once Isaiah bowed in fear;
    sweet the countless tongues united
    to entrance the prophet's ear.

2 Round the Lord in glory seated,
  cherubim and seraphim
  filled his temple and repeated
  each to each the alternate hymn:

3 *f* 'Lord, your glory fills the heaven,
    earth is with its fulness stored;
    to your name be glory given:
    Holy, holy, holy Lord!'

4 *mf* Heaven is still with glory ringing,
    earth takes up the angels' cry:
    'Holy, holy, holy' singing,
    'Lord of hosts, the Lord most high!'

5 With his seraphim before him,
  with his holy church below,
  thus united, we adore him –
  let our glorious anthem flow:

6 *f* 'Lord, your glory fills the heaven,
earth is with its fulness stored;
to your name be glory given:
Holy, holy, holy Lord!'

from Isaiah 6
R. Mant (1776–1848)
© in this version Jubilate Hymns†

Descant and arrangement C. Macpherson (1870–1927)

Descant

6 'Lord, your glo-ry fills   the hea-ven, earth is with its   ful - ness stored;＿

to   your   name   be   glo   -   ry: Ho-ly,   ho - ly Lord!'

579

EASTER SONG 8 8 4 4 8 8 and Alleluias

Geistliche Kirchengesang Cologne 1623
arranged R. Vaughan Williams (1872–1958)
arrangement © Oxford University Press

1 By every nation, race and tongue,
worship and praise be ever sung;
praise the Father: Alleluia!
For pardoned sin, death overcome,
and hopes that live beyond the tomb:
Alleluia, alleluia;
alleluia, alleluia, alleluia!

2 Saints who on earth have suffered long,
 for Jesus' sake enduring wrong,
  ever-faithful: Alleluia!
 Where faith is lost in sight, rejoice
 and sing with never-wearied voice:
  Alleluia . . .

3 Let earth and air and sea unite
 to celebrate his glorious might,
  their creator: Alleluia!
 Sun, moon and stars in endless space
 echo the song of every race:
  Alleluia . . .

H. B. George (1838–1910)

580

DEUS TUORUM MILITUM   8 8 8 8 (LM)   *Grenoble Antiphoner* 1753
arranged G. H. Knight (1908–1979)
arrangement © Hymns Ancient & Modern

1 From all who live beneath the skies
 let the Creator's praise arise!
 let the Redeemer's name be sung
 through every land, by every tongue!

2 Eternal are your mercies, Lord,
 eternal truth attends your word;
 your praise shall sound from shore to shore
 till suns shall rise and set no more.

from Psalm 118
I. Watts (1674–1748)

Alternative tunes: MORNING HYMN (264)
EASTER SONG (579) adding alleluias as appropriate.

581

ODE TO JOY 8 7 8 7 D   L. van Beethoven (1770–1827)

1 Glory be to God in heaven,
  peace to those who love him well;
  on the earth let all his people
  speak his grace, his wonders tell:
  Lord, we praise you for your glory,
  mighty Father, heaven's king;
  hear our joyful adoration
  and accept the thanks we bring.

2 Only Son of God the Father,
  Lamb who takes our sin away,
  now with him in triumph seated –
  for your mercy, Lord, we pray:
  Jesus Christ, most high and holy,
  Saviour, you are God alone
  in the glory of the Father
  with the Spirit: Three-in-One!

from *Gloria in Excelsis*
© Michael Perry (born 1942)†

Alternative tune: ABBOT'S LEIGH (494)

582

CUDDESDON 6 5 6 5 D

W. H. Ferguson (1874–1950)
© Oxford University Press

1 Glory in the highest
            to the God of heaven!
   Peace to all your people
            through the earth be given!
   Mighty God and Father,
            thanks and praise we bring,
   singing Alleluia
            to our heavenly king.

2 Jesus Christ is risen,
            God the Father's Son!
   With the Holy Spirit,
            you are Lord alone!
   Lamb once killed for sinners,
            all our guilt to bear,
   show us now your mercy,
            now receive our prayer.

3 Christ the world's true Saviour,
            high and holy one,
   seated now and reigning
            from your Father's throne:
   Lord and God, we praise you!
            Highest heaven adores:
   in the Father's glory,
            all the praise be yours!

from *Gloria in Excelsis*
© Christopher Idle (born 1938)†

583

AUSTRIA 8 7 8 7 D

Croatian folk tune
adapted F. J. Haydn (1732–1809)
descant T. H. Ingham (1878–1948)
descant © Oxford University Press

Descant

2 Praise the Lord, for he is glo - rious, nev - er shall his pro-mise fail;

God has made his saints vic-tor-ious, sin and death shall not pre - vail.

Praise the God of our sal-va - tion! hosts on high, his power pro-claim;

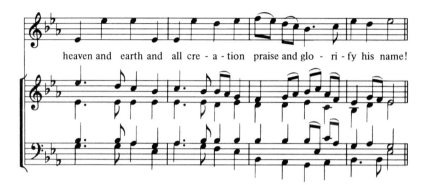

heaven and earth and all cre - a - tion praise and glo - ri - fy his name!

1 Praise the Lord, you heavens, adore him;
  praise him, angels in the height;
  sun and moon, rejoice before him;
  praise him, all you stars and light.
  Praise the Lord, for he has spoken,
  worlds his mighty voice obeyed;
  laws which never shall be broken
  for their guidance he has made.

2 Praise the Lord, for he is glorious,
  never shall his promise fail;
  God has made his saints victorious,
  sin and death shall not prevail.
  Praise the God of our salvation!
  hosts on high, his power proclaim;
  heaven and earth and all creation
  praise and glorify his name!

anonymous
Foundling Hospital Collection (1796)

584

TO GOD BE THE GLORY   11 11 11 11 and refrain   W. H. Doane (1832–1916)

Praise the Lord, praise the Lord! let the earth hear his voice;

1 To God be the glory! great things he has done;
 so loved he the world that he gave us his Son
 who yielded his life an atonement for sin,
 and opened the life-gate that all may go in.
       Praise the Lord, praise the Lord!
       let the earth hear his voice;
       praise the Lord, praise the Lord!
       let the people rejoice:
       O come to the Father through Jesus the Son
       and give him the glory;
            great things he has done.

2 O perfect redemption, the purchase of blood!
 To every believer the promise of God:
 the vilest offender who truly believes,
 that moment from Jesus a pardon receives.
       Praise the Lord! . . .

3 Great things he has taught us,
            great things he has done,
 and great our rejoicing through Jesus the Son:
 but purer and higher and greater will be
 our wonder, our gladness, when Jesus we see!
       Praise the Lord! . . .

Frances J. van Alstyne (1820–1915)

585

TALLIS' CANON   8 8 8 8 (LM)   Shortened form of melody by Thomas Tallis
(c. 1505–1585)
from T. Ravenscroft's *Psalter* 1621

Praise God from whom all blessings flow,
in heaven above and earth below;
one God, three persons, we adore –
to him be praise for evermore!

after T. Ken (1637–1710)
© in this version Jubilate Hymns†

(see also traditional version, 586)

For other hymns on this theme, see:
Liturgical Hymns index
  Doxologies (p. vi)
Song Section
  Come into his presence (S.2)
  I will sing, I will sing (S.15)

APPENDIX:
TRADITIONAL TEXTS

586

COME TOGETHER   8 8 8 8 (LM)

Jimmy Owens
arranged David Peacock (born 1949)†
© Lexicon Music Inc, Word Music (UK)

Praise God from whom all blessings flow:
praise him, all creatures here below,
praise him above, ye heavenly host –
praise Father, Son, and Holy Ghost.

T. Ken (1637–1710)

(see also revised version, 585)

587(i)

MILES LANE   8 6 8 6 (CM) extended

Later form of melody by W. Shrubsole
(c. 1759–1806)
as in *The Australian Hymn Book* 1977

crown him, crown him,
crown ___ him, crown him Lord of ___ all.

1 All hail the power of Jesus' name!
   let angels prostrate fall;
   bring forth the royal diadem
   to crown him Lord of all.

2 Crown him, you morning stars of light,
   who fixed this floating ball;
   now hail the Strength-of-Israel's might
   and crown him Lord of all.

3 Crown him, you martyrs of our God,
   who from his altar call;
   extol the Stem-of-Jesse's rod
   and crown him Lord of all.

4 You seed of Israel's chosen race
   .and ransomed from the fall,
   hail him who saves you by his grace
   and crown him Lord of all.

5 Hail him, you heirs of David's line,
   whom David 'Lord' did call,
   the God incarnate, Man divine –
   and crown him Lord of all.

587(ii)

DIADEM   8 6 8 6 (CM) extended   J. Ellor (1819–1899)

crown _____

crown him,   crown him,   crown him,

him,

crown him,   crown him,   crown him, crown him, and crown him Lord of   all.

crown _____

6 Sinners, whose love cannot forget
   the wormwood and the gall,
   go spread your trophies at his feet
   and crown him Lord of all.

7 O that with every tribe and tongue
   we at his feet may fall,
   lift high the universal song
   and crown him Lord of all.

E. Perronet (1725–1792) and
J. Rippon (1751–1836)

(see also revised version, 203)

588

SAGINA   8 8 8 8 8 8 extended   T. Campbell's *Bouquet* 1825

1 And can it be that I __ should gain an in - terest in the __ Sa - viour's blood? Died he for me, __ who caused his pain; for me, __ who him __ to death pur - sued? A - mazing love! — how __ can __ it __ be __ that thou, __ my God, shouldst die __ for me?

A - ma - zing love! — how can it be that

A - ma - zing love! — how can it be

thou, my God,

that thou, my God, shouldst __ die for me?

1 And can it be that I should gain
   an interest in the Saviour's blood?
   Died he for me, who caused his pain;
   for me, who him to death pursued?
   Amazing love! – how can it be
   that thou, my God, shouldst die for me?

2 'Tis mystery all! – the Immortal dies, –
   who can explore his strange design?
   In vain the first-born seraph tries
   to sound the depths of love divine!
   'Tis mercy all! – Let earth adore;
   let angel minds inquire no more.

3 He left his Father's throne above –
   so free, so infinite his grace –
   emptied himself of all but love,
   and bled for Adam's helpless race.
   'Tis mercy all, immense and free;
   for, O my God, it found out me.

4 Long my imprisoned spirit lay
   fast bound in sin and nature's night:
   thine eye diffused a quickening ray;
   I woke – the dungeon flamed with light.
   My chains fell off, my heart was free;
   I rose, went forth, and followed thee.

5 No condemnation now I dread;
   Jesus, and all in him, is mine!
   Alive in him, my living head,
   and clothed in righteousness divine,
   bold I approach the eternal throne
   and claim the crown through Christ my own.

C. Wesley (1707–1788)

(see also revised version, 452)

589

VENI CREATOR   8 8 8 8 (LM)
Mode viii (Mechelen version)

'Praise to thy eternal merit, Father, Son, and Holy Spirit.'

1   Come, Holy Ghost, our souls inspire,
    and lighten with celestial fire:
    thou the anointing Spirit art,
    who dost thy sevenfold gifts impart.

2   Thy blessèd unction from above
    is comfort, life, and fire of love:
    enable with perpetual light
    the dulness of our blinded sight.

3   Anoint and cheer our soilèd face
    with the abundance of thy grace:
    keep far our foes, give peace at home –
    where thou art guide no ill can come.

4   Teach us to know the Father, Son,
    and thee of both to be but One:
    that, through the ages all along,
    this may be our endless song:
        'Praise to thy eternal merit,
        Father, Son, and Holy Spirit.' Amen

after R. Maurus (c.776–856)
J. Cosin (1594–1671)

(see also revised version, 232)

A - men.

590

MONKS GATE   6 5 6 5 6 6 6 5

English traditional melody
arranged R. Vaughan Williams (1872–1958)
arrangement © Oxford University Press

1 He who would valiant be
      'gainst all disaster,
  let him in constancy
      follow the Master:
  there's no discouragement
      shall make him once relent
  his first avowed intent
      to be a pilgrim.

2 Who so beset him round
      with dismal stories
  do but themselves confound –
      his strength the more is:
  no foes shall stay his might,
      though he with giants fight;
  he will make good his right
      to be a pilgrim.

3 Since, Lord, thou dost defend
      us with thy Spirit,
  we know we at the end
      shall life inherit:
  then, fancies, flee away!
      I'll fear not what men say,
  I'll labour night and day
      to be a pilgrim.

after J. Bunyan (1628–1688)
P. Dearmer (1867–1936)

(see also revised version, 537)

591(i)

CRIMOND 8 6 8 6 (CM)

J. S. Irvine (1836–1887)
arranged D. Grant (1833–1893)
descant W. Baird Ross (1871–1950)
descant © Paterson's Publications Ltd

Descant

5 Good-ness and mer-cy all my life shall sure-ly fol-low me;

and in God's house for ev-er-more my dwell-ing-place shall be.

1 The Lord's my shepherd: I'll not want;
   he makes me down to lie
   in pastures green: he leadeth me
   the quiet waters by.

2 My soul he doth restore again,
   and me to walk doth make
   within the paths of righteousness,
   e'en for his own name's sake.

3 Yea, though I walk through death's dark vale,
   yet will I fear no ill;
   for thou art with me, and thy rod
   and staff me comfort still.

591(ii)

BROTHER JAMES' AIR   8 6 8 6 (CM) extended   J. L. Macbeth Bain (died 1925)
                                              © arranged John Barnard (born 1948)†

When this tune is used the last two lines of each verse are repeated.

4   My table thou hast furnishèd
    in presence of my foes;
    my head with oil thou dost anoint
    and my cup overflows.

5   Goodness and mercy all my life
    shall surely follow me;
    and in God's house for evermore
    my dwelling-place shall be.

from Psalm 23
W. Whittingham (c.1524–1579) and others

(see also revised version, 45)

592

NATIONAL ANTHEM 6 6 4 6 6 6 4

Melody from *Thesaurus Musicus*
London 1745

1 God save our gracious Queen,
   long live our noble Queen,
   God save the Queen!
   Send her victorious,
   happy and glorious,
   long to reign over us:
   God save the Queen!

2 Thy choicest gifts in store
   on her be pleased to pour:
   long may she reign!
   May she defend our laws,
   and ever give us cause
   to sing with heart and voice:
   God save the Queen!

unknown (c. 1745)

(see also revised version, 326)

593*

PETRA 777777   R. Redhead (1820–1901)

1 *mf* Rock of ages, cleft for me,
        let me hide myself in thee;
        let the water and the blood
        from thy riven side
            which flowed,
        be of sin the double cure,
        cleanse me from its guilt
            and power.

2   Not the labours of my hands
        can fulfil thy law's demands;
        could my zeal no respite know,
        could my tears for ever flow,
        all for sin could not atone:
        thou must save, and thou alone.

3 *mp* Nothing in my hand I bring,
        simply to thy cross I cling;
        naked, come to thee for dress,
        helpless, look to thee for grace;
        foul, I to the fountain fly:
        wash me, Saviour, or I die!

4   While I draw this fleeting breath,
        when my eyelids close in death,
   mf when I soar
            through tracts unknown,
        see thee on thy judgement
            throne:
        Rock of ages, cleft for me,
        let me hide myself in thee.

A. M. Toplady (1740–1778)

(see also revised version, 444)

Alternative tune: TOPLADY (444)

*Please note: Hymns 593–612 do not appear in the first edition of *Hymns for Today's Church*.

594

NICAEA   11 12 12 10

J. B. Dykes (1823–1876)
descant C. S. Lang (1891–1971)
descant © Novello & Co Ltd

Descant

4 Ho-ly, ho-ly, ho - ly, Lord God al-might - y!

all thy works shall praise thy name, in earth and sky and sea:

Ho - ly, ho - ly, ho - ly! — mer - ci-ful and might - y,

God in three per - sons, bless-ed _ Tri - ni - ty.

1 Holy, holy, holy, Lord God almighty!
   early in the morning our song
        shall rise to thee:
   Holy, holy, holy! – merciful and mighty,
   God in three persons, blessèd Trinity.

2 Holy, holy, holy! All the saints adore thee,
   casting down their golden crowns
        around the glassy sea;
   cherubim and seraphim falling down before thee:
   God from of old who evermore shall be!

3 Holy, holy, holy! – though the darkness hide thee,
   though the eye of sinful man
        thy glory may not see;
   only thou art holy, there is none beside thee
   perfect in power, in love and purity.

4 Holy, holy, holy, Lord God almighty!
   all thy works shall praise thy name,
        in earth and sky and sea:
   Holy, holy, holy! – merciful and mighty,
   God in three persons, blessèd Trinity.

R. Heber (1783–1826)

(see also revised version, 7)

Alternative tune: TERSANCTUS (7ii)

595

MANNHEIM 878787

F. Filitz (1804–1876)

1 *mf* Lead us, heavenly Father, lead us
o'er the world's tempestuous sea;
guard us, guide us, keep us, feed us –
for we have no help but thee,
yet possessing every blessing
if our God our Father be.

2 *mp* Saviour, breathe forgiveness o'er us:
all our weakness thou dost know,
thou didst tread this earth before us,
thou didst feel its keenest woe;
through the dreary desert, weary,
in obedience thou didst go.

3 *mf* Spirit of our God, descending,
fill our hearts with heavenly joy,
love with every passion blending,
pleasure that can never cloy:
f thus provided, pardoned, guided,
nothing can our peace destroy.

J. Edmeston (1791–1867)

(see also revised version, 525)

596

HEREFORD   8 8 8 8 (LM)   S. S. Wesley (1810–1876)

1 O thou who camest from above
the pure celestial fire to impart,
kindle a flame of sacred love
on the mean altar of my heart!

2 There let it for thy glory burn
with inextinguishable blaze;
and trembling to its source return,
in humble prayer and fervent praise.

3 Jesus, confirm my heart's desire
to work and speak and think for thee;
still let me guard the holy fire,
and still stir up thy gift in me:

4 Ready for all thy perfect will,
my acts of faith and love repeat,
till death thy endless mercies seal
and make the sacrifice complete.

C. Wesley (1707–1788)

(see also revised version, 552)

597

ADESTE FIDELES   Irregular

Eighteenth-century melody probably by
J. F. Wade (1711–1786)
arranged mainly W. H. Monk (1823–1889)

1 *f* O come, all ye faithful,
joyful and triumphant;
O come ye, O come ye to Bethlehem;
come and behold him, born the king of angels!
   O come, let us adore him,
   O come, let us adore him,
   O come, let us adore him, Christ the Lord!

2   God from God,
      Light from light –
      lo, he abhors not the virgin's womb!
      Very God, begotten, not created.
          O come . . .

3 *mf* See how the shepherds
      summoned to his cradle,
      leaving their flocks, draw nigh with lowly fear:
      we too will thither bend our joyful footsteps.
          O come . . .

4   Led by the starlight,
      Magi, Christ adoring,
      offer him incense, gold, and myrrh;
      we to the Christ-child bring our hearts' oblations.
          O come . . .

5 *mp* Child, for us sinners,
      poor and in the manger,
      we would embrace thee with love and awe:
      who could not love thee, loving us so dearly?
          O come . . .

6 *f* Sing, choirs of angels,
      sing in exultation!
      Sing, all ye citizens of heaven above,
      'Glory to God in the highest!'
          O come . . .

7   Yea, Lord, we greet thee,
      born for our salvation;
      Jesus, to thee be glory given!
      Word of the Father now in flesh appearing.
          O come . . .

OR on Christmas morning:

7   Yea, Lord, we greet thee,
      born this happy morning;
      Jesus, to thee be glory given!
      Word of the Father now in flesh appearing.
          O come . . .

                         after J. F. Wade (1711–1786)
                         F. Oakeley (1802–1880) and others

An arrangement and descant for verses 6 and 7 appear overleaf.

(see also revised short version, 65)

597 – O come, all ye faithful

Descant and arrangement © Christopher Robinson (born 1935)

For alternative descant and arrangement see 65.

598

NARENZA 6 6 8 6 (SM)

Adapted from J. Leisentritt
Catholicum Hymnologium 1584
arranged W. H. Havergal (1793–1870)

1 You servants of the Lord
who for his coming wait:
observe with care his heavenly word –
be watchful at his gate.

2 Let all your lamps be bright
and guard the living flame;
be ready always in his sight,
for awesome is his name.

3 Await your Lord's command:
the bridegroom shall appear,
for his returning is at hand,
and while we speak he's near.

4 O happy servants they
who wide awake are found
to greet their master on that day,
and be with honour crowned!

5 Christ shall the banquet spread
with his own royal hand,
and raise each faithful servant's head
amid the angelic band.

from Luke 12
P. Doddridge (1702–1751)
© in this version Word & Music†

599

CRÜGER   7 6 7 6 D

J. Crüger (1598–1662)

1   O bless the God of Israel
      who comes to set us free;
  who visits and redeems us,
      with love for all to see.
  The prophets spoke of mercy,
      of rescue and release:
  God shall fulfil his promise
      and bring our people peace.

2   He comes! the Child of David,
      the Son whom God has given;
  he comes to live among us
      and raise us up to heaven:
  before him goes his servant –
      forerunner in the way,
  the prophet of salvation,
      the herald of the Day.

3   Where once were fear and darkness,
      the sun begins to rise –
  the dawning of forgiveness
      upon the sinner's eyes.
  He guides the feet of pilgrims
      along the paths of peace:
  O bless our God and Saviour,
      with songs that never cease!

from *Benedictus* (Luke 1)
© Michael Perry (born 1942)†

Alternative tune: MORNING LIGHT (535)

600

CRANHAM Irregular

G. Holst (1874–1934)

1 In the bleak mid-win - ter frost-y wind made moan,
2 Hea-ven can-not hold him, nor the earth sus - tain;
3 E-nough for him whom cher - u- bim wor-ship night and day — a
4 What can I give him, poor as I am?

earth stood hard as ir - on, wa - ter like a stone;
heaven and earth shall flee a - way when he comes to reign:
breast - ful of milk and a man -ger full of hay; e -
If I were a shep - herd I would give a lamb,

snow had fall - en, snow on snow, snow on snow,
in the bleak mid - win - ter a sta - ble-place suf -ficed
- nough for him whom an - gels fall down be - fore — the
if I were a wise man I would do my part; yet

in the bleak mid - win - ter long a - go.
God, the Lord al - migh - ty, Je - sus Christ.
wise men and the shep - herds who a - dore!
what I can I give him — give my heart.

1　In the bleak mid-winter
　　　frosty wind made moan,
　　earth stood hard as iron,
　　　water like a stone;
　　snow had fallen, snow on snow,
　　　snow on snow,
　　in the bleak mid-winter
　　　long ago.

2　Heaven cannot hold him,
　　　nor the earth sustain;
　　heaven and earth shall flee away
　　　when he comes to reign:
　　in the bleak mid-winter
　　　a stable-place sufficed
　　God, the Lord almighty,
　　　Jesus Christ.

3　Enough for him whom cherubim
　　　worship night and day –
　　a breastful of milk
　　and a manger full of hay;
　　enough for him whom angels
　　　fall down before –
　　the wise men and the shepherds
　　　who adore!

4　What can I give him,
　　　poor as I am?
　　If I were a shepherd
　　　I would give a lamb,
　　if I were a wise man
　　　I would do my part;
　　yet what I can I give him –
　　　give my heart.

Christina Rossetti (1830–1894)

601

WINCHESTER NEW   8 8 8 8 (LM)   *Musikalisches Handbuch* Hamburg 1690

1 On Jordan's bank the Baptist's cry
    announces that the Lord is nigh:
    awake and listen for he brings
    glad tidings of the King of kings.

2 Let every heart be cleansed from sin,
    make straight the way for God within,
    and so prepare to be the home
    where such a mighty guest may come.

3 For you are our salvation, Lord,
    our refuge and our great reward;
    without your grace we waste away
    like flowers that wither and decay.

4 To heal the sick, stretch out your hand,
    and make the fallen sinner stand;
    shine out, and let your light restore
    earth's own true loveliness once more.

5 To you, O Christ, all praises be,
    whose advent sets your people free;
    whom with the Father we adore
    and Holy Spirit evermore!

after C. Coffin (1676–1749)
J. Chandler (1806–1876)
© in this version Word & Music†

Descant and arrangement © John Barnard (born 1948)†

Descant

5 To you,— O Christ, all prais - es be, whose ad - vent sets your peo - ple free; whom with the Fa - ther we a - dore and Ho - ly— Spi - rit— ev - er - more!

602

PASSION CHORALE 7 6 7 6 D

Melody from H. L. Hassler (1564–1612)
arranged J. S. Bach (1685–1750)

1 We come as guests invited
   when Jesus bids us dine,
   his friends on earth united
   to share the bread and wine;
   the bread of life is broken,
   the wine is freely poured
   for us, in solemn token
   of Christ our dying Lord.

2 We eat and drink, receiving
   from Christ the grace we need,
   and in our hearts believing
   on him by faith we feed;
   with wonder and thanksgiving
   for love that knows no end,
   we find in Jesus living
   our ever-present friend.

3 One bread is ours for sharing,
   one single fruitful vine,
   our fellowship declaring
   renewed in bread and wine –
   renewed, sustained and given
   by token, sign and word,
   the pledge and seal of heaven,
   the love of Christ our Lord.

© Timothy Dudley-Smith (born 1926)

603(i)

GWALCHMAI 7 4 7 4 D

J. D. Jones (1827–1870)

1 King of glory, king of peace
       I will love you;
   since your mercies never cease,
       faith shall prove you!
   You have granted my request,
       you have heard me;
   though my sinful soul transgressed,
       you have spared me.

2 Praises with my utmost art
       I will bring you;
   songs of triumph from my heart
       I will sing you.
   Though my sins against me cried,
       this shall cheer me:
   God in Christ has justified
       and will clear me.

603(ii)

REDLAND 7 4 7 4 D

© Malcolm Archer (born 1952)

3   Seven whole days – not one in seven –
       I will praise you;
    worship lifts the heart to heaven,
       love obeys you!
    Once you died, when no-one sought
       to console you;
    now eternity's too short
       to extol you!

G. Herbert (1593–1633)
© in this version Word & Music†

604(i)

HUMILITY 7 7 7 7 and refrain

J. Goss (1800–1880)

1 Bless the Lord, creation sings;
    earth and sky his hand proclaim.
    Praise him, all created things;
    angel hosts, exalt his Name.

2 Bless the Lord! To heaven's throne
    songs of endless glory rise;
    in the clouds his praise be shown,
    sun and moon and starry skies.

3 Bless the Lord with ice and snow,
    bitter cold and scorching blaze,
    floods and all the winds that blow,
    frosty nights and sunlit days.

604(ii)

UNIVERSITY COLLEGE   7 7 7 7   H. J. Gauntlett (1805–1876)

4 Bless the Lord in mist and cloud,
   lightnings shine to mark his way;
   thunders speak his name aloud,
   wind and storm his word obey.

5 Bless the Lord who brings to birth
   life renewed by sun and rain;
   flowing rivers, fruitful earth,
   bird and beast on hill and plain.

6 Bless the Lord! From earth and sky,
   ocean depths and furthest shore,
   all things living bear on high
   songs of praise for evermore.

7 Bless the Lord! His name be blessed,
   worshipped, honoured, loved, adored;
   and with holy hearts confessed,
   saints and servants of the Lord.

8 Bless the Lord! The Father, Son,
   and the Holy Spirit, praise;
   high exalt the Three-in-One,
   God of everlasting days!

from *A Song of Creation/Benedicite*
© Timothy Dudley-Smith (born 1926)

For a shorter version of this hymn verses 1, 7 and 8 may be sung, using the tune
UNIVERSITY COLLEGE.

605

WÜRTTEMBERG   77776   *Hundert Arien* Dresden 1694

1   Great and wonderful your deeds,
    God from whom all power proceeds:
    true and right are all your ways –
    who shall not give thanks and praise?
        To your name be glory!

2   King of nations, take your crown!
    every race shall soon bow down:
    holy God and Lord alone,
    justice in your deeds is shown;
        all have seen your glory.

3   To the one almighty God,
    to the Lamb who shed his blood,
    to the Spirit now be given
    by the hosts of earth and heaven;
        love and praise and glory!

606

NICOLAUS 8 6 8 8 6

Nicolaus Herman (c. 1485–1561)
arranged J. S. Bach (1685–1750)

1 *f* All glory be to God on high,
his peace on earth proclaim;
to all his people tell abroad
the grace and glory of the Lord,
and bless his holy Name.

2 In songs of thankfulness and praise
our hearts their homage bring
to worship him who reigns above
almighty Father, Lord of love,
our God and heavenly King.

3 *mp* O Christ, the Father's only Son,
O Lamb enthroned on high,
O Jesus, who for sinners died
and reigns at God the Father's side,
in mercy hear our cry.

4 *f* Most high and holy is the Lord,
most high his heavenly throne;
where God the Father, God the Son,
and God the Spirit, ever One,
in glory reigns alone.

from *Gloria in Excelsis*
© Timothy Dudley-Smith (born 1926)

607

ST. ALBINUS 7 8 7 8 4

H. J. Gauntlett (1805–1876)

1 Jesus, Saviour of the world,
   you have bought your people's freedom
   by your cross, your life laid down:
   now bring in your glorious kingdom:
      Come to help us!

2 Christ, who once on Galilee
   came to your disciples' rescue:
   we, like them, cry out for help –
   free us from our sins, we ask you.
      Come to save us!

3 Lord, make known your promised power;
   show yourself our strong deliverer:
   so our prayer shall turn to praise –
   hear us, stay with us for ever:
      Come to rule us!

4 When you come, Lord Jesus Christ,
   filling earth and heaven with wonder,
   come to make us one with you –
   heirs of life, to reign in splendour:
      Alleluia!

from *Saviour of the World*
© Christopher Idle (born 1938)†

608

ASTHALL 7 8 7 8

© John Barnard (born 1948)†

Descant

3 So may we who watch or rest bless the Lord of

earth and hea-ven; and by him our-selves be blessed,

grace and peace and mer - cy giv - en.

1   Bless the Lord as day departs;
let your lamps be brightly burning,
lifting holy hands and hearts
to the Lord, till day's returning.

2   As within the darkened shrine,
faithful to their sacred calling,
sons and priests of Levi's line
blessed the Lord as night was falling:

3   So may we who watch or rest
bless the Lord of earth and heaven;
and by him ourselves be blessed,
grace and peace and mercy given.

from Psalm 134
© Timothy Dudley-Smith (born 1926)

609

ST. CLEMENT 9 8 9 8

C. C. Scholefield (1839–1904)

1   Come, praise the Lord, all you his servants,
    who stand within his house by night!
    Come, lift your hands and hearts in worship;
    make him your praise and your delight:

2   Come, bless the Lord, all those who love him,
    who serve within his holy place:
    may God who made both earth and heaven
    grant us the blessings of his grace.

from Psalm 134
© Christopher Idle (born 1938)†

610

ORIENTIS PARTIBUS (ii)   7 7 7 7

P. de Corbeil (died 1222)
arranged R. Vaughan Williams (1872–1958)
arrangement © Oxford University Press

1 Bless the Lord, our fathers' God,
   bless the name of heaven's king;
   bless him in his holy place,
   tell his praise, his glories sing.

2 Bless the Lord who reigns on high
   throned between the cherubim;
   bless the Lord who knows the depths,
   show his praise and worship him.

3 Bless the Lord for evermore;
   bless the Holy Trinity:
   bless the Father, Spirit, Son,
   sing his praise eternally!

from *Bless the Lord*
© Christopher Idle (born 1938)†

611(i)

NORTH COATES 6 5 6 5   T. R. Matthews (1826–1910)

1 *mp* Lord, now let your servant
    go his way in peace;
your great love has brought me
    joy that will not cease:

2 *mf* For my eyes have seen him
    promised from of old –
saviour of all people,
    shepherd of one fold:

3 *f* Light of revelation
    to the gentiles shown,
light of Israel's glory
    to the world made known.

from *Nunc Dimittis* (Luke 2)
J. E. Seddon (1915–1983)
© Mrs. M. Seddon†

611(ii)

FAWLEY LODGE   6 5 6 5   © Norman Warren (born 1934)†

1 *mp* Lord, now let your servant
   go his way in peace;
  your great love has brought me
   joy that will not cease:

2 *mf* For my eyes have seen him
   promised from of old –
  saviour of all people,
   shepherd of one fold:

3 *f* Light of revelation
   to the gentiles shown,
  light of Israel's glory
   to the world made known.

   from *Nunc Dimittis* (Luke 2)
   J. E. Seddon (1915–1983)
   © Mrs. M. Seddon†

612

NARENZA   6 6 8 6 (SM)

Adapted from J. Leisentritt
Catholicum Hymnologium 1584
arranged W. H. Havergal (1793–1870)

1 *mf* Before the heaven and earth
were made by God's decree,
the Son of God all-glorious dwelt
in God's eternity.

2 Though in the form of God
and rich beyond compare,
he did not stay to grasp his prize;
nor did he linger there.

3 From heights of heaven he came
to this world full of sin,
to meet with hunger, hatred, hell,
our life, our love to win.

4 The Son became true Man
and took a servant's role;
with lowliness and selfless love
he came, to make us whole.

5 *mp* Obedient to his death –
that death upon a cross,
no son had ever shown such love,
nor father known such loss.

6 *f* To him enthroned on high,
by angel hosts adored,
all knees shall bow, and tongues confess
that Jesus Christ is Lord.

from *The Song of Christ's Glory* (Philippians 2)
© Brian Black (born 1926) and Word & Music†

Descant and arrangement © John Barnard (born 1948)†

Descant and arrangement © John Barnard (born 1948)†

SONG SECTION

S.1

BURNING HEART

© Norman Warren

(Alleluia, alleluia!)

1 As we walk along beside you,
and we hear you speak of mercy,
then it seems our hearts are burning
for we find you in the sharing of the word.

2 As we ask that you stay with us
   and we watch what you are doing,
   then our eyes begin to open
   for we see you in the breaking of the bread.

3 As we reach for you believing
   and we go to love and serve you,
   then our lives will be proclaiming
   that we know you in the rising from the dead.

   (Lord, alleluia!)

from Luke 24
© Michael Perry†

S.2

COME INTO HIS PRESENCE

Unknown
© arranged David Wilson†

1 Come into his presence singing,
   Alleluia, alleluia, alleluia!

2 Come into his presence singing
   Jesus is Lord, Jesus is Lord, Jesus is Lord!

3 Come into his presence singing,
   Worthy the Lamb, worthy the Lamb,
              worthy the Lamb!

4 Come into his presence singing,
   Glory to God, glory to God, glory to God!

unknown

S.3

Don Fishel
arranged Norman Warren
© Word of God Music
descant Angela Reith

Al-le-lu - ia, al-le-lu - ia, thanks to the ris-en Lord!

Al - le - lu - ia, al - le - lu - ia, praise to his name!

Alleluia, alleluia,
give thanks to the risen Lord!
Alleluia, alleluia,
give praise to his name!

1   Jesus is Lord of all the earth;
    he is the king of creation:
        Alleluia . . .

2   Spread the good news o'er all the earth –
    Jesus has died and has risen:
        Alleluia . . .

3   We have been crucified with Christ;
    now we shall live for ever:
        Alleluia . . .

4(5)   Come let us praise the living God;
    joyfully sing to our saviour:
        Alleluia . . .

Don Fishel
© 1973 and arranged © 1982 by The Word of God,
P.O. Box 8617, Ann Arbor, Michigan 48107, USA.
All rights reserved, used by permission

S.4

BIND US TOGETHER

Bob Gillman
arranged Norman Warren

Bind us together, Lord,
bind us together
with cords that cannot be broken;
bind us together, Lord,
bind us together,
O bind us together in love!

There is only one God,
there is only one King,
there is only one Body –
that is why we sing:
 Bind us together . . .

Bob Gillman
© 1977 Thankyou Music, P.O. Box 75,
Eastbourne BN23 6NW.
Reprinted by permission

S.5

FATHER, WE ADORE YOU

Terrye Coelho
© Maranatha! Music/Word Music (UK)

1 Father, we adore you,
  lay our lives before you:
  how we love you!

2 Jesus, we adore you,
  lay our lives before you:
  how we love you!

3 Spirit, we adore you,
  lay our lives before you:
  how we love you!

Terrye Coelho
© 1972 Maranatha! Music/Word Music (UK)
9 Holdom Avenue, Bletchley, Milton Keynes MK1 1QU

S.6

BROKEN FOR ME

Janet Lunt
arranged Andrew Maries
© Mustard Seed Music

Bro-ken for me, _____ bro-ken for you,

the bo-dy of Je - sus _____ broken for you.

1 He offered his bo - dy, _____ he poured out his soul,

Jesus was bro - ken ____ that we might be whole:

the bo-dy of Je - sus ____ broken for you.

The harmony versions of the refrain and verse printed on the next page may be used, in conjunction with the accompaniment above, for any verse. Rhythms need to be adjusted to fit the words.

Broken for me, broken for you,
the body of Jesus broken for you.

1 He offered his body, he poured out his soul,
Jesus was broken that we might be whole:
Broken for me . . .

2 Come to my table and with me dine,
eat of my bread and drink of my wine:
Broken for me . . .

3 This is my body given for you,
eat it remembering I died for you:
Broken for me . . .

4 This is my blood I shed for you,
for your forgiveness, making you new:
Broken for me . . .

Janet Lunt
© 1978/9 Mustard Seed Music
9 Holdom Avenue, Bletchley, Milton Keynes MK1 1QU

S.6 – Broken for me

S.7

HE IS LORD

Unknown
© arranged Norman Warrent
descant © Angela Reith

He is Lord, he is Lord,
he is risen from the dead, and he is Lord!
Every knee shall bow, every tongue confess
that Jesus Christ is Lord.

from Philippians 2
© Marvin Frey

S.8

MICHAEL, ROW THE BOAT

Traditional melody
© arranged David Wilson†

1 Come and praise the Lord our king,
come and praise the Lord our king.

Alleluia,
alleluia!

2 Christ was born in Bethlehem,
Son of God and Son of Man.

Alleluia,
alleluia!

3 He grew up an earthly child
in the world, but undefiled.

Alleluia,
alleluia!

4   He who died at Calvary
    rose again triumphantly.   Alleluia,
                                            alleluia!

5   He will cleanse us from our sin
    if we live by faith in him.   Alleluia,
                                            alleluia!

6   Come and praise the Lord our king,
    come and praise the Lord our king.   Alleluia,
                                            alleluia!

                                            unknown

S.9

SOVEREIGN LORD   Peter Jackson
                                                 arranged Norman Warren
                                                 © Word Music (UK)

Sovereign Lord, Sovereign Lord,
you made all things by your word;
my creator, redeemer, my King of kings adored,
sovereign Lord, sovereign Lord!

Peter Jackson
© 1980 Word Music (UK)
9 Holdom Avenue, Bletchley, Milton Keynes MK1 1QU

S.10

I AM THE BREAD OF LIFE

Suzanne Toolan
© GIA Publications Inc
arranged Christian Strover

1   Come, let us worship Christ
    to the glory of God the Father,
    for he is worthy of all our love;
    he died and rose for us!
    praise him as Lord and saviour.
            And when the trumpet shall sound
            and Jesus comes in great power,
            then he will raise us to be with him
            for evermore!

2   'I am the bread of life;
    he who comes to me shall not hunger:
    and all who trust in me shall not thirst' –
    this is what Jesus said:
    praise him as Lord and saviour.
            And when the trumpet . . .

3   'I am the door to life;
    he who enters by me is saved,
    abundant life he will then receive' –
    this is what Jesus said:
    praise him as Lord and saviour.
            And when the trumpet . . .

4   'I am the light of the world;
    if you follow me, darkness ceases,
    and in its place comes the light of life' –
    this is what Jesus said:
    praise him as Lord and saviour.
            And when the trumpet . . .

5   Lord, we are one with you;
    we rejoice in your new creation:
    our hearts are fired by your saving love –
    take up our lives, O Lord,
    and use us for your glory.
            And when the trumpet . . .

after Suzanne Toolan
© Michael Baughen
and GIA Publications Incorporated

S.11

GIVE ME JOY

Traditional
© arranged Christian Strover †

Sing ho-san -na, sing ho-san-na, sing ho-san-na to the King of kings;

sing ho-san - na, sing ho-san - na, sing ho-san-na to the King.

1 Give me joy in my heart, keep me praising;
   give me joy in my heart, I pray:
   give me joy in my heart, keep me praising –
   keep me praising till the break of day.
        Sing hosanna, sing hosanna,
        sing hosanna to the King of kings;
        sing hosanna, sing hosanna,
        sing hosanna to the King.

2 Give me peace in my heart, keep me resting;
   give me peace in my heart, I pray:
   give me peace in my heart, keep me resting –
   keep me resting till the break of day.
        Sing hosanna . . .

3 Give me love in my heart, keep me serving;
   give me love in my heart, I pray:
   give me love in my heart, keep me serving –
   keep me serving till the break of day.
        Sing hosanna . . .

unknown

S.12

FREELY, FREELY

Jimmy Owens
arranged David Iliff
© Lexicon Music Inc/Word Music (UK)

He said: Free-ly, free-ly you have re-ceived, free-ly, free-ly give; ___ go in my name and be-cause you be-lieve, oth-ers will know that I live. ___

1   God forgave my sin in Jesus' name;
    I've been born again in Jesus' name,
    and in Jesus' name I come to you
    to share his love as he told me to.
            He said:
            Freely, freely you have received,
            freely, freely give;
            go in my name and because you believe,
            others will know that I live.

2   All power is given in Jesus' name,
    in earth and heaven in Jesus' name;
    and in Jesus' name I come to you
    to share his power as he told me to.
            He said . . .

from *Come Together* by Jimmy and Carol Owens
© 1972 Lexicon Music Inc./Word Music (UK)
9 Holdom Avenue, Bletchley, Milton Keynes MK1 1QU

S.13

GOD HAS SPOKEN

Israeli folk song
© arranged Norman Warren†
descant © Angela Reith

God has spo-ken to his peo-ple, Al-le-lu - ia,

and his words are words of wis-dom. Al -le-lu - ia!

Fine

God has spoken to his people,   Alleluia,
and his words are words of wisdom.   Alleluia!

1   Open your ears, O Christian people,
    open your ears and hear good news;
    open your hearts, O royal priesthood,
    God has come to you, God has come to you.
       God has spoken . . .

2   They who have ears to hear his message,
    they who have ears, then let them hear;
    they who would learn the way of wisdom,
    let them hear God's word,
           let them hear God's word!
       God has spoken . . .

3   Israel comes to greet the saviour,
    Judah is glad to see his day;
    from east and west the peoples travel,
    he will show the way, he will show the way.
       God has spoken . . .

S.14

HOLY, HOLY

Jimmy Owens
arranged Noël Tredinnick
© Lexicon Music Inc/Word Music (UK)

vv. 2-4

1 Holy, holy, holy, holy,
  holy, holy, Lord God Almighty!
  and we lift our hearts before you
  as a token of our love:
  holy, holy, holy, holy!

2 Gracious Father, gracious Father,
  we're so glad to be your children,
    gracious Father;
  and we lift our heads before you
  as a token of our love,
  gracious Father, gracious Father.

3 Precious Jesus, precious Jesus,
  we're so glad that you've
    redeemed us, precious Jesus;
  and we lift our hands before you
  as a token of our love,
  precious Jesus, precious Jesus.

4 Holy Spirit, Holy Spirit,
  come and fill our hearts anew,
    Holy Spirit!
  and we lift our voice before you
  as a token of our love,
  Holy Spirit, Holy Spirit.

from *Come Together* by Jimmy and Carol Owens
© 1972 Lexicon Music Inc./Word Music (UK)
9 Holdom Avenue, Bletchley, Milton Keynes MK1 1QU

S.15

I WILL SING, I WILL SING

Max Dyer
© Celebration Services/Thankyou Music

Repeat for refrain

1 I will sing, I will sing a song unto the Lord,
  I will sing, I will sing a song unto the Lord,
  I will sing, I will sing a song unto the Lord:
  Alleluia, glory to the Lord:
      Allelu, alleluia, glory to the Lord,
      allelu, alleluia, glory to the Lord,
      allelu, alleluia, glory to the Lord,
      alleluia, glory to the Lord!

2 We will come, we will come
              as one before the Lord . . .
  Alleluia, glory to the Lord!
      Allelu, alleluia . . .

3 If the Son, if the Son shall make you free . . .
  you shall be free indeed:
      Allelu, alleluia . . .

4 They that sow in tears shall reap in joy . . .
  Alleluia, glory to the Lord!
      Allelu, alleluia . . .

Max Dyer
© 1974, 1975 Celebration Services/Thankyou Music
PO Box 75, Eastbourne BN23 6NW

S.16

I WANT TO WALK

Swiss folk tune
© arranged Noël Tredinnick†

Fol-low him, fol-low him, yield your life to him — he has con-quered death, he is King of kings; ac - cept the joy which he gives to those who yield their lives _ to him! _____ him! _____

1   I want to walk with Jesus Christ
    all the days I live of this life on earth;
    to give to him complete control
    of body and of soul.
        Follow him, follow him,
        yield your life to him –
        he has conquered death,
        he is King of kings;
        accept the joy which he gives to those
        who yield their lives to him!

2   I want to learn to speak to him,
    to pray to him, confess my sin,
    to open my life and let him in,
    for joy will then be mine.

3   I want to learn to speak of him –
    my life must show that he lives in me;
    my deeds, my thoughts, my words must speak
    of his great love for me.

4   I want to learn to read his word,
    for this is how I know the way
    to live my life as pleases him,
    in holiness and joy.

5   O Holy Spirit of the Lord,
    now enter into this heart of mine;
    take full control of my selfish will
    and make me yours alone!
        Follow him . . .

S.17

JESUS IS LORD

David Mansell

Je - sus is Lord, Je - sus is Lord!

Praise him with al - le - lu - ias, for Je - sus is Lord!

1 *mf* Jesus is Lord! creation's voice proclaims it,
for by his power each tree and flower
was planned and made.
Jesus is Lord! the universe declares it –
sun, moon and stars in heaven cry: 'Jesus is Lord!'
Jesus is Lord, Jesus is Lord!
Praise him with alleluias,
for Jesus is Lord!

2 *mp* Jesus is Lord! yet from his throne eternal
in flesh he came to die in pain on Calvary's tree.
mf Jesus is Lord! from him all life proceeding –
yet gave his life a ransom thus setting us free.
Jesus is Lord . . .

3 *f* Jesus is Lord! o'er sin the mighty conqueror;
from death he rose and all his foes
shall own his name.
Jesus is Lord! God sends his Holy Spirit
to show by works of power that Jesus is Lord.
Jesus is Lord . . .

David Mansell
© 1979 Springtide/Word Music (UK)
9 Holdom Avenue, Bletchley, Milton Keynes MK1 1QU

S.18

CALHOUN MELODY

Traditional melody
© arranged David Wilson†
descants © Ivor Keys

1 Let us praise, let us praise God togeth-er, let us praise; ____

3 Let us serve, let us serve, let us serve; ____

let us praise God to-geth-er all our days: ____

let our lives show his goodness through each day: ____

1 Let us praise God together,
    let us praise;
  let us praise God together
    all our days:
  he is faithful in all his ways,
  he is worthy of all our praise,
    his name be exalted on high!

2 Let us seek God together,
    let us pray;
  let us seek his forgiveness
    as we pray:
  he will cleanse us from all our sin,
  he will help us the fight to win,
    his name be exalted on high!

he is faith-ful in all his ways, he is wor-thy of all our praise,

Christ the Lord is the world's true light – let us serve him with all our might,

vv. 1, 2 | v. 3

his name be ex-alt-ed on high!

vv. 1, 2 | v. 3

his name be ex - alt-ed on high!

vv. 1, 2 | v. 3

The descants may be used separately or together for any verses, adapting the
words accordingly. Alternatively Descant 1 may be played on a solo organ stop.

3 Let us serve God together,
        him obey;
    let our lives show his goodness
        through each day:
    Christ the Lord is the world's true light –
    let us serve him with all our might,
        his name be exalted on high!

J. E. Seddon
© Mrs. M. Seddont

S.19

ST. FRANCIS

Sebastian Temple
arranged John Barnard
© Franciscan Communications

1   Make me a channel of your peace:
    where there is hatred let me bring your love,
    where there is injury, your pardon, Lord,
    and where there's doubt, true faith in you:
        O Master, grant that I may never seek
        so much to be consoled as to console;
        to be understood as to understand,
        to be loved, as to love with all my soul!

2   Make me a channel of your peace:
    where there's despair in life let me bring hope,
    where there is darkness, only light,
    and where there's sadness, ever joy:
        O Master grant . . .

v. 3

Fine Mas-ter, grant that I may nev-er seek so much to be consoled as to con-sole; ___ to be un-der-stood as to un-der-stand, to be loved, as to love with all my soul! ___

poco rall.

The refrain may be sung in 2-part harmony as indicated by the tails pointing upwards in the piano accompaniment.
The descant should be sung to *Ah* throughout.

3   Make me a channel of your peace:
     it is in pardoning that we are pardoned,
     in giving of ourselves that we receive,
     and in dying that we're born to eternal life.

from the traditional prayer
Sebastian Temple
© 1975 Franciscan Communications Center
Los Angeles, CA 90015, USA.
Reprinted by permission

S.20

MOTHER TERESA   © Norman Warren†

1   Make us worthy, Lord,
    to serve our neighbour's need
    throughout the world,
    who live in poverty and hunger,
        in poverty and hunger,
        in poverty and hunger.

2   Give them through our hands
    this day their daily bread
    and, by our understanding love,
    give peace and joy,
        give peace and joy,
        give peace and joy!

after Mother Teresa

S.21

HE IS LOVE

Carey Bonner
© arranged David Wilson†

1 Praise him, praise him,
everybody praise him –
he is love, he is love;
praise him, praise him,
everybody praise him –
God is love, God is love!

2 Thank him, thank him,
everybody thank him –
he is love, he is love;
thank him, thank him,
everybody thank him –
God is love, God is love!

3 Love him, love him,
everybody love him –
he is love, he is love;
love him, love him,
everybody love him –
God is love, God is love!

4 Alleluia,
glory, alleluia;
he is love, he is love;
alleluia,
glory, alleluia!
God is love, God is love!

unknown (c.1890)
© in this version Jubilate Hymns†

S.22

SING ALLELUIA

Optional 2nd part

(Lord!)   1 Sing al-le-lu-ia to the Lord,

1 Sing al-le-lu-ia to the Lord,   sing al-le-lu-ia to the

sing al-le-lu-ia, __ al - le - lu - ia,

Lord,   sing al-le-lu - ia, sing al-le-lu - ia,

v. 4

sing al - le - lu - ia to the   own.

sing al - le - lu - ia to the Lord!

1 Sing alleluia to the Lord,
sing alleluia to the Lord,
sing alleluia, sing alleluia,
sing alleluia to the Lord!

2 Jesus is risen from the dead,
Jesus is risen from the dead,
Jesus is risen, Jesus is risen,
Jesus is risen from the dead!

3 Jesus is Lord of heaven and earth,
Jesus is Lord of heaven and earth,
Jesus is Lord, Jesus is Lord,
Jesus is Lord of heaven and earth!

4 Jesus is coming for his own,
Jesus is coming for his own,
Jesus is coming, Jesus is coming,
Jesus is coming for his own.

S.23 and S.24

SPIRIT OF THE LIVING GOD

Unknown
arranged W. G. Hathaway

S.23   Spirit of the living God, fall afresh on me;
Spirit of the living God, fall afresh on me:
break me, melt me, mould me, fill me –
Spirit of the living God, fall afresh on me!

Daniel Iverson
© Moody Press, 820 North Lasalle Drive,
Chicago, Illinois 60610, USA

S.24   Spirit of the living God, move among us all;
make us one in heart and mind, make us one in love:
humble, caring, selfless, sharing –
Spirit of the living God, fill our lives with love!

© Michael Baughen†

S.25

THE VIRGIN MARY

West Indian traditional melody
© collected Boosey & Hawkes
arranged John Barnard

Unison

1 The vir - gin Ma - ry had a ba - by__ boy,__ the
2 The an - gels sang when the ba - by was born,__ the
3 The shep-herds came where the ba - by was born,__ the

vir - gin Ma - ry had a ba - by__ boy,__ the vir - gin Ma - ry had a
an - gels sang__when the ba - by was born,__ the an - gels sang__when the
shep-herds came where the ba - by was born,__ the shep-herds came where the

O yes, be-liev - er! He come from the glo - ry, he come from the glo - rious king-dom.

after v. 3

West Indian carol
© collected Boosey & Hawkes Inc.

When choirs use this arrangement they may wish to clap at the ♩ signs.
Where 2-part harmony is suggested the lower part should be sung by the men at printed pitch, not an octave lower.
The addition of claves playing the rhythm ♩ ♩. ♩ will be found effective.

S.26

NEW COMMANDMENT

Unknown
© arranged Norman Warren†

The new commandment that I give to you
　　is to love one another as I have loved you;
　　is to love one another as I have loved you.
By this shall people know you are my disciples:
　　if you have love one for another;
by this shall people know you are my disciples:
　　if you have love one for another.

from John 13

S.27

NO GREATER NAME   © Michael Baughen†

1 There's no greater name than Jesus,
  name of him who came to save us;
  in that saving name so gracious
  every knee shall bow.

2 Let everything that's beneath the ground,
  let everything in the world around,
  let everything exalted on high
  bow at Jesus' name!

3 In our minds, by faith professing,
  in our hearts, by inward blessing,
  on our tongues, by words confessing,
  Jesus Christ is Lord.

S.28

THIS IS THE DAY

Fiji folk song
© arranged Norman Warren†

This is the day that the Lord has made, we will rejoice and be glad in _ it;

this is the day, this is the day that the Lord has made.

1   This is the day, this is the day,
    that the Lord has made, that the Lord has made;
    we will rejoice, we will rejoice,
    and be glad in it, and be glad in it:
        This is the day that the Lord has made,
        we will rejoice and be glad in it;
        this is the day, this is the day
        that the Lord has made.

2   This is the day, this is the day
    when he rose again . . .

3   This is the day, this is the day
    when the Spirit came . . .

from Psalm 118

S.29

WE HAVE COME INTO THIS HOUSE

Bruce Ballinger
© Sound III Inc.
arranged Norman Warren

We have come into this house
and gathered in his name
   to worship him;
we have come into this house
and gathered in his name
   to worship him;
we have come into this house
and gathered in his name
   to worship Christ the Lord,
worship him, Christ the Lord.

S.30

YOU ARE WORTHY

Pauline Michael Mills

You are worthy, you are worthy,
you are worthy, O Lord;
you are worthy to receive glory,
glory and honour and power:
for you have created, have all things created,
for you have created all things
and for your pleasure they are created:
you are worthy, O Lord!

S.31*

KUM BA YAH

Traditional melody
© arranged David Peacock†

1 Praise the Lord our God, praise the Lord;
   praise him from the heights, praise the Lord;
   praise him, angel throngs, praise the Lord –
   praise God, all his host!

2 Praise him, sun and moon, all the stars;
   praise him, sky and clouds, wind and rain;
   let them praise his name, works of God –
   all creatures, praise the Lord!

3 Praise him, wind and storm, mountains steep;
   praise him, fruitful trees, cedars tall;
   beasts and cattle herds, birds that fly –
   all creatures, praise the Lord!

4 Kings of earth, give praise, rulers all;
   all young men and girls, praise the Lord;
   old men, children small, praise the Lord –
   all people, praise the Lord!

from Psalm 148
© Richard Bewes†

*Please note: S.31 and S.32 do not appear in the first edition of *Hymns for Today's Church*.

S.32(i)

SONG OF CREATION   © Norman Warren

1 Angels, praise him,
  heavens, praise him,
  waters, praise him,
      Alleluia!
  creatures of the Lord,
  all praise him
      for evermore:

2 Sun, praise him,
   moon, praise him,
   stars, praise him,
      Alleluia!
   showers, praise him,
   dews, praise him
      for evermore:

3 Wind, praise him,
   fire, praise him,
   heat, praise him,
      Alleluia!
   winter, praise him,
   summer, praise him
      for evermore:

4 Nights, praise him,
   days, praise him,
   light, praise him,
      Alleluia!
   lightnings, praise him,
   clouds, praise him
      for evermore:

5 Earth, praise him,
   mountains, praise him,
   hills, praise him,
      Alleluia!
   green things, praise him,
   wells, praise him
      for evermore:

6 Seas, praise him,
   rivers, praise him,
   fish, praise him,
      Alleluia!
   birds, praise him,
   beasts, praise him
      for evermore:

7 Nations, praise him,
   churches, praise him,
   saints, praise him,
      Alleluia!
   all his people,
   join to praise him
      for evermore!

from *A Song of Creation (Benedicite)*
© Michael Perry†

S.32(ii)

LITTLE BARRINGTON

© John Barnard†

1 An-gels, praise him, hea-vens, praise him, wa-ters, praise him, Al-le-lu - ia! crea-tures of the Lord, all ___ praise him for ___ ev - er - more: 2 Sun,
praise him, moon,___ praise him, stars ___ praise him, Al-le-lu - ia! showers,___ praise ___ him, dews, ___ praise him for ___ ev - er - more:

3 Wind, praise him, fire, ___ praise him, heat, praise him, Al-le-lu - ia! win - ter, praise him, sum-mer, praise him for ___
praise him, mountains, praise him, hills, praise him, Al-le-lu - ia! green things, praise him, wells,___ praise him for ___

ev - er - more: 4 Nights, praise him, days, __
ev - er - more: 6 Seas, praise him, ri - vers,

praise him, light, praise him, Al - le - lu - ia! light-nings
praise him, fish, praise him, Al - le - lu - ia! birds, __

praise him, clouds, praise him for __ ev - er - more: 5 Earth, __
praise him, beasts, praise him for __ ev - er - more: 7 Na - tions,

praise him, churches, praise him, saints, praise him, Al - le - lu - ia! all his

peo - ple, join to praise him for ___ ev - er - more!

from *A Song of Creation/Benedicite*
© Michael Perry†

BIBLICAL INDEX

i

iv

LITURGICAL HYMNS AND CANTICLES

A General Thanksgiving	Thank you, O Lord – 43
A Song of Creation	Angels, praise him – S.32
(Benedicite)	Bless the Lord – 604
Benedictus (Luke 1:68–79)	O bless the God of Israel – 599
Bless the Lord	Bless the Lord – 610
Cantate Domino (Psalm 98)	Joy to the world – 197
	New songs of celebration – 343
	Sing a new song – 349
	Sing to God – 352
Credal Hymns	Firmly I believe – 429
	God the Father of creation – 427
	I believe in God – 434
	We believe in God – 10
Deus Misereatur (Psalm 67)	God of mercy – 293
	May God be gracious – 330
Easter Anthems	Now lives the Lamb – 159
Gloria in Excelsis	All glory be to God – 606
	Glory be to God – 581
	Glory in the highest – 582
Glory and Honour	Heavenly hosts in ceaseless worship – 570
(Revelation 4–5)	
Great and Wonderful	Great and wonderful – 605
(Revelation 15:3–4)	
Jubilate Deo (Psalm 100)	All people that on earth – 14
	Before Jehovah's awesome throne – 15
	Come, rejoice – 17
Magnificat (Luke 1:46–57)	Tell out, my soul – 42
Nunc Dimittis	Faithful vigil – 55
(Luke 2:29–32)	Jesus, hope of every nation – 58
	Lord, now let your servant – 611
Phos Hilaron	Hail, gladdening light – 275
	Light of gladness – 277
Psalm 134	Bless the Lord – 608
	Come, praise the Lord – 609
Saviour of the World	Jesus, Saviour of the World – 607
Te Deum Laudamus	God of gods – 340
	God, we praise you – 341
Te Lucis Ante Terminum	Before the ending of the day – 276
The Lord's Prayer	Father God in heaven – 358
The Song of Christ's Glory	Before the heaven and earth – 612
(Philippians 2:5–11)	Empty he came – 127
Veni Creator Spiritus	Come, Holy Ghost – 589
	Creator Spirit, come – 232
Venite (Psalm 95)	Come with all joy – 16
	Come, worship God – 18

Doxologies

These hymns have a straightforward doxology as their last verse

All creatures of our God and king – 13
All people that on earth do dwell – 14
Alleluia, alleluia! hearts to heaven – 151
Alleluia! raise the anthem – 205
Angel voices ever singing – 307
Awake, my soul – 264
Before the ending of the day – 276
Bless the Lord, creation sings – 604
Bless the Lord, our fathers' God – 610
Christ is made the sure foundation – 559
Christ is the world's light – 321
Come to us, creative Spirit – 308
Come with all joy – 16
Creator Spirit, come – 232
Father eternal, Lord of the ages – 1
Father most holy – 3
Firmly I believe and truly – 429
Glory to you, my God this night – 274
Great and wonderful – 605
Hark! a trumpet call is sounding – 192
I believe in God the Father – 434
Jesus, hope of every nation – 58
Jesus our hope, our heart's desire – 178
Light's glittering morning – 157
My God, accept my heart – 551
My Lord of light – 4
Now thank we all our God – 33
O Trinity, O Trinity – 6
Praise God from whom all blessings – 585, 586
Praise the Father, God of justice – 8
Roar the waves – 289
Sing, my tongue – 142
Songs of praise the angels sang – 350
Spring has come for us today – 160
Thank you, O Lord of earth and heaven – 43
Through all the changing scenes of life – 46
We give immortal praise – 11
You choirs of new Jerusalem – 168

SUNDAY THEMES

Lectionary themes of the Alternative Service Book 1980 – see ASB page 1092

1   9 before Christmas: The Creation

All hymns, 'Lord and Father – Creating
and Sustaining' – 13–27
Some hymns, 'Work and Leisure: Art and
Science' – 306–314
All things bright – 283
Alleluia! raise the anthem – 205
Angels, praise him – S.32
At the name of Jesus – 172
Bless the Lord, creation sings – 604
Breathe on me, breath of God – 226
Bright the vision – 578
Christ whose glory – 266
Creator of the earth – 320
For the beauty of the earth – 298
For the fruits of his creation – 286
Give to our God immortal praise (from
Psalm 136) – 31
God, whose almighty word – 506
Great is your faithfulness – 260
Heavenly hosts in ceaseless worship
(from *Glory and honour*) – 570
Jesus is Lord – S.17
Lord, be my vision – 545
Lord of the changing year – 261
Love divine – 217
Morning has broken – 265
My God, how wonderful you are – 369
New songs of celebration (from *Cantate
Domino*, Psalm 98) – 343
O Lord of heaven – 287
Praise be to Christ – 220
Praise the Lord, you heavens (from
Psalm 148) – 583
Praise to the Lord, the almighty – 40
Roar the waves – 289
Shout for joy – 348
Sing a new song (from *Cantate Domino*,
Psalm 98) – 349
Songs of praise the angels sang – 350
The Lord is King (from Psalm 97) – 183
Timeless love! We sing the story (from
Psalm 89) – 47
We believe in God (a credal hymn) – 10
You are worthy (from Revelation 4)
– S.30

2   8 before Christmas: The Fall

Creator of the earth and skies – 320
Father of heaven – 359

Glory be to Jesus – 126
Joy to the world (from *Cantate Domino*,
Psalm 98) – 197
Judge eternal – 329
Just as I am – 440
Lift up your hearts – 366
Lord God, your love – 480
O Lord, our guardian (from Psalm 17)
– 374
Praise to the Holiest – 140
Restless souls, why do you scatter – 443
Shout for joy – 348
Sing, my tongue – 142
The Lord made man – 143
There is a fountain – 144

3   7 before Christmas: The Election of
God's People: Abraham

Father, hear the prayer – 360
God is working his purpose out – 191
God of light – 561
Have faith in God – 431
I bind myself to God – 5
Lord, be my vision – 545
My Lord, I did not choose you – 107
O God of Jacob – 35
O happy band of pilgrims – 530
O Lord, who came – 552
Rejoice today – 347
The God of Abraham – 9
Through the night of doubt – 466

4   6 before Christmas: The Promise of
Redemption: Moses

All my hope on God is founded – 451
Bread of heaven – 398
Guide me, O my great Redeemer – 528
I hunger and I thirst – 409
Jesus, the joy – 413
Lord, enthroned – 416
O bless the Lord (from Psalm 103) – 34
O God of Jacob – 35
O God, unseen – 421
Revive your church – 515
There is a land of pure delight – 575
Through all the changing scenes (from
Psalm 34) – 46
Through the night of doubt – 466

17 Epiphany 6: Revelation: Parables

All hymns, 'Lord and Spirit –
  Word of Truth: the Scriptures' –
  247–255
Happy are they – 473
Lord Jesus, once you spoke – 112
O changeless Christ – 108
Wake, O wake – 199
When Jesus walked – 317

18 9 before Easter: Christ the Teacher

Blessed are the pure in heart – 110
Father of mercies – 247
Lord Jesus, once you spoke – 112
Lord, speak to me – 510
Lord, teach us how to pray – 367
O bless the Lord (from Psalm 103) – 34
O changeless Christ – 108
Praise, my soul – 38
Praise to the Holiest – 140
Praise to the Lord – 40
Tell his praise (from Psalm 34) – 41
Through all the changing scenes (from
  Psalm 34) – 46
You are the way – 113
When Jesus walked – 317

19 8 before Easter: Christ the Healer

All hymns, 'God's World: Health and
  Healing' – 315–319
Bread of heaven – 398
Fill your hearts with joy (from Psalm
  147) – 30
From you all skill – 310
Great Shepherd of your people – 363
Here, Lord, we take – 404
How sweet the name – 211
I'll praise my maker (from Psalm 146)
  – 20
Immortal love – 105
Just as I am – 440
Lord Jesus, when your people – 371
Now thank we all our God – 33
O bless the Lord (from Psalm 103) – 34
Praise, my soul (from Psalm 103) – 38
Praise to the Lord – 40
See Christ was wounded – 137
When all your mercies – 39
With loving hands – 106

**20 7 before Easter: Christ the Friend
of Sinners**

All hymns, 'God's Church: Penitence
  and Prayer' – 355–374

A purple robe, a crown of thorns – 122
Here within this house of prayer – 563
How sweet the name – 211
I come with joy – 408
Immortal love – 105
Jesus calls us – 104
Jesus, come – 109
Jesus, good above all other – 96
King of glory – 603
Let us praise God – S.18
Lord, be my vision – 545
Lord of all hopefulness – 101
My Lord, I did not choose you – 107
My Lord, you wore – 118
O sacred head – 139
Son of God, eternal Saviour – 102
The kingdom of God – 333
When all your mercies – 39

**21 Lent 1: The King and the Kingdom:
Temptation**

Father of heaven – 359
Forty days and forty nights – 103
God is our fortress – 523
He lives in us – 457
Lead us, heavenly Father – 525
Let us love and sing – 215
Lift up your hearts – 366
Listen to my prayer (from Psalm 61)
  – 365
Lord of our life – 529
O Christ of all the ages – 262
O Jesus, I have promised – 531
Safe in the shadow (from Psalm 91)
  – 445
Still near me, O my Saviour – 464
Where high the heavenly temple – 184

**22 Lent 2: The King and the Kingdom:
Conflict**

All hymns, 'God's Church: Conflict and
  Endurance' – 522–537
Before the ending of the day – 276
How firm a foundation – 430
How sweet the name – 211
I love you, O Lord (from Psalm 18)
  – 475
Listen to my prayer (from Psalm 61)
  – 365
My Lord, you wore – 118
Son of God, eternal Saviour – 102
Take up your cross – 114
The church's one foundation – 501
Through the night – 466

At the name of Jesus – 172
Christ whose glory – 266
Come and praise – S.8
Come, let us worship the Christ – 207
Crown him with many crowns – 174
Empty he came (from *Song of Christ's Glory*) – 127
Father in heaven – 2
Great God, we praise – 299
He is Lord – S.7
I bind myself to God – 5
In Christ shall all – 459
In the quiet consecration – 411
Jesus is Lord – S.17
Jesus, stand among us – 364
Let us talents and tongues – 414
Light of the minds – 477
Lord, enthroned – 416
Lord Jesus Christ – 417
Lord of the changing year – 261
Lord of the cross of shame – 548
No weight of gold – 138
O Christ of all the ages – 262
O Christ the great foundation – 502
Praise the Father, God of justice – 8
Praise we offer – 346
Risen Lord, whose name – 500
Saviour Christ – 216
Shout for joy – 348
Sing alleluia to the Lord – S.22
Sing to God (from *Cantate Domino*, Psalm 98) – 352
The hands of Christ – 141
This is the day, this is the day (from Psalm 118) – S.28
Through all our days – 145
Through the night – 466
We have a gospel – 519
We were not there – 121

28   Easter 1: (1) The Upper Room

All hymns, 'God's Church: The Lord's Day' – 375–380
All creatures of our God – 13
Alleluia, raise the anthem – 205
Blow upon the trumpet – 186
Christ the Lord is risen – 153
Comes Mary to the grave – 152
Great Shepherd of your people – 363
Jesus, stand among us – 364
O God, unseen – 421
Stand up and bless – 351
The day of resurrection – 161
This is the day, this is the day (from Psalm 118) – S.28
We were not there – 121

(2) The Bread of Life

Some hymns, 'God's Church: Holy Communion' – 391–424
As we walk – S.1
Bread of heaven – 398
Bread of the world – 396
Broken for me – S.6
Christian soldiers – 524
Come, let us worship Christ – S.10
Come, risen Lord – 399
Guide me, O my great Redeemer – 528
I hunger and I thirst – 409
Jesus lives – 156
Jesus, the joy – 413
Join all the glorious names – 214
O God, unseen – 421
Revive your church – 515
The day of resurrection – 161
The strife is past – 163
Through all the changing scenes (from Psalm 34) – 46

29   Easter 2: (1) The Emmaus Road

Abide with me – 425
Ah, holy Jesus – 123
As we walk – S.1
Christ the Lord is risen again – 153
Come, risen Lord – 399
Jerusalem the golden – 573
Light of the minds – 477
The head that once – 182
The Lord is King (from Psalm 97) – 183

(2) The Good Shepherd

All hymns from Psalms 95 and 100 – 14–18
Faithful Shepherd, feed me – 29
I will sing the wondrous story – 212
In heavenly love abiding – 458
Loving Shepherd – 305
O Lord, our guardian (from Psalm 17) – 374
Restless souls, why do you scatter – 443
The king of love (from Psalm 23) – 44
The Lord my shepherd (from Psalm 23) – 45
The Lord's my Shepherd (from Psalm 23) – 591
Yours for ever, God of love – 556

30   Easter 3: (1) The Lakeside

As water to the thirsty – 470
God, whose almighty word – 506
Jesus lives – 156

There's a spirit in the air – 245
This is the truth – 388
We know that Christ is raised – 389

36   Pentecost 2: (1) The People of God

As sons of the day – 490
Bless the Lord, our fathers' God – 610
Christ, from whom all blessings – 491
Christ is our corner-stone – 564
Church of God – 504
City of God, Jerusalem – 187
Come with all joy (from *Venite*, Psalm 95) – 16
Come, worship God (from *Venite*, Psalm 95) – 18
Give praise for famous men – 568
How sweet the name – 211
Jesus, Lord, we pray – 302
Lord of the church – 499
Lord, you can make our spirits shine – 512
O God of Jacob – 35
The church's one foundation – 501
The day you gave us – 280
Your hand, O God, has guided – 536

(2) The Church's Unity and Fellowship

All hymns, 'God's Church: Unity and Growth' – 489–503
Bind us together – S.4
Born of the water – 382
Christ is the world's true light – 323
Christians, lift up your hearts . . . Praise for the Spirit – 229
Father eternal – 1
Filled with the Spirit's power – 233
God is here – 560
God, our Father and creator – 562
Great Shepherd of your people – 363
Help us to help each other – 540
How good a thing (from Psalm 133) – 497
In Christ there is no east or west – 322
Jesus, Lord, we pray – 302
Jesus shall reign (from Psalm 72) – 516
My God, now is your table – 418
O Spirit of the living God – 513
One holy apostolic church – 514
Onward, Christian soldiers – 532
The day you gave us – 280
Through the night of doubt – 466
Your hand, O God – 536

37   Pentecost 3: (1) The Life of the Baptized

Some hymns, 'God's Church: Christian Initiation': 381–390
Some hymns, 'God's Church: Faith and Trust' – 425–447
Some hymns, 'God's Church: Commitment and Character' – 538–557
Alleluia, alleluia! hearts to heaven – 151
Born of the water – 382
Breathe on me, breath of God – 226
Christ is the King – 492
Church of God – 504
Come, O fount of every blessing – 337
Fill now my life – 541
God is here – 560
He lives in us – 457
I want to walk – S.16
In heavenly love – 458
Jesus, priceless treasure – 461
Lift high the cross – 508
Look, Lord, in mercy – 498
Love divine – 217
O Christ, the great foundation – 502
O Jesus, I have promised – 531
One holy apostolic church – 514
Revive your church – 515
Shout for joy – 348
The church's one foundation – 501
We know that Christ – 389
We love the place – 558

(2) The Church's Confidence in Christ

Most hymns, 'God's Church: Faith and Trust' – 425–447
Most hymns, 'God's Church: Hope and Confidence' – 448–467
At the name of Jesus – 172
Bring to the Lord (from Psalms 149–150) – 336
Christ is made the sure foundation – 559
Christ is our corner-stone – 564
Christ's church shall glory – 522
Come, let us worship the Christ – 207
Eternal light, shine – 339
God of eternity – 495
Hail, our once-rejected Jesus – 175
How sweet the name – 211
I know that my redeemer lives – 169
Jesus is Lord – S.17
Jesus! the name high over all – 213
Join all the glorious names – 214
Let all the world – 342

Name of all majesty – 218
O changeless Christ – 108
O for a thousand tongues – 219
Onward, Christian soldiers – 532
Praise the Lord, his glories show (from Psalm 150) – 345
Praise to the Lord, the almighty – 40
Saviour Christ, in praise we name him – 216
Sing praise to the Lord (from Psalm 150) – 354
Tell out, my soul (from *Magnificat*) – 42
To the name of our salvation – 222

38 Pentecost 4: (1) The Freedom God gives

Amazing grace – 28
And can it be – 452
As sons of the day – 490
Born by the Holy Spirit's breath – 225
Christ is the world's true light – 323
Church of God – 504
Freedom and life – 544
He lives in us – 457
I will sing – S.15
In Christ there is no east or west – 322
Jesus shall reign (from Psalm 72) – 516
Lead us, heavenly Father – 525, 595
Lord God, your love – 480
O for a heart to praise – 483
O for a thousand tongues – 219
O Lord of heaven – 287
Praise, my soul (from Psalm 103) – 38
Spirit of God within me – 243

(2) The Church's Mission to the Individual

How shall they hear – 507
I will sing, I will sing – S.15
Jesus, your blood – 460
Lord Jesus, let these eyes – 549
Lord Jesus, think of me – 316
Lord, speak to me – 510
May God be gracious (from *Deus Misereatur*, Psalm 67) – 330
O for a thousand tongues – 219
O love that will not let me go – 486
O Master Christ – 553
Restless souls – 443
The king of love (from Psalm 23) – 44
We love the place – 558

39 Pentecost 5: (1) The New Law

Awake, my soul – 264
Beloved, let us love – 468

Blessed are the pure in heart – 110
Father of all, whose laws – 539
Happy are they – 473
Holy Spirit, truth divine – 235
Love is his word – 481
Now let us learn – 503
The new commandment – S.26
This is the day of light – 380
We share a new day's dawn – 271

(2) The Church's Mission to All

All hymns, 'God's Church: Mission and Ministry' – 504–521
All people that on earth do dwell (from *Jubilate Deo*, Psalm 100) – 14
Can we by searching – 426
Christ is the world's true light – 323
Filled with the Spirit's power – 233
Forth in the peace of Christ – 542
From all who live (from Psalm 117) – 580
God forgave my sin – S.12
God has spoken – S.13
God is working his purpose out – 191
God of mercy (from *Deus Misereatur*, Psalm 67) – 293
How can we sing – 362
In Christ there is no east or west – 322
Let all the world – 342
Look, Lord, in mercy – 498
Make us worthy – S.20
May God be gracious (from *Deus Misereatur*, Psalm 67) – 330
Rejoice, O land – 331
Remember, Lord – 332
Soldiers of the cross – 534

40 Pentecost 6: Made New in Christ

And can it be – 452
Christ, our king before creation – 428
Come down, O Love divine – 231
Come, praise the name – 538
He lives in us – 457
I bind myself to God – 5
Jesus, Lord we pray – 302
Lord, I was blind – 437
Lord Jesus, let these eyes – 549
Lift up your hearts – 366
O for a heart to praise my God – 483
O Holy Spirit, giver of life – 239
O Lord, who came – 552
O love that will not let me go – 486
Songs of praise – 350
Thank you, O Lord of earth – 43
The Lord made man – 143

xvi

xviii

My Father, for another night – 269
O Christ, the Master Carpenter – 135
O God, our help (from Psalm 90) – 37
Take up your cross – 114
We share a new day's dawn – 271
When I survey – 147

53 Pentecost 19: The Life of Faith

All hymns, 'God's Church: Faith and
  Trust' – 425–447
Come down, O Love divine – 231
Fight the good fight – 526
For all the saints – 567
In heavenly love – 458
King of glory – 603
Lord, be my vision – 545
O God beyond all praising – 36
O God of Jacob – 35
O for a closer walk – 368
O for a thousand tongues – 219
There is a green hill – 148

54 Pentecost 20: Endurance

All hymns, 'God's Church: Conflict and
  Endurance' – 522–537
Christ is the world's true light – 323
Father, hear the prayer – 360
Give praise for famous men – 568
God of grace – 324
Have faith in God – 431
He lives in us – 457
Judge eternal – 329
O God beyond all praising – 36
O Lord my love – 485
O Lord, who came – 552
Unto the hills (from Psalm 121) – 48
Yours for ever – 556

55 Pentecost 21: The Christian Hope

All hymns, 'God's Church: Hope and
  Confidence' – 448–467
At the name of Jesus – 172
By every nation – 579
God is our strength (from Psalm 46)
  – 527
Hail to the Lord's anointed (from Psalm
  72) – 190
Jesus, our hope – 178
King of glory – 603

Man of sorrows – 130
Rejoice, the Lord is king – 180
Thank you – 43
There is a fountain – 144

56 Pentecost 22: The Two Ways

Some hymns, 'God's Church: Conflict
  and Endurance' – 522–537
Come with all joy (from *Venite*, Psalm
  95) – 16
Come, worship God (from *Venite*, Psalm
  95) – 18
How sure the Scriptures – 249
Just as I am – 440
Lord, your word – 251
May we, O Holy Spirit – 236
Son of God, eternal Saviour – 102
The Lord is king (from Psalm 97) – 183
You are the way – 113
Your way, not mine – 555
Yours be the glory – 167

57 Last Sunday after Pentecost: Citizens of Heaven

All hymns, 'God's Church: The Church
  Triumphant: Heaven' – 565–577
Born of the water – 382
Bright the vision – 578
Bring to the Lord (from Psalms 149–150)
  – 336
By every nation – 579
Come, let us join – 206
Glorious things – 494
God of gods (from *Te Deum Laudamus*)
  – 340
God, we praise you (from *Te Deum
  Laudamus*) – 341
Holy, holy, holy – 7
I'll praise my maker (from Psalm 146)
  – 20
Jesus! the name – 213
Look, you saints – 179
O bless the God – 599
O changeless Christ – 108
There's a song – 304
Through the night of doubt – 466
You holy angels bright – 353
You servants of God – 520
You servants of the Lord – 598

AUTHORS AND SOURCES OF WORDS

Jesus, the name high over all – 213
Let saints on earth – 574
Love divine – 217
O come, our all-victorious Lord – 441
O for a heart to praise my God – 483
O for a thousand tongues – 219
O Lord, who came – 552
O thou who camest from above – 596
Rejoice, the Lord is king – 180
Soldiers of Christ, arise – 533
Still near me, (verse 1) – 464
To us a child of royal birth – 64
You servants of God – 520
Wesley, John (1703–1791)
Author of life divine – 395
Before Jehovah's awesome throne – 15
Jesus, your blood – 460
O Lord my love, my strength – 485
Still near me (verses 2 and 3) – 464
White, Henry Kirke (1785–1806)
Christian soldiers, onward go – 524
Whiting, William (1825–1878)
Eternal Father, strong to save – 285
Whittier, John Greenleaf (1807–1892)
Dear Lord and Father of mankind – 356
Immortal love for ever full – 105
Whittingham, William (1524–1579)
The Lord's my shepherd – 591
Wigmore, Paul (born 1925)
May we, O Holy Spirit – 236
Wilkinson, Katie (Barclay) (1859–1928)
May the mind of Christ – 550
Williams, Isaac (1802–1865)
O Lord, our guardian – 374
Williams, Peter (1721–1796)
Guide me, O my great Redeemer – 528
Williams, William (1717–1791)
Guide me, O my great Redeemer – 528
Willis, Love Maria (1824–1908)
Father, hear the prayer – 360
Winkworth, Catherine (1827–1878)
All my heart this night rejoices – 76
Christ the Lord is risen again – 153
Deck yourself, my soul – 400
Jesus, priceless treasure – 461
Now thank we all our God – 33
Praise to the Lord, the almighty – 40
Winslow, John Copley (1882–1974)
Come, sing the praise of Jesus – 208
Lord of all power – 547
**Woodward, George Ratcliffe
(1848–1934)**
This joyful Eastertide – 165
Wordsworth, Christopher (1807–1885)
Alleluia, alleluia! hearts to heaven – 151
Holy Spirit, gracious guest – 474

Lord, make your word my rule – 250
O Lord of heaven and earth – 287
See the conqueror mounts – 181
Songs of thankfulness and praise – 98
Wren, Brian Arthur (born 1936)
Christ upon the mountain peak – 115
I come with joy to meet my Lord – 408
Lord God, your love has called us – 480
Praise God for the harvest – 288
There's a spirit in the air – 245
When Christ was lifted – 335

Young, John Freeman (1820–1885)
Silent night, holy night – 95

**Zinzendorf, Nikolaus Ludwig Graf von
(1700–1760)**
Jesus, your blood – 460

Hymn texts in English
with unknown authorship

Away in a manger (verses 1–2) – 72
Behold the eternal King and Priest – 397
God rest you merry, gentlemen – 84
God save our gracious Queen – 592
Jesus Christ is risen today – 155
Praise the Lord, you heavens – 583
The first nowell – 93

Authors of songs (in addition
to names included above)

Ballinger, Bruce
We have come into this house – S.29
Coelho, Terrye
Father, we adore you – S.5
Dyer, M.
I will sing, I will sing – S.15
Fishel, Don
Alleluia, alleluia, give thanks – S.3
Frey, Marvin
He is Lord – 57
Gillman, B.
Bind us together – S.4
Iverson, D.
Spirit of the living God, fall afresh – S.23
Jabusch, Willard F.
God has spoken to his people – S.13
Jackson, Peter
Sovereign Lord – S.9
Lunt, Janet
Broken for me – S.6
Mansell, David J.
Jesus is Lord – S.17

COMPOSERS, ARRANGERS AND SOURCES OF TUNES

Poitiers Antiphoner 1746: 391
Polish melody: 86
Praetorius, Michael (1571–1621): 49, 118
Prichard, Rowland Hugh (1811–1887): 170, 212
Prys (Edmund) *Psalter* 1621: 372
Psalmes (T. Este) 1592: 94
Psalmes (W. Damon) 1579: 316, 436
Psalmodia Evangelica (T. Williams) 1789: 31, 516
Psalter (J. Day) 1562: 421
Psalter (E. Prys) 1621: 372
Psalter (T. Ravenscroft) 1621: 193, 274, 313, 585
Purcell, Henry (1659–1695): 559

Ravenscroft (Thomas) *Psalter* 1621: 193, 274, 313, 585
Redhead, Richard (1820–1901): 178, 444, 578, 593
Reinagle, Alexander Robert (1799–1877): 211, 551
Reith, Angela (born 1952): S.3, S.7, S.13
Rheinhardt, J. H. (1754): 344
Rigby, Charles Walter (1901–1962): 210
Robinson, Christopher (born 1935): 597
Ross, William Baird (1871–1950): 591
Routley, Erik Reginald (1917–1982): 89, 100, 132
Rowlands, William Penfro (1860–1937): 217, 373, 570
Runyan, William Marion (1870–1957): 260
Rusbridge, Arthur Ewart (1917–1969): 86
Russian melody: 411

Sacred Melodies (W. Gardiner) 1815: 16, 144, 310, 519
Sandys (William) *Christmas Carols* 1833: 493
Sankey, Ira David (1840–1908): 471
Scheffler (Johann) *Heilige Seelenlust* Breslau 1657: 258, 491
Schein, Johann Hermann (1586–1630): 64, 510
Scholefield, Clement Cotterill (1839–1904): 280, 609
Schulz, Johann Abraham Peter (1747–1800): 292
Scott-Gatty, Alfred Scott (1847–1918): 437
Scottish melody: 220
Scottish Psalter Edinburgh 1615: 71, 368, 540, 574
Scottish Psalter Edinburgh 1635: 332, 426, 509

Sharp, Cecil James (1859–1924): 575
Shaw, Geoffrey Turton (1879–1943): 37, 83, 110, 143, 156, 298, 374, 438, 566
Shaw, Martin Edward Fallas (1875–1958): 63, 77, 101, 133, 166, 242, 259, 261, 267, 283, 360, 466, 488, 545
Sheldon, Robin Treeby (born 1932): 38, 309
Shrubsole, William (c. 1759–1806): 203, 587
Sibelius, Jean (1865–1957): 446
Silcher, Philipp Friedrich (1789–1860): 29
Silesian Folk Songs Leipzig 1842: 209
Slater, Gordon Archbold (1896–1979): 390, 484
Smart, George Thomas (1776–1867): 46
Smart, Henry Thomas (1813–1879): 30, 102, 128, 179, 293, 440, 511
Smith, Alfred Morton (1879–1971): 399
Smith, Henry Percy (1825–1898): 294, 413
Smith, Isaac (1734–1805): 363, 374
Smith, Kenneth Donald (born 1928): 8
Somervell, Arthur (1863–1937): 140
Southgate, Thomas Bishop (1814–1868): 131
Spencer Palmer, Peggy (born 1900): 19
Stainer, John (1840–1901): 52, 85, 93, 121, 160, 217, 275, 304, 316, 395, 403, 434, 443, 469, 474, 479
Stanford, Charles Villiers (1852–1924): 5, 204, 389
Stanton, Walter Kendall (1891–1978): 209, 381
Stassen, Linda: S.22
Steggall, Charles (1826–1905): 98, 565
Steiner, Johann Ludwig (1668–1761): 360
Stralsund Gesangbuch 1665: 40
Strover, Martin Christian Tinne (born 1932): 58, 340, 408, 443, S.10, S.11
Sullivan, Arthur Seymour (1842–1900): 87, 151, 268, 281, 291, 295, 504, 532
Swiss melody: 276, S.16

Tallis, Thomas (c. 1505–1585): 274, 313, 585
Tans'ur (William) *Harmony of Syon* 1734: 111, 407
Taylor, Cyril Vincent (born 1907): 250, 489, 494
Temple, Sebastian: S.19
Terry, Richard Runciman (1865–1938): 314, 362, 422
Teschner, Melchior (1584–1635): 120

TUNES: ALPHABETICAL

TUNES: METRICAL, WITH STAVES

3 5 3 3
SAVIOUR CHRIST, 216

4 4 4 4 4 4 8
GARTAN, 5

4 8 8 4
ENIGMA, 106

4 9 4 8 9 9 4
THE INFANT KING (SING LULLABY), 92

5 5 5 5 5 5 5 4
HARROW WEALD, 2

5 5 5 5 D
VICTOR'S CROWN, 185

5 5 5 11
ARDWICK, 224

5 5 7 D
PASSFIELD, 382

5 5 8 D
SCHÖNSTER HERR JESU, 209

SILCHESTER, 209, 381

5 5 8 8 5 5
ARNSTADT (THURINGIA), 279, 302

5 6 6 4
SOMMERLIED, 393

TENHEAD, 546

6 4 4 4 6
WINGS OF JOY, 327

6 5 6 4
CHRIST AROSE, 158

6 5 6 5
CASWALL, 126, 364

FAITHFUL VIGIL, 55

FAWLEY LODGE, 55, 611

LISTENING, 365

NORTH COATES, 384, 611

PASTOR PASTORUM (SILCHER), 29

QUIETUDE, 253

6 5 6 5 D
CAMBERWELL, 172

CUDDESDON, 582

EVELYNS, 172

NOËL NOUVELET, 166

6 5 6 5 Triple
ST. GERTRUDE, 532

WYE VALLEY, 463

6 5 6 5 6 6 6 5
MONKS GATE, 537, 590

6 6 4 6 6 6 4
MOSCOW, 506

NATIONAL ANTHEM, 326, 592

6 6 5 5 6 6 6 4
ALL MAJESTY, 218

MAJESTAS, 218

6 6 5 6 6 5 7 8 6
JESU, MEINE FREUDE, 461

6 6 6 6
BEWELEY, 250

ECCLES, 409

IBSTONE, 250, 409, 555

PARKSTONE, 503

QUAM DILECTA, 558

RAVENSHAW, 251

ST. CECILIA, 334

6 6 6 6 4 4 4 4 – see 6 6 6 6 8 8

6 6 6 6 6 5 5 3 9
PERSONENT HODIE (THEODORIC), 311, 348

6 6 6 D
LAUDES DOMINI, 223

LUDGATE, 230

6 6 6 6 D
CHESTERTON, 251

6 6 6 6 8 8
AUTHOR OF LIFE, 395

CHRISTCHURCH, 565

CROFT'S 136TH, 11, 159, 214, 249

DARWALL'S 148TH, 171, 353

EASTVIEW, 214

GOLDINGTON, 261

GOPSAL, 180

HAREWOOD, 564

LITTLE CORNARD, 242, 259, 261, 488

LOVE UNKNOWN, 136

ST. JOHN, 129

SAMUEL, 268

6 6 7 7 7 8 5 5
IN DULCI JUBILO (GOOD CHRISTIAN MEN REJOICE), 85

6 6 8 4 D
LEONI, 9

6 6 8 6
SUTTON COMMON, 319

6 6 8 6 (S M)
CARLISLE, 226, 351, 515

DOMINICA, 380

FRANCONIA, 110

HOLYROOD, 497

MEMENTO, 316

NARENZA, 568, 598, 612

ROSSLEIGH, 290

SAIGON, 68

ST. BRIDE, 435

ST. ETHELWALD, 431, 533

ST. PAUL'S, 316

ST. THOMAS, 415

SANDYS, 493

SONG 20, 439

SOUTHWELL – DAMON, 316, 436

STEEPLE ASHTON, 497

UNITED MAN, 497

VENICE, 34, 515

6 6 8 6 6 6

CARDINGTON, 164

VINEYARD HAVEN, 164

6 6 8 6 D (D S M)

DIADEMATA, 174

FROM STRENGTH TO STRENGTH, 533, 544

6 6 11 D

CROSS OF SHAME, 548

DOWN AMPNEY, 231

PHILIP JAMES, 186

6 7 6 7

HERMITAGE, 62

6 7 6 7 6 6 6 6

GRACIAS, 33

NUN DANKET, 33

RINKART, 323

6 7 6 7 D

VRUECHTEN, 165

6 7 7 11

CHURCH CLOSE, 152

EASTER MORNING, 152

PASCHAL DAWN, 152

7 4 7 4 D

GWALCHMAI, 272, 603

HARVEY, 272

REDLAND, 603

7 5 7 5 D
DEDICATION, 257

7 6 7 6
ALL THINGS BRIGHT AND BEAUTIFUL, 283

KOCHER, 530

MORDEN PARK, 138

ROYAL OAK, 283

ST. ALPHEGE, 557

7 6 7 6 6 6 4 4 6
OASIS, 470

7 6 7 6 6 7 6
ES IST EIN' ROS' (A GREAT AND MIGHTY WONDER),
49

7 6 7 6 D
ARGENT, 138

AURELIA, 477, 501, 502

AVE VIRGO, 200

CRÜGER, 190, 599

ELLACOMBE, 161, 244

EWING, 573

ICH REDE, 69

KING'S LYNN, 477

MORNING LIGHT, 535

OFFERTORIUM, 107

PASSION CHORALE, 139, 602

PENLAN, 301, 458

ST. THEODULPH, 120

STAND UP, 538

TEMPUS ADEST FLORIDUM, 160

THORNBURY, 521, 536

WIR PFLÜGEN, 292

WOLVERCOTE, 531

7 6 7 7
PUER NOBIS, 83

7 6 8 6
CHERRY TREE CAROL, 75

7 6 8 6 D
ALFORD, 576

HOLY APOSTLES, 75

7 6 8 6 8 6 8 6
LIVING FLAME, 243

7 7 5 7 5 7 3
IT WAS A MAN, 456

7 7 7 3
VIGILATE, 355

1

7 7 7 4 D

ROXETH, 325

7 7 7 5

CAPETOWN, 12

CHARITY, 474

GUILDFORD CATHEDRAL, 474

7 7 7 5 7 7 11

DAM BUSTERS MARCH, 527

7 7 7 7

ASCENSION, 176

BUCKLAND, 305

CHISLEHURST, 176

CRUCIS MILITES, 534

CULBACH, 258, 491

EASTER HYMN, 155

FAIRMILE, 60

HARTS, 447

HEINLEIN, 103

HUMILITY, 90, 604

INNOCENTS, 566

JESUS LOVES ME, 303

KING DIVINE, 210

LAUDS, 245

LLANFAIR, 176, 345

LÜBECK, 554

MELLING, 566

MONKLAND, 23

NEWINGTON, 556

NORTHAMPTON, 350

NOTTINGHAM, 554

ORIENTIS PARTIBUS (i), 472, 534

ORIENTIS PARTIBUS (ii), 534, 610

SAVANNAH, 150

SONG 13, 235

UNIVERSITY COLLEGE, 524, 604

7 7 7 7 4

WÜRTTEMBERG, 150, 153

7 7 7 7 6

WÜRTTEMBERG, 605

7 7 7 7 7 7

ARFON, 398

ASHBURTON, 298, 563

7 7 7 7 7 7 continued

BREAD OF HEAVEN, 398

DIX, 99, 563

ENGLAND'S LANE, 298

HEATHLANDS, 293

LUCERNA LAUDONIAE, 27

NORICUM, 27

PETRA, 444, 593

RATISBON, 266

TOPLADY, 444

7 7 7 D

VENI, SANCTE SPIRITUS, 227

7 7 7 7 D

ABERYSTWYTH, 438

CALON LÂN, 482

EVERLASTING LOVE, 482

HOLLINGSIDE, 438

HOLY CHILD, 60

LITTLE HEATH, 438

MENDELSSOHN, 59

ST. EDMUND, 98

ST. GEORGE'S, WINDSOR, 98, 284

7 7 7 7 Triple

GLORIOUS COMING, 201

7 7 7 8

MAN OF SORROWS (GETHSEMANE), 130

7 7 8 7 8 7 6 8 8 8 6

BATTLE HYMN, 208

7 7 11 8

LITTLEBOURNE, 349

ONSLOW SQUARE, 349

7 8 7 8

ASTHALL, 608

7 8 7 8 4

ST. ALBINUS, 115, 156, 607

7 8 7 8 8 8

LIEBSTER JESU, 394

7 9 9 8 7

GRACIOUS GOD, 330

8 3 3 6 D

ALL MY HEART, 76

BONN, 76

8 4 8 4 8 8 8 4

ALL THROUGH THE NIGHT (AR HYD Y NOS), 81

EAST ACKLAM, 286

lii

848857
THURLEIGH, 317

8583
BULLINGER, 433

8585
SHARNBROOK, 496

UNION, 496

858579
CHRIST TRIUMPHANT, 173

GUITING POWER, 173

858587
ANGEL VOICES, 307

ARTHOG, 308

CREATIVE SPIRIT, 308

86767676
IN MEMORIAM, 304

8684
ST. CUTHBERT, 241

WICKLOW, 241

8686 (C M)
ABRIDGE, 363, 374

ALBANO, 135

AMAZING GRACE, 28

ANTIOCH, 197

ARDEN, 572

BALLERMA, 374

BANGOR, 111, 407

BARCHESTER FAIR, 408

BEATITUDO, 240

BEDFORDSHIRE MAY-DAY CAROL, 45

BELMONT, 144, 310

BEULAH, 108

BILLING, 362

BINCHESTER, 386, 473

BISHOPTHORPE, 105, 379

BRISTOL, 193

BROTHER JAMES' AIR, 45, 591

CAITHNESS, 368, 426

CHORUS ANGELORUM (SOMERVELL), 140

CONTEMPLATION, 39

CREATOR GOD, 445

CRIMOND, 591

DIADEM, 203, 587

8 6 8 6 (C M) continued

DUNDEE (FRENCH), 71, 574

DUNFERMLINE, 540

GERONTIUS, 140

HORSLEY, 148

IRISH, 363

JACKSON, 572

KILMARNOCK, 448

LITTLE HINTON, 441

LONDON NEW, 332, 509

LYDIA, 213

LYNGHAM, 219

MARTYRDOM, 35

McKEE, 322

MENDIP, 575

METZLER (REDHEAD NO. 66), 178, 484

MILES LANE, 203, 587

NATIVITY, 206

NUN DANKET ALL (GRÄFENBERG), 134

OSWALD'S TREE, 363

RICHMOND, 140, 541

ROSELAND, 410

ST. AGNES – DYKES, 478

ST. ANNE, 37

ST. BERNARD, 484

ST. BOTOLPH, 390, 484

ST. COLUMBA, 238

ST. FLAVIAN, 421

ST. FRANCIS XAVIER, 479

ST. FULBERT, 168

ST. HUGH, 367

ST. JAMES, 113

ST. MAGNUS, 182

ST. PETER, 211, 551

ST. STEPHEN, 483

ST. TIMOTHY, 269

SALTFLEETBY ALL SAINTS, 412

SAN ROCCO, 335

SONG 67, 372

SOUTHWELL – IRONS, 247, 457, 569

STANTON, 445

STOCKTON, 483

STRACATHRO, 144

THIS ENDRIS NYGHT, 50

UNIVERSITY, 219, 408

WALSALL, 124

WESTMINSTER, 369

WILTSHIRE, 46

WINCHESTER OLD, 94

8 6 8 6 7 7 8 8
TRINITY, 6

8 6 8 6 8 6
MORDEN, 455

8 6 8 6 D (D C M)
CHRISTMAS CAROL, 88, 498

FOREST GREEN, 88

KINGSFOLD, 457

LADYWELL, 514, 577

NOEL, 87

RACHEL, 211

SELFLESS LOVE, 405

8 6 8 6 Triple
A PURPLE ROBE, 122

8 6 8 6 8 8
O JESU, 507

PEMBROKE, 507

8 6 8 8 6
BINNEY'S, 553

GATESCARTH, 256

NEWCASTLE, 454

NICOLAUS, 606

REPTON, 356, 553

8 6 8 8 8 6
REVELATION, 177

8 7 8 5
ST. LEONARD'S, 550

8 7 8 7
ACH, GOTT UND HERR (BECCLES), 387, 423

ALL FOR JESUS, 434, 469

ANIMAE HOMINUM, 443

BARBARA ALLEN, 4

BIRABUS, 58

COME REJOICE, 17

lv

8 7 8 7 continued

CROSS OF JESUS, 52, 403, 443

DOMINUS REGIT ME, 44

EVERSLEY, 58

GOTT WILL'S MACHEN, 360

HALTON HOLGATE (SHARON), 370, 429

IRIS, 77

LAUS DEO (REDHEAD NO. 46), 578

LOVE DIVINE, 217

MARCHING, 360, 466

MERTON, 192

OTTERY ST. MARY, 429

ST. ANDREW–THORNE, 104

ST. COLUMBA, 404

SHIPSTON, 282, 427, 429

SICILIAN MARINERS, 337

STENKA RAZIN, 411

STUTTGART, 8

SUSSEX, 360

THE FOLLOWERS, 44

8 7 8 7 3 3 7

MABLEDON, 79

MEINE HOFFNUNG, 228, 451

MICHAEL, 228, 451

8 7 8 7 4 7

BRYN CALFARIA, 528

CWM RHONDDA, 528

HELMSLEY, 196

PORCHESTER, 255

8 7 8 7 6 6 6 6 7

EIN' FESTE BURG (A STRONGHOLD SURE), 347, 522, 523

8 7 8 7 6 8 6 7

GREENSLEEVES, 145

8 7 8 7 7 7

ALL SAINTS, 215, 561

BUSHEY HALL, 561

HIGHEST HEAVEN, 97

IRBY, 67

OTTAWA, 97

ST. LEONARD, 562

8 7 8 7 8 7

ALLELUIA, DULCE CARMEN (BITHYNIA/TANTUM ERGO), 346

8 7 8 7 8 8 7
LUTHER, 189

PALACE GREEN, 189

8 7 8 7 8 8 7 7
INFANT HOLY (POLISH CAROL), 86

8 7 8 7 8 8 8 7
GOD OF GODS, 340

8 7 8 8 7
BOURNE, 487

ST. JUDE, 487

8 7 8 8 7 7 7 7 7
BEVERLEY, 202

8 8 4 4 8 8
EASTER SONG (LASST UNS ERFREUEN), 13, 157, 579

8 8 6 8 8 6
CORNWALL, 299

8 8 8 4
ALMSGIVING, 287

VICTORY, 163

VULPIUS (GELOBT SEI GOTT), 154, 163, 492

8 8 8 5
KUM BA YAH, 358

8 8 8 6
MISERICORDIA, 440

SAFFRON WALDEN, 440

WOODWORTH, 440

8 8 8 6 D
FRAMLINGHAM, 424

8 8 8 7
EWHURST, 432

LORD OF LOVE, 70

OLD YEAVERING, 32

QUEM PASTORES LAUDAVERE, 32, 74, 96, 277

8 8 8 8
ADORAMUS, 19

CELESTE, 450

8 8 8 8 (L M)
ANGELS' SONG (SONG 34), 306

ANGELUS, 315

BIRLING, 143

BODMIN, 437

BOW BRICKHILL, 146, 262

BRESLAU, 114, 146, 453

CHURCH TRIUMPHANT, 169, 183, 254

COME TOGETHER, 586

DANIEL, 133, 267

DEEP HARMONY, 377

DEUS TUORUM MILITUM (GRENOBLE), 580

DUKE STREET, 526, 542

EISENACH, 64, 510

FESTUS, 442

FOSSEBRIDGE, 388

FULDA, 16, 519

GALILEE, 376, 460

GIDEON, 131

GONFALON ROYAL, 262, 413, 513

HAWKHURST, 137

HEREFORD, 552, 596

HERONGATE, 131, 133, 549

IVYHATCH, 320

KILLIBEGS, 419

MARYTON, 294, 413

MELCOMBE, 270, 318, 397

MORNING HYMN, 264

O WALY WALY, 82, 147

OLD CLARENDONIAN, 517, 526

OLD 100TH, 14, 15

OMBERSLEY, 146

RIMINGTON, 31

RIVAULX, 359

ROCKINGHAM, 147, 418

RUSHFORD, 397

ST. LAURENCE, 133, 512

SARAH RACHEL, 339

SEVEN SEAS, 339

SOLOTHURN, 276

SPLENDOUR, 118

TALLIS' CANON, 274, 313, 585

TE LUCIS, 276

THE HOLY SON, 143

TRURO, 31, 516

VENI CREATOR, 232, 589

WAREHAM, 331, 371, 413

WARRINGTON, 184

8 8 8 8 (L M) continued

WHITSUN PSALM, 225

WINCHESTER NEW, 112, 119, 601

8 8 8 8 4

MEDFIELD STREET, 141

8 8 8 8 6

ST. MARGARET, 486

8 8 8 8 8

PACHELBEL (WAS GOTT THUT), 271

8 8 8 8 8 8

ABINGDON, 132

CREDO, 121

DAS NEUGEBORNE KINDELEIN, 116

LONDON ROAD, 125

MADRID, 375

MELITA, 273, 285, 480

MONMOUTH, 20

PATER OMNIUM, 485

RYBURN, 480, 539

SAGINA, 452, 588

ST. CATHERINE, 462

ST. CHRYSOSTOM, 476

ST. MATTHIAS, 296, 464, 476, 485

SURREY, 117, 462

VENI EMMANUEL, 66

8 8 8 8 8 8 8 7

O TANNENBAUM, 73

8 8 8 8 D

SCHMÜCKE DICH, 400

TREWEN, 449

8 8 8 8 D (D L M)

JANE, 475

JERUSALEM, 336

ST. PATRICK, 5

YE BANKS AND BRAES, 220

8 8 8 8 10 8

CALYPSO PRAISE, 414

8 8 9 7 10 7

CRESSWELL, 481

8 9 8 D 6 6 4 8 8

WACHET AUF! (SLEEPERS, WAKE!), 199

8 9 9 9 9 8

MORWENSTOW, 53

SECRET BIRTH, 53

9 8 8 8 8 3

LIVING LORD, 417, 518

9 8 9 8

ST. CLEMENT, 280, 609

SPIRITUS VITAE, 43, 237

STEEPLE BELLS, 378

9 8 9 8 8 8

NEUMARK (BREMEN), 100

9 8 9 8 9 8

BERGERS (FRAGRANCE/QUELLE EST CETTE ODEUR), 63

9 8 9 8 D

RENDEZ À DIEU, 343, 396

9 9 9 9 10 9

SUSSEX CAROL, 239

10 4 6 6 6 6 10 4

HERBERT, 342

LUCKINGTON, 342

10 4 10 4 10 10

ALBERTA, 48

10 8 10 8

BUNESSAN, 51

10 9 10 9

BUNESSAN, 265

10 10

CRUCIFER, 508

EASTER SKIES, 149

ELBERTON, 401

PAX TECUM, 467

SONG 46 (SONG 47), 149, 468

10 10 7 7

BEKESBOURNE, 127

KENOSIS, 127

10 10 10 4

CREATION, 204

ENGELBERG, 204, 389

SINE NOMINE, 567

10 10 10 9

FELMERSHAM, 1

10 10 10 10

BEACON HILL, 57

ELLERS, 281

EVENTIDE, 425

FARLEY CASTLE, 361

GO FORTH, 42, 505

LAVENDON, 236, 399

MALVERN HILLS, 233

ST. AGNES – LANGRAN, 406

SLANE, 545

10 10 10 10 continued

SURSUM CORDA, 399

WOODLANDS, 42, 357, 366

YANWORTH, 366, 459, 505

10 10 10 10 4

BEYOND ALL KNOWLEDGE, 471

IT PASSETH KNOWLEDGE, 471

10 10 10 10 10 10

SONG 1, 392, 420

UNDE ET MEMORES, 392

YORKSHIRE (STOCKPORT), 78

10 10 11 10

YVONNE, 162

10 10 11 11

HANOVER, 24, 333

LAUDATE DOMINUM, 354, 490

PADERBORN, 520

10 11 11

ELMSDALE, 198

10 11 11 6

CHRISTE SANCTORUM, 321

10 11 11 11

CHEDWORTH, 547

MACCABAEUS, 167

10 11 11 12

SLANE, 101

11 10 11 10

BARNARD GATE, 207

EPIPHANY HYMN, 338, 495

GREAT IS THY FAITHFULNESS, 260

HIGHWOOD, 314, 422

LIVING WORD, 252

LORD OF THE YEARS, 328

O PERFECT LOVE, 297

O QUANTA QUALIA, 18, 252, 571

PUTNEY, 314

SPEAN, 207

STRENGTH AND STAY, 300

YVONNE, 252

11 10 11 10 11 10

FINLANDIA, 446

11 10 11 10 D

EPIPHANY, 338

LONDONDERRY AIR, 499

SALVATOR MUNDI, 263

Irregular continued

RECTORY MEADOW, 89

SALVE FESTA DIES, 229, 383

SEBASTE, 275

STILLE NACHT (SILENT NIGHT), 95

THE FIRST NOWELL, 93

Song Section

ALLELUIA NO. 1, S.3

BIND US TOGETHER, S.4

BROKEN FOR ME, S.6

BURNING HEART, S.1

CALHOUN MELODY, S.18

COME INTO HIS PRESENCE, S.2

FATHER, WE ADORE YOU, S.5

FREELY, FREELY, S.12

GIVE ME JOY (SING HOSANNA), S.11

GOD HAS SPOKEN, S.13

HE IS LORD, S.7

HE IS LOVE (PRAISE HIM), S.21

HOLY, HOLY, S.14

I AM THE BREAD OF LIFE, S.10

I WANT TO WALK, S.16

I WILL SING, I WILL SING, S.15

JESUS IS LORD, S.17

KUM BA YAH, S.31

LITTLE BARRINGTON, S.32

MICHAEL, ROW THE BOAT, S.8

MOTHER TERESA, S.20

NEW COMMANDMENT, S.26

NO GREATER NAME, S.27

ST. FRANCIS (MAKE ME A CHANNEL), S.19

SING ALLELUIA, S.22

SONG OF CREATION, S.32

SOVEREIGN LORD, S.9

SPIRIT OF THE LIVING GOD, S.23, S.24

THE VIRGIN MARY, S.25

THIS IS THE DAY, S.28

WE HAVE COME INTO THIS HOUSE, S.29

YOU ARE WORTHY, S.30

HYMNS: WITH TUNES

Italics indicate former first line.